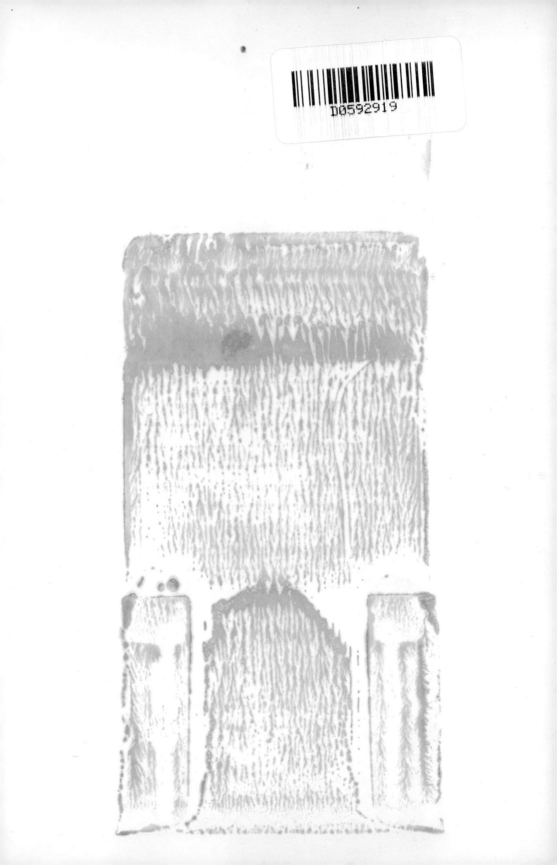

Third Edition

YOUNG HOMEMAKERS'

EQUIPMENT GUIDE

Third Edition

YOUNG HOMEMAKERS'

EQUIPMENT GUIDE

LOUISE J. PEET, Ph.D.

*Professor of Household Equipment, College of Home Economics,
Iowa State University*

IOWA STATE UNIVERSITY PRESS, AMES, IOWA

THE AUTHOR

Professional competence—unsurpassed in her discipline—teamed with years of teaching and counseling in widely separated geographic areas have established LOUISE PEET as an authority in the field of equipment science. Her warm personality and talent for understanding young people have given her a unique insight into their modes, manners, and needs. An important need is for help in adapting their intelligence to the successful operation of a home.

Before her appointment to Iowa State University, where for 22 years she was head of the department of household equipment, she taught at William Woods College, Fulton, Missouri, and Istanbul Women's College in Turkey. She also has been visiting professor at the University of Illinois, the University of Wyoming, Oregon State College, Brigham Young University, and Utah State University. She holds bachelor of arts and master of arts degrees from Wellesley College and a doctor of philosophy degree from Iowa State University. The alumni association of this university has awarded her a Faculty Citation for outstanding teaching and achievement in her field.

Stock No. 1810

First edition, 1958
Second printing, 1959
Third printing, 1960

Second edition, 1963

Third edition, 1967
Second printing, 1967
Third printing, 1968

Library of Congress Catalog Card Number: 66–24399

MARIA PARLOA, *one of the early leaders in the home economics movement, once said:* "**Household duties are something more than tasks. They have an important relation to life.**" *Happy housekeeping is a big factor in happy homemaking.*

INTRODUCTION . . . *in which you will discover why*

this book was written and where to find certain information.

Have you ever stopped to think what a home would be like without the present-day modern equipment—without gas and electricity and the appliances they operate? In the kitchen there would be no range and refrigerator, food waste disposer, and dishwasher. There would be no small electric appliances such as the toaster, coffee maker, electric frypan and mixer, not to mention the rotisserie, roaster, waffle baker, can opener, and knife sharpener. Cutlery and kitchen tools such as graters and sifters would be missing, as well as the utensils for oven and surface cookery. Laundry and cleaning equipment, too—washers, dryers, irons, water heaters, vacuum cleaners, and the more recently available floor scrubbers and waxers—would be absent. And we still haven't mentioned electric lights and air conditioners, dehumidifiers and fans—all adjuncts of the modern home.

Equipment is interesting. Modern space-age living is exciting and it has invaded the kitchen. Meat is tenderized automatically, ovens are cleaned automatically, ice cubes are produced automatically. A growing number of manufacturers announce the use of solid-state controls on appliances. But as Mr. John Martin of Frigidaire says, "Miracle products are one thing, but reliable miracle products make space-age living a reality." Emphasis is on longevity, and reliability—qualities proven by up-to-date methods of testing appliances before they are put on the market. Mr. Martin asks, "Do you know that a refrigerator compressor during its comparatively few—10 to 15—years of operation pumps refrigerant four times as often as a human heart beats in 70 years? Or that a certain spring in an automatic washer is compressed and released over 37 million times during the washer's lifetime?" He further reports that service calls on all products manufactured by his company have been reduced more than half in the last five years, indicating the "extreme reliability" of many present-day appliances.

We don't have to go back to the times when our ancestors cooked in the fireplace and washed beside a stream, dipping the water into a hand boiler to be heated over an outdoor fire, although many people in the world still live this way, having none of the conveniences we take so much for granted.

Our grandmothers saw the beginnings of modern equipment. The first electric range was manufactured in 1910, the first electric washer about the same time, refrigerators even somewhat later. So you who are marrying now are fortunate.

Young women marry at a much earlier age than they did twenty or thirty years ago. In fact, one out of six girls between the ages of fifteen and nineteen years is now married. The peak age for marrying is eighteen, and eighty per cent of all girls are married within five years after graduation from high school. The married couple is no longer a phenomenon in college, and a majority of young wives continue to work for a period after marriage. During the years that they study or work before marriage, many young women live together in a cooperative homemaking arrangement.

Many of you will start homemaking in rented apartments where none of the furnishings will be of your choosing, where manufacturer's instructions for use and care of equipment have been destroyed, and previous occupants have given no thought to improving working conditions or arrangements. This book will help you develop initiative in getting the most out of what you have to work with, so those first weeks of adventure will be cheerful instead of tearful.

With more wives studying or working at least part time, husbands are finding that sharing household tasks and responsibilities can be pleasant, and they are developing an increased interest in selection and efficient operation of household appliances and utensils.

The sharing of mutual problems opens new fields for young women also. The complexities of lighting, plumbing, and heating once were considered too difficult for the feminine mind. Today's young homemaker finds it useful to have a working knowledge of these and other technical subjects such as electricity, gas, thermostats, insulation, or the properties of metals, or the characteristics of glass, plastics, and synthetics. Chapters 14 and 15 explain in condensed and simplified form how these principles can be used advantageously in homemaking.

The new chapter (16) "Selecting Equipment as Gifts," by Betty Jeanne Sundling, adds a new dimension to the practical adaptation of household equipment—giving consideration to the selection of equipment pieces as gifts that will be cherished by both the beginning and the more mature homemaker and her family.

Representative laboratory projects and experiments found at the end of each chapter offer opportunity to make use of some of the knowledge acquired. They are suggestive of the problems you will find in your own home. You or your teacher may think of others. The questions will help you review some of the points covered.

Certain illustrations have been selected to show features of construction not always seen when you look at equipment. Descriptions under the pictures should be read carefully as they add information not given in the text. A classified listing of illustrations supplements the index.

A book like this, supplying information on the selection, use, and care of the equipment in your home, should prove as useful as your cook books. In fact cooking operations and kitchen appliances are quite inseparable, each dependent on the other for the ultimate success of the finished product.

I would like to acknowledge the friendly cooperation of the manufacturers who provided up-to-date information and illustrations. Also I express my very sincere thanks to Miss Betty Jeanne Sundling, member of the Engineering Home Economics Department of Whirlpool Corporation, for her help in providing me with articles on new equipment, for calling my attention to other available sources of recent factual material, and for her contribution of the new chapter, "Selecting Equipment as Gifts."

Reference lists in the back of the book contain names of other published materials that are readily obtainable at little or no cost. Addresses have been included as far as possible. You will find separate listing (with addresses) for associations and manufacturers who will supply additional information on equipment they represent or produce.

Changes occur constantly—in the science of nutrition, in ideas of child care, in textiles and types of clothing—and even more rapidly in the field of home equipment. Most changes are improvements, but some are in style, only. When you are fortified with basic knowledge about home equipment, you can adapt to changes that are desirable. The objective of this book is to supply that essential knowledge.

LOUISE J. PEET

TABLE OF CONTENTS

Third Edition

YOUNG HOMEMAKERS'

EQUIPMENT GUIDE

Chapter One

SELECTION FACTORS

IN BUYING EQUIPMENT

Y ou can't keep house without a certain amount of equipment. Efficient use of equipment includes the correct selection, arrangement, operation, and care of appliances so that the homemaker may accomplish the maximum amount of work in the shortest possible time with a minimum of effort. From year to year manufacturers improve their products so they are easier to operate and require less servicing. New automatic features often save energy and time. The manufacturer has done his best; now it is up to you. Enjoyment in the use of appliances involves mastery of operation and that in turn requires knowledge—not only how to use the appliance correctly, but how to care for it that it may give continued service for years, preventing irritation and forestalling needless expenditure for repairs or replacement.

But cost must still be considered. Money is, however, only one of the resources of the family. Other important ones are health and, consequently, energy of the homemaker, and attitudes of the family members. When the homemaker has some physical disability, appliances that will save her strength should be purchased, even if other members of the family do without some cherished desire. If the family can be satisfied with a bottom-of-the-line appliance, even if the neighbors have top-of-the-line models, the family will find that all the essential operating features are there. The less-expensive range will not have indicator lights to show when a burner or unit is in operation and may lack a platform light, but many such lights are too low to illuminate the inside of any utensil but a frypan. The less-expensive washer will not have detergent and bleach injectors, lint screens, and the so-called program washing controls, but it will wash the clothes.

When the homemaker works outside the home, she will have to decide whether automatic appliances within the home or community facilities such as the laundromat will increase the ease with

3

which she manages two jobs. The size and age of the children play an important part in reaching a decision. A family conference in which each one can express an opinion is often a good way to settle the matter.

In any case the income of the family, the amount that can be invested, other needs, and commitments already made must be taken into consideration.

Once the various conditions have been evaluated and a decision to buy has been reached, other factors must be examined if the purchase of an appliance or utensil is to give lasting satisfaction. These factors will be listed in an outline form, which is sufficiently suggestive to afford an opportunity for you to apply the information in any specific case.

Selection Factors To Be Considered in Making a Wise Purchase

1. Reliability of manufacturer and dealer:
   How long have they been in business?
   Relationship with employees.
   Do they carry on research?
   Do they employ a home economist to get a woman's point of of view?
   What service training is given to dealers and servicemen?
2. Availability of servicing:
   From how far must serviceman come when needed?
   Are manufacturer and dealer interested if appliance should get out of order?
3. Construction of appliance:
   Appearance, design, color, trim, and size.
   Hidden values—is base metal treated against corrosion?
   Convenience features and ease of cleaning.
   Special features, how essential to you?
   Does it meet your needs?
4. Guarantees, operation directions, and specification sheets:
   Are they informative?
   Are they honest and dependable?
      Who promises what?
      Fair-trade practice versus discount houses?
5. Costs:
   Initial
   Installation
   Operating
   Servicing

Factors That Affect Initial Cost of Equipment

1. Raw materials
2. Transportation, distance from source to company location
3. Labor, benefits provided—hospitalization, recreation, and pensions
4. Manufacuring processes, buildings, equipment, packaging, and number of models
5. Design—simple or intricate
6. Research carried on
7. Guarantees and replacements
8. Competition

Where can you go to obtain this needed information? There are various sources: catalogues from mail-order companies, magazine articles, extension bulletins from state universities, books on equipment such as this volume, advertisements, current issues of Consumer Reports, (usually available in your public library) or information from neighbors or friends who have models you are interested in. Inquire regarding local rates for gas, electricity, and water from your utility companies, and from the appliance nameplate, figure the operating costs of the equipment for the approximate time you will use it. Information on page 277 will help you do this.

Before you finally buy, a few last thoughts. Do you really need the appliance? Will it aid in the effective performance of a given task? Have you space to use it comfortably and store it satisfactorily? Will it increase safety in the home? Or will it increase noise and heat in your working area? Will it change and perhaps complicate rather than complement your work habits? If you can answer these questions convincingly, you are ready to buy.

Chapter Two

GAS AND ELECTRIC RANGES

G<small>AS AND ELECTRIC RANGES</small> are used widely in present-day homes, and for the protection of the users, must pass certain tests. These guarantees are in the form of Seals of Approval which should be visible to the purchaser. A detailed discussion of the seals and what they identify appears at the end of this chapter. Each range should be accompanied by a complete and understandable use and care booklet. This should be studied carefully before the range is put in use. Reputable dealers will see to it that all electric ranges are grounded. This requirement should be checked carefully by the homemaker when moving into a home where the range was installed previous to her occupancy.

The frames of both types of range are made of steel, the parts welded together. The free-standing range is usually finished in porcelain enamel, but when a built-in range with a wall oven and separate surface heating units is installed, stainless steel frequently is used. The top of the range, known as the cooking top, is backed by the back splasher or backguard, names that clearly indicate its function of protecting the wall. Free-standing ranges are of two designs, table-top and high-oven. At present the high-oven models make up 22 per cent of all ranges sold (Fig. 2.1). Table-top ranges (Fig. 2.2) are available in three sizes: the standard range, 36 to 40 inches wide, the 30-inch model, and the 24-inch apartment size. Built-in ranges may have the oven and surface units installed separately or may be the all-in-one type with under-counter oven.

SURFACE UNITS
Electric

The source of heat in the electric range is called a unit and is controlled by a switch. Surface units are 6 inches and 8 inches in diameter and four in number. On standard and apartment size ranges the units are commonly grouped together; on the 30-inch model they may be divided, two on each side with a narrow work space between, or occasionally placed in an L position, two on one side and the other two across the back.

The unit is the tubular type, a coil of nickel-chromium wire enclosed in a tube of an iron-nickel alloy, from which it is insulated by magnesium oxide. The tube may be narrow, containing a single coil of wire, or wide with two or three coils. Occasionally two narrow tubes are used.

FIG. 2.1. A range with four cooking levels: an extra large top oven with a broiler in addition to the separate bottom broiler. The oven features semi-rigid aluminum liners that can be cleaned at the sink. Upper oven features center-divided doors which eliminate interference with burners below. All oven doors are removable.—Roper.

FIG. 2.2. This 30-inch gas range of Early American style features a cook-and-keep oven, oven door seal, dripless seamless top, and a controlled surface burner that cooks food a preset length of time, then reduces to serving temperature which it will maintain indefinitely. Coppertone with Early American handles.—Roper.

Because of their low mass and because some of the tube material is very thin, tubular units heat rapidly. They vary in power rating from about 2,760 to 1200 watts.

Some ranges feature a "jet speed" unit that supplies an initial intense heat for about 20 to 30 seconds to start the cooking operation rapidly and then reduces to rated wattage. For example, a 236-volt, 1600-watt, 6-inch unit may operate as a 3,000-watt unit at 250 volts for the first half minute. When a glass utensil is used over the high heat of an electric unit, a metal grid should be placed below the glass to prevent direct contact with the unit; otherwise, the excessive heat may cause a slight circular depression in the bottom of the glass utensil. Glass tends to soften above 1200 F.

Switches

Most switches indicate five heat positions, from high heat to simmer, and an off position, but a number of manufacturers are now featuring surface units with infinite heat control. Some ranges control the heat by means of push buttons, a separate one for each heat, so that the heat desired may be obtained immediately without turning a switch through intermediate positions. On the more expensive models lights behind the switches show when a unit is in operation and also, perhaps, will indicate by a variety of colors which heat is being used. Switches and push buttons are usually located on the backguard, but may be on a panel at the side of the cooking top.

Gas Surface Burners

In the gas range the source of heat is appropriately known as a burner. Depending upon their Btu rating (British thermal unit of heat, explained on p. 280), burners are the giant or regular, each of them with a simmer position and sometimes also with a warm position (Fig. 2.3). The giant burner uses 12,000 Btu per hour, the regular, 9,000; but a high-speed 18,000-Btu burner, with slots instead of ports, is also available. It brings water to the boil very rapidly and then may be turned to a low position to maintain simmering. Burners are of cast iron or aluminum. The holes, called ports, are drilled horizontally on the outer rim and horizontally, vertically, or at a 45° angle on the inner cone, depending upon the manufacturer.

A valve handle directs the flow of gas from the manifold pipe, located behind the front panel of the range, through the

FIG. 2.3. The ALLTROL burner. The gas range allows selection of the exact heat needed, from tiny "keep warm" to gentle "simmer," to "medium high," to "high" heat. Once the water reaches the boiling temperature, the simmer position should be used. If the container is covered, the simmer flame will maintain boiling and at the same time save on gas consumption.— Harper-Wyman.

orifice into the mixing head and throat of the burner. Here the gas mixes with air which is drawn in through openings in the shutter on the mixer head (Fig. 2.4). The gas-air mixture then flows through the ports and is ignited by a pilot light that burns continuously near the center of a group of burners. Occasionally each burner has its own miniature pilot light. The heat given

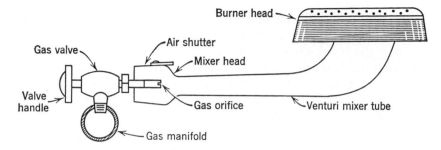

FIG. 2.4.   All burners are constructed to mix gas and air as shown in this diagram.—American Gas Association.

off from this tiny pilot is minimal. Cooking utensils are supported over the burner by a grate made of cast iron which tends to be brittle and should be handled with care to avoid breakage.

Four burners are the usual number and they commonly are arranged two on a side with work space between. The valve handles are placed on the front panel, only rarely on the back-guard.

RANGE OVENS

Ovens in the standard and apartment ranges have the conventional dimensions, approximately 16 to 19 inches wide, 19 inches deep, and 15 inches high; while in the 30-inch range the width of the oven is at least 21 and often 24 inches. When a range features two ovens on the same level, the second one is generally only 10 or 12 inches wide; this is true whether the two ovens are below the cooking surface or at eye level. However, in the split-level range with two large ovens, one below and one above the cook surface, both may be of the same width and height, although the upper oven may be somewhat narrower. This oven is always shallower in depth to avoid interference with the surface units. Ovens are lined with the first dark coat of porcelain enamel, the cobalt coat, or frequently with a gray titanium enamel coat (p. 294), and less commonly with a shiny metal, stainless or chromium-plated steel. The shiny surface reflects the radiant heat better than the dark material, but discolors unless cleaned regularly.

Oven shelves should be of corrosion-resistant wires or ribbons, of stainless steel or chromium-plated steel, occasionally nickel-plated steel, spaced close together to support small baking utensils without tipping. There should be a positive stop so the shelves may be pulled out far enough to eliminate stooping or danger of burning the hand when baking dishes are removed. A rail at the rear prevents utensils from slipping off the back as the shelf is pulled forward. The usual oven shelf is on a level with the side supports on which it rests, but a special offset shelf is constructed so the central rods on which the utensil is placed are 1½ to 2 inches lower than the supports along the oven side. This shelf may be reversed, allowing a range of 3 to 4 inches in the between-shelf space.

A sufficient number of shelf supports should be provided to permit versatility in arranging shelves to accommodate utensils of various sizes. Ovens usually are insulated with Fiberglas, and the door may be sealed with a removable silicone gasket. The temperature is controlled by a hydraulic-type thermostat (Fig. 2.5)

Thermostats

Four companies specializing in the manufacture of thermostatic controls make new types of oven thermostats developed to provide low-temperature heat control, 140 to 250 F. This control allows cooked foods to be held at the desired degree of doneness and warmth, without overcooking, until ready to serve. To maintain these low temperatures, the gas flame may cycle off and on.

The action of the thermostats in gas and electric ovens is slightly different. If the thermostat dial on the electric oven has been set for 350 F., when the switch is turned on, the oven units will operate until a temperature of perhaps 425 F. or more is reached. This is known as the preheat overshoot and allows the cold food to be placed in the oven and the consequent opening of the door without too much loss of heat. At the end of the preheat period the electric current is shut off automatically and the temperature drops, probably slightly below that indicated on the thermostat dial. The current then is turned on again and it cycles off and on as shown in Figure 2.6 (left) frequently about 10 degrees above and below the dial setting.

In heating the gas oven there is also a preheat overshoot, but then the heat settles down to a fairly constant quantity, as shown in Figure 2.6 (right). The gas valve is partly closed, allowing only enough gas to flow to maintain the preset temperature. Some new gas ranges that feature low temperatures, 250 to 140 F., also use

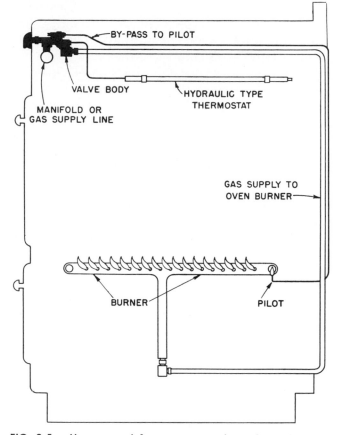

FIG. 2.5.   Heat control for gas oven reduces flow of gas to burner when temperature set on thermostat has been reached.—Robertshaw-Fulton.

the cycling principle, but the amplitudes of the curve are smaller than in the electric range. There is a possibility that in the not too distant future all temperatures in certain gas ovens may be maintained by cycling. The temperature in the food, of course, does not cycle, but continues to rise until the food is cooked.

An oven light is usually a standard feature. It is activated when the door is opened and on many ovens with a window may be turned on by a switch on the front panel or back splasher if the homemaker desires to follow the progress of the baking without opening the door.

Vents

A vent carries away volatile products given off in the cooking process, and also products of combustion. The vent from the electric oven usually opens into the center of a rear unit; in the gas oven the vent opening is on the back splasher, placed so as to direct any vapors away from the wall. A range hood or kitchen ventilating fan helps remove these vapors before they condense on the kitchen walls.

In the built-in oven the vent may open into a flue connected to the outside of the house, or into an upper cabinet supplied with a fan that draws the volatile materials through a screen. In some cases this screen may be removed from time to time and washed in hot, soapy water to get rid of collected grease and other deposits.

Another type of vent for a high-oven range embodies a filtering system that cleanses the air thoroughly before returning it to the kitchen (Fig. 2.7 a and b).

Heating Units in Ovens

Electric. Two units, commonly of the tubular type, are found in the electric oven, one at the top and the second at the bottom.

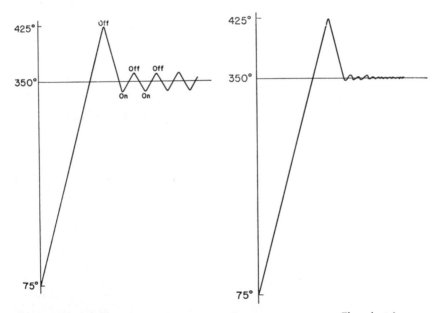

FIG. 2.6. Heating curves of electric and gas range ovens. The electric oven (left) has a cycling control, the gas oven (right), a modulating control which decreases the size of the burner flame.

FIG. 2.7a. Hi-oven range with special Vacuum-Aire Filter Vent. "Teflon"-coated slide-out oven panels can be washed at the sink or sponged clean right at the range.—Hotpoint.

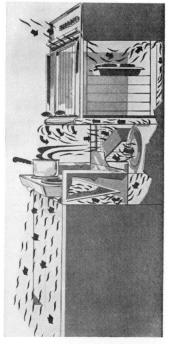

FIG. 2.7b. Detail of Vacuum-Aire Filter Vent showing how surface cooking, oven, and broiler odors, smoke, and grease are directed into the filtering system before they can enter the kitchen. Broiling is done with the oven door closed.—Hotpoint.

Both units are operated during the preheat period, then for broiling, the upper unit is used by itself; the bottom unit may be used alone for baking, although in most present-day ovens a section of the top unit is heated with the bottom unit during the baking process to give a more even browning to the baked product.

The broiling unit frequently is backed by a reflector to speed the operation. The switch may be the single-dial oven control in which the switch and thermostat settings are combined, or the two devices may be separate. The door of the electric range oven is counterbalanced to allow it to be partly open during the broiling operation. At least one manufacturer features closed-door broiling, with a special filter-vent system to remove smoke and volatile oils.

Gas. In the gas oven the burner is below the oven bottom, which is cut away at the corners or sides so that the currents of heated air may circulate freely. If the same burner is used also for broiling, the broiler compartment is below the burner. In the standard range, however, the broiler may be in a separate compartment beside the oven, either in a drawer—the front of which is hinged so that it may fold down—or the broiler pan is attached to a door so it swings out when the door is opened. Automatic oven and broiler pilots are required on all gas ranges carrying the Blue Star Seal (Fig. 2.20).

Broiling food by radiant heat always has been considered the most desirable method, one that the electric range provides. Manufacturers of gas ranges have sought, therefore, to appeal to the consumer's interest by installing metal wire screening below the burner. This material is heated to a glow stage by the burner, then gives off radiant heat. In one model a perforated, unglazed porcelain sheet is placed below the burner; in another, a built-in surface grill is supplied with radiant heat from glowing ceramic coals placed on a screen beneath the grid. The coals are heated by a gas burner below them (Fig. 2.8). Both electric and gas broiler pans should be of the smokeless type. The pan should be fairly deep and covered with a rack which is perforated by narrow slits through which the juices and liquid fats drip so that they are protected from contact with the high heat that would cause smoking. One electric range manufacturer claims to obtain spatter-free broiling by using a pan with extra-deep sides so that the spatters stay in the pan and do not reach the walls of the oven. The broiler pan is in two parts; the lower, shallower section is

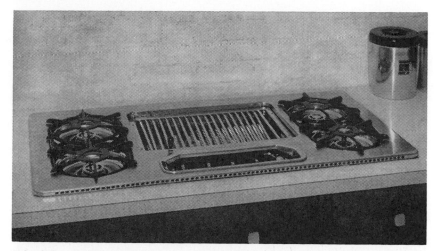

FIG. 2.8.   Built-in cooking top with grill beneath which ceramic coals are spread over a grate that rests on a firebox above a burner. May be used as a barbecue or rotisserie (three spits are provided) or for broiling steaks, etc. —Tappan.

partially filled with cold water. A vertical broiler is featured in some ranges, and in one range, broiling is carried on under a glass plate which protects the electric coils.

Special Features

So far the basic characteristics of gas and electric ranges have been discussed. Many ranges, especially those of de luxe quality, have additional features, the importance of which the homemaker must evaluate in the light of her own needs.

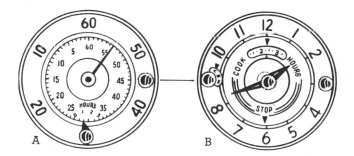

FIG. 2.9.   (A) The 4-hour timer may be set to remind home-maker of completion of any task; (B) automatic clock turns oven on and off at times selected by the homemaker. —American Gas Association.

Heat-Control Devices

The interval timer (A in Fig. 2.9), either electrically or manually controlled, may be set to indicate the time an operation will finish. It then buzzes or rings a bell. The automatic clock and timing device (B in Fig. 2.9) is used to turn the oven, or occasionally one of the surface units, on and off at the desired time without anyone being at home. This is a convenience if the homemaker works or is active in civic or social affairs that frequently take her away from home. She may prepare the meal ahead of time, place it in the oven, set the clock, and return to find her meal cooked and ready to serve. On most ovens the time control must be turned back to M (Manual) at the end of the baking operation, or the oven will not heat when used again without the control. Electric outlets usually are installed on the range, and if one of these is connected to the automatic clock, any small electric appliance such as the coffee maker may also be controlled automatically. This outlet has a separate fuse or circuit breaker since any small electric appliance attached to the outlet will be wired for only 120 volts, and the electric range itself is installed on a 240-volt circuit. In the case of the gas range, the outlet is attached to a general purpose or appliance circuit.

When an oven heating system automatically changes at a specified time from one temperature to another, usually from a cooking to a keep-warm temperature, it is known as oven programming.

There are two types of programming systems, the single thermostat and the double thermostat system, but in either system it is only necessary to turn the thermostat to the cooking temperature and then set the program timer. The oven heats immediately, and when the food is cooked the temperature is reduced automatically to a keep-warm temperature until served. From the viewpoint of bacterial growth, the cooking of the food first is preferable to the common automatic clock and timing device method of putting the food in the oven and setting the clock to turn the oven on perhaps several hours later.

Foods requiring an exact baking time should not be programmed; for example, biscuits, pies, cakes, etc. Soufflés, which must be served immediately when the cooking period is ended, cannot be prepared by this method. Any foods that hold well at low temperatures, especially roasts and certain vegetables, may be used; some foods will hold better than others. The homemaker should experiment to discover which foods are best suited to this treatment. When food is to be served immediately, without any holding period, the cooking time may need to be increased 10 to 15 minutes.

Lights indicate when a unit or burner is on and, sometimes, the individual setting. Self-latching valve handles prevent a burner from being turned on accidentally—especially desirable when there are young children in the home. Storage drawers furnish additional space in the kitchen; when heated, they may be used to keep food or dishes warm. As has been noted, miniature pilots for each burner keep unnecessary heat out of the kitchen, and electric ignition on a gas range cuts down heat still further.

Some surface units and burners are supplied with a central-sensitive disk (Fig. 2.10) mounted on a spring so that it will make contact with the bottom of the utensil. The disk is connected to a thermostat of the hydraulic type or occasionally of the bimetallic type (p. 282). When the cooking temperature set on the switch or valve handle is reached, the control operates to maintain this temperature. One range has an added control, a push-button selector to vary the size of the heated surface so that it may be used with a 4-inch, 6-inch, or 8-inch saucepan. Such a thermostatic control is equivalent to using an automatic frypan or saucepan and tends to eliminate the overcooking and scorching of food products (Fig. 2.11). It is advisable to have food cover the center of the pan, for the action of the thermostat is controlled by the temperature of the center of the utensil in contact with the thermal ele-

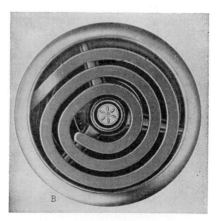

FIG. 2.10—Central-sensitive disks in some surface units and burners are thermostatically controlled. The bottom of the utensil in contact with the thermal element of the disk regulates the flow of heat. Thus any utensil acquires the characteristics of an automatic appliance. (A) Gas burner. —Tappan. (B) Electric surface unit.— Frigidaire.

FIG. 2.11. Too high a temperature for grill at top produces unattractive and unpalatable bacon; controlled heat for grill at bottom reduces curling, prevents scorching, and preserves flavor. —Robertshaw-Fulton.

ment of the disk. This is especially important when frying meats. Most satisfactory results are obtained when the utensil has a flat bottom and is a good conductor (p. 286).

Robertshaw-Fulton has developed a top burner heat control with a "Flame-Set" feature that is especially useful when cooking is done in nonaluminum utensils (Fig. 2.12). When the control is used with aluminum utensils, the dial is turned to the high setting to light the burner, then lowered to the temperature desired for

FIG. 2.12. The Flame-set top burner heat control allows the homemaker to adjust size of flame before setting the temperature of cooking. Recommended for use with all nonaluminum utensils.—Robertshaw-Fulton.

the cooking. With nonaluminum utensils the dial is again turned to high to light the burner, then to Flame-set where the home-maker reduces the flame to about half before turning the dial to the proper temperature for the cooking operation.

Surface grills are supplied with some ranges. On one range the grill with its own automatic temperature control is plugged directly into an outlet on the back splasher. Along the front edge is a recess for grease from which excess fat may be removed with a spoon. On another range the grill is used over the controlled temperature unit and shares the advantage of the "just-right" heat, without need of plugs or connecting cords.

Some electric ovens have built-in barbecue attachments or rotisseries with their own motors to turn the spit; others, a central unit by which the oven may be divided into sections, so that the homemaker may broil in the lower part and bake in the upper at the same time. Certain gas ranges also provide rotisseries with the motor controlled by a switch on the front panel.

A number of ranges feature a type of meat thermometer as an oven accessory (Fig. 2.13). One part, the probe, is inserted into the roast, the other part into a special outlet in the interior oven wall. A dial on the back panel of the range indicates the degree of doneness of the meat—rare, medium, or well done. In some range models the roasting process is automatically stopped when the correct internal temperature is reached and a bell or buzzer signal notifies the cook. In other models, however, the tempera-ture of the oven will be reduced automatically to the internal temperature of the meat and held at that temperature without further cooking until ready to serve. Do not immerse the roast-meter spear and plug in water.

At least two companies place a thermometer dial on the probe to indicate the temperatures that may be used for obtaining different degrees of doneness. This information aids in setting the oven thermostat correctly. One probe may be set to start the roast-ing when the homemaker is away from the house.

Speed of broiling is usually regulated by the distance of the broiler rack from the heat, but one range has a two-way broiler valve that provides a small bead flame around the burner in addition to the standard flame, and several electric ranges have a broiler control that may be set for any degree of doneness. This control dials the doneness desired without the need of shifting the height of the broiler pan. In certain broilers another type of

FIG. 2.13. A meat thermometer, connected to a special outlet in the side of the oven, cooks roasts to any desired degree of doneness.—Whirlpool Corporation.

control either raises or lowers the broiler pan without need for removing it; or even more unusual, raises or lowers the broiler unit to the correct distance above the food.

At least two manufacturers advertise an oven that will tenderize meat (Fig. 2.14). Automatic meat tenderizing employs a long, slow, low-temperature cooking system, similar to that used by many master chefs. After an initial cooking time at 325 F., the oven automatically cuts back for longer-term cooking at a controlled low temperature. The slow heating rate causes a chemical action which breaks down connective tissues, resulting in more tender, juicier meats, even with budget-priced cuts. Homemakers also benefit from reduced meat shrinkage with the new process.

Tabular information is furnished for the conventional heat control, and the Meat Minder and Tender-matic controls, with settings marked for the type and weight of meat and for the degree of doneness desired. The shape of the roast, amount of fat, and extent of aging of the meat will affect the cooking results. A shal-

FIG. 2.14. Double wall oven shown here has special control for tenderizing roasts—even budget cuts—automatically. Windows in doors of both ovens swing down 180 degrees for cleaning.—Frigidaire.

low roasting pan is recommended; with the meat placed on a grid or rack, which allows the heat to reach all areas equally and gives more even cooking and tenderizing results. At first the oven heat control turns the temperature to 325 F., then at the proper time the heat control automatically turns itself down to the chosen tenderizing temperature. Eight hours is the minimum roasting time provided and 12 to 14 hours is suggested for certain cuts—chuck, rolled rump, and sirloin tip. Turkeys may be roasted for an even longer time. Roasts with no outer layer of fat will be darker in color than when roasted conventionally; lean meat may be covered with a layer of suet or bacon. If rare meat is preferred, it should be roasted not more than eight hours, or the conventional method should be chosen. Neither a commercial tenderizer nor a meat thermometer should be used.

FIG. 2.15. Cooking units fold back out of the way when not in use, leaving most of counter free as work area. May be installed at any location in kitchen, family room, play room, or near patio.—Frigidaire.

Built-in Surface Units and Ovens

Brief reference has been made to the separate built-in surface units and burners and oven-broiler compartments. A variety of arrangements is possible, from the single unit installed in the work counter to separate units in two different locations in the kitchen. When working space is limited, the hinged unit can be folded back out of the way against a rear panel when not in use, leaving counter space free for other activities (Fig. 2.15). A more efficient use of counter and cabinet space may result when ovens are placed away from the surface units. When more than one person prepares food, it is helpful to have more than one work center.

The built-in oven also may be at any height, a feature welcomed by many.

Something new has been developed in glass oven doors—a new plating process makes it possible for the glass to double as a mirror (Fig. 2.16).

ELECTRONIC RANGES

In the electronic range, now available for homes, food is cooked by the action of electronic waves generated by a new

FIG. 2.16. Through a new plating process a mirror-finish oven window that will withstand constant exposure to high temperatures is now available. It casts a reflection when the oven light is off, provides a view of baking foods when the light is on.—Roper.

microtron power unit that has reduced the warm-up period from 75 seconds to 7 seconds. In most models of electronic ovens the 230- to 240-volt alternating current used in the ordinary electric range is transformed into 5,000-volt direct current and this direct current activates the microtron tube which converts the current into high-frequency microwave energy. A fan is installed in the oven to distribute the microwaves throughout the oven, and the metal lining reflects them back to the food.

Metal utensils also will reflect the waves, but glass and paper transmit the waves, and therefore are used for the cooking utensils —glass for roasting, baking, and where liquids are present; paper for snacks and the absorbing of fat from foods such as bacon. Some china and pottery may be used for short cooking processes, but gold-trimmed china should not be used, for microwaves will tend to discolor the gold permanently, and some pottery dishes contain lead or other metals that reflect high-frequency waves.

Microwaves penetrate the food rather than heating the surface. The waves, passing back and forth very rapidly through the food, agitate the molecules of the food, thus producing the heat that cooks the food. On the average the waves penetrate about two inches into the food. In thicker foods, such as poultry and certain cuts of meat, the outer heat is then transferred to the center of the food. High-frequency waves cook very rapidly; for example, a potato bakes in 4 minutes, a frozen, 19-pound turkey in an hour and a half, and an egg, frankfurter, two or three strips of bacon, etc. in a matter of seconds. Although electronic cookery is so much more rapid—2 to 10 times faster than by usual methods—larger quantities of food require a longer cooking time; baking several potatoes takes 2 to 3 times as long as baking one potato, because the electronic oven does not store energy, it produces energy at a given rate without any relation to temperature. Consequently, when you increase the quantity of food, you sacrifice the advantage of speed.

When the cooking process continues for twenty minutes or longer, the surface of the food is usually browned sufficiently. If not, it may be browned under a broiler unit. One company includes such a unit in the top of the electronic oven, so designed that the unit coils do not interfere with the passage of the high-frequency waves. Other companies supply a standard oven installed above or below the electronic oven.

A new General Electric range combines a standard two-level

FIG. 2.17. New Electronic oven range looks like a conventional 2-level range and will fit into same space in kitchen. It has all the features of a conventional range and can be used with or without electronic elements. Here a soufflé has been cooked on the electronic shelf.—General Electric.

range with an electronic unit in the lower oven. This electronic unit is removable and the range may be used for surface cookery and for baking and broiling in the usual way. Or the electronic unit may be placed within the oven and used by itself, or in combination with the standard bake or broil unit, which then produces the browned surface that is considered desirable by most homemakers. The power unit, a magnetron tube, is contained in the drawer below the oven. It converts electric power into ultra-high frequency (UHF) radio waves, and this energy is transmitted up the back of the oven and through a window in the top of the oven. The UHF energy has a frequency of 915 mega-cycles compared to 2,450 megacycles used by other electronic ovens. The 915-megacycle wave is 2½ times the length of the 2,450 megacycle wave and penetrates deeper into the food. The longer the wave, the greater the depth of penetration. In this new range the size of the magnetron tube has been greatly reduced. Under normal operating conditions the tube has an average life of 10 years. A fan maintains efficient operating temperatures.

To provide safety the door is surrounded by a gasket of metal mesh over silicone which makes a tight seal and also grounds the door and liner, once the door is latched.

A perforated metal shelf in the oven is connected to the elec-tronic unit. The shelf is circular in shape and rotates during the cooking process, thus bringing all areas of the food into equal contact with the waves of energy. The oven provides two settings, high and low power, 700 and 150 watts, respectively. Most foods need high power; the low setting allows the use of metal pans for muffins, cup cakes, and similar foods, when definitely specified in a G.E. recipe.

A complete oven should be capable of cooking all types of food. This new range does just that. The chief advantage of the electronic unit is its speed, but it also reduces heat in the kitchen.

Cool and Safe Operation

In the use of the electronic oven by itself the utensils and the oven remain cool to the touch—only the food heats—so utensils may be removed from the oven without the use of a holder. Unless the food is transferred immediately to a serving dish, several precautions should be observed. As the food stands on the counter outside the oven it will continue to cook, a fact that should be taken into consideration to prevent overcooked steaks, roasts, etc. Moreover, as the food stands, heat will be transferred to the container and it will become sufficiently hot, perhaps, to require the use of a pad. The food may dry onto the surface of the container and tend to stick to it, conditions which do not occur when the food is removed immediately to the serving plate.

Electronic methods of cooking are entirely safe, since the opening of the oven door instantly stops the production of micro-wave energy. The metal screen in the door is so designed that no waves can pass through it. There is no thermostat setting; the control sets the required cooking time and the closing of the door activates the electronic tube system. At the end of the preset time the cooking process automatically shuts off.

It is interesting to note that electronic ovens must have their wave lengths assigned by the Federal Trade Commission so that the use of the oven will not interfere with radio or TV reception.

CARE OF RANGES

The length of time that equipment will give satisfactory service depends in large part upon the care that it receives. To prevent scarring, avoid pulling cooking utensils across the porcelain enameled cooking top. Never use harsh abrasives for cleaning. If soap and water are not adequate, use baking soda; it is effective and harmless, but may discolor aluminum because of its alkalinity. Even though the enamel is acid proof or at least acid resistant, certain foods, especially spilled milk, may etch it, and should be wiped up immediately with a paper towel or a dry cloth. Once the range is cool, the enameled surface should be washed with a cloth wrung from warm soapy water and then clear water. Wetting the porcelain enamel when it is hot may cause it to contract more rapidly than the steel base and consequently crack or craze. Utensils extending beyond the edge of the electric unit may also cause crazing; and setting a saucepan of cold water on the hot range surface has a similar effect.

One range has a glass covered control panel, very easily cleaned; on other ranges the switch and valve handle knobs may be removed. Several ranges have raised edges around the cook top to catch spill-overs.

Tubular units on electric ranges rarely need to be cleaned, as heat from the unit usually chars any spillage, which can then be brushed off, or occasionally wiped with a damp cloth. Some reflector pans or bowls beneath units may be removed and washed; others are of disposable aluminum foil. Several manufacturers supply hinged surface units or even an entire hinged top for ease in cleaning beneath them (Fig. 2.18a). The units on one range are removable, but should not be immersed in water.

Gas burners should be removed from the range occasionally, and the mixing head and throat brushed out with a soft brush. They may be washed in soapy water, rinsed in clear water, then placed upside down in a warm oven until the interior passageways

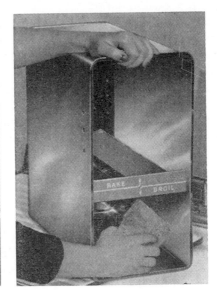

FIG. 2.18a. Present-day ranges have many features that increase ease of cleaning: top surfaces tilt up, oven doors slip off, and the full-width storage drawer slides out so the floor beneath may be mopped clear to the wall.—Philco. (See also Figs. 2.1 and 2.7.)

FIG. 2.18b. Oven linings pull out or are entirely removable and may be taken to the sink for cleaning. — Philco, Frigidaire.

have dried. The top of the thermal element in the thermo-statically controlled surface burner should be kept clean at all times.

Oven shelves should be removed and the entire interior sur-face wiped after each use if possible. The oven walls may look clean, but certain volatile material is given off in any cooking operation and tends to deposit on the lining; this is easily washed off when fresh, but once it has baked on during a subsequent heat-ing of the oven, it is removed with difficulty. Should such stub-born spots occur, they may be covered with a cloth moistened with undiluted household ammonia. If left covered for about thirty minutes, the spot may then be washed off with soap and water. Or a commercial oven cleaner may be used; directions for use should be followed carefully, noting any suggested precautions. Once clean, certain commercial spray materials are available for covering the oven surfaces to protect against future build-up of grease and other baked-on deposits. When soiled, this coating may be washed from the oven walls with a soapy sponge or cloth and the walls then retreated. Again directions and cautionary advice should be followed. A partial list of commonly available oven cleaners and oven sprays includes:

Oven cleaners	*Oven sprays*
Aladdin	Fuller Oven-spray
Dow Oven Cleaner	Oven-Gard
Easy-off	
Glamorene	

Tubular units in the electric oven that fold down or up add to the ease of reaching all areas. Oven doors that lift off or may be dropped down 180 degrees flat against the front of the range also increase the facility with which all parts of the oven may be reached (Fig. 2.18a). Occasionally the glass window in the door is removable for cleaning. Pull-out linings also make all areas more accessible (Fig. 2.18b). One range has removable side and back walls of "Teflon" from which any deposits are easily wiped; another features throw-away oven linings of aluminum foil.

Certain new ranges have ovens that clean themselves with electric heat, without the use of any commercial cleaner and with-out smoke or odor. The oven door is locked and cannot be opened during the operation, then controls are set so that the

FIG. 2.19. Transformation of oven soil (left) to a wisp of ash (right) was,
achieved automatically in Electri-clean oven; not only the oven walls were
cleaned, but also the racks.—Frigidaire.

oven heats gradually to approximately 900 F., a temperature at which any soil is decomposed (Fig. 2.19). At the end of the preset time the heat turns off automatically. A Lock Light comes on at the beginning of the process and turns off again when the oven has cooled sufficiently to be opened. About the same amount of heat is noticed in the kitchen as when a meal is cooked in the conventional oven. This method of oven cleaning is a built-in feature of the range, which is especially insulated because of the high temperature needed for the cleaning process, and cannot be added to other models. The device is UL-approved and the operating cost is about eight cents per cleaning.

Leaving the door partly open when the heat is first turned on and again when the oven is cooling prevents condensation of moisture which may reach hidden areas and cause corrosion. Chromium trim should be wiped with a damp cloth and polished with a dry one.

The installation of hoods over ranges, especially built-in surface units and burners and wall ovens, has helped to maintain a clean kitchen. Some hoods are vented to the outside of the house; others are supplied with two or three permanent filters that are removable and washable.

SEALS OF APPROVAL

A Seal of Approval is in no way connected with the price of a range, but does assure the purchaser or user that the equipment has met numerous tests for durable construction, acceptable performance, and safe operation. The American Gas Association testing laboratories issues two seals of approval. The Blue Star Seal (a blue star on a silver background) assures that the range meets all requirements for adequate construction, performance, and safety (Fig. 2.20). The Gold Star Seal (Fig. 2.21) identifies the superior quality gas range, meeting 28 requirements in addition to those of the standard tests of the Blue Star Seal, and also that the range has from two to five optional features. It must always have automatic ignition for broiler and oven burners and at least one thermostatically controlled surface burner.

Electric ranges may be tested by the Underwriters' Laboratories, Inc., a nonprofit organization with headquarters in Chicago and branch testing Laboratories in New York and San Francisco. They follow up the initial tests with subsequent inspections, either at the factory where the article is manufactured or in their own laboratories on items purchased on the open market. Lists of equipment checked and approved are published at frequent intervals. The homemaker should use only those appliances that have the UL Seal. Their seal (Fig. 2.22), frequently a black UL

FIG. 2.20. The American Gas Association's Blue Star Seal of Approval for standard competency.

FIG. 2.21. The AGA Gold Star Seal indicates a range that has met rigid requirements for operation and construction.

on an orange background surrounded by a red circle, indicates the appliance is safe, free from hazards to life and from fire. This seal appears on all reputable electric appliances but in the case of ranges it cannot guarantee this safety unless the range is adequately grounded. This grounding frequently is accomplished by an attachment to the plumbing, so it is imperative that these connections are not disturbed by the homemaker.

Suggestions for Economical Use of Gas and Electricity

1. Keep all parts of range clean.
2. Use a small burner or unit whenever possible.
3. Put the utensil on before turning on the heat. Turn off heat before removing utensil.
4. Boil only amount of water needed. You save fuel, prevent heat in kitchen, and speed up the job.
5. When water begins to boil, turn unit or burner to low or simmer position. Slowly boiling water is as hot as rapidly boiling water.
6. Use covered utensils if feasible.
7. Use thermostatic surface heat control for all frying, if such a heat is provided. Fat will not smoke. (See Figs. 2.10, 2.11, and 2.12).
8. Do not preheat oven too long before use.
9. Obtain circulation of heat in oven by placing pans in alternate positions on racks.
10. When baking or roasting, use oven to capacity. Cook food for another day.
11. Avoid raising pot covers and opening the oven door during cooking.
12. Use accurate baking temperatures. Too high a temperature causes a cake to be compact in texture with a cracked upper crust; too low a temperature produces a coarse texture with a sticky, pitted top surface.
13. When oven is well insulated, turn off heat a few minutes before end of baking period, and finish baking with retained heat.

FIG. 2.22. The Underwriters' Laboratories Seal of approval for all electric appliances and cords.

14. Do not preheat the broiler. The grid is easier to clean if the food is placed on a cold rack.

EXPERIMENTS AND PROJECTS

1. To inspect gas and electric ranges for:
   Sizes and arrangements of surface units and burners, controlled unit.
   Position of switches and valve handles, number of heats.
   How ovens are heated, how heat is controlled, type of shelves, position of vents.
   Type of broiler, construction of broiler pan.
   Special features (evaluate importance of these features for you as a homemaker).
   Nameplate information; how useful is it? (See p. 276.)
2. Inspect your home ranges and compare with those in laboratory.
3. To demonstrate automatically controlled gas surface burner:
   Add 2 cups of water to 1-quart glass saucepan. Place over automatic burner and bring water to vigorous boil. Note height of flame. Add 4 ice cubes to boiling water. Note height of flame.
4. To test a thermostatically controlled surface burner or unit:
   a. To pop corn:
      Add 2 tablespoons vegetable oil to 2-quart covered saucepan. Add ½ cup popcorn. Cover pan. Place over surface burner or unit with temperature set at 375 F. Time 5 to 8 minutes. Follow same process using an electric frypan and compare results.
   b. To fry in deep fat:
      Pour 1 pint vegetable oil into a 2-quart, covered saucepan. Heat with temperature control set at 400 F. (about 10 minutes). Open can of biscuits and cut each biscuit into 4 to 6 pieces. Deep fry in hot fat until golden brown. Remove biscuit miniatures from fat. Drain. Toss in paper bag containing sugar-cinnamon mix (½ cup sugar to ½ teaspoon cinnamon). Note advantage of controlled heat.
   c. To cook pancakes:
      Using pancake mix, cook pancakes on griddle over thermo-

statically controlled surface burner or unit; then cook some in an electric frypan. Compare ease of manipulation and desirability of product.

5. To demonstrate use of 8-inch surface unit on electric range for baking:
Use 9- or 10-inch covered aluminum frypan. Cover bottom of frypan with 4 layers of wax paper. Use white cake mix, following mixing directions on box. Pour into a greased or "Teflon"-coated frypan and cover. Place over 8-inch unit, turn heat to highest setting for one minute, then to low (not simmer) for 40 to 45 minutes. Do not peek for 30 minutes. Cake will be done when it shrinks from side of pan. Remove cover. Cool 5 to 10 minutes before removing from pan. Top of cake will be white, but may be covered with frosting. Sides and bottom will be attractively browned. Compare cooking on surface unit with cooking in oven for cost and desirability of cake.

6. To test baking-sheet materials:
Use cookie sheets of aluminum, tin, and Russian iron. Preheat oven to 375 F. Use ice-box cookies, either commercially prepared or made from any standard recipe at previous class laboratory session and stored in refrigerator. Cut cookies into $\frac{1}{8}$-inch slices. Bake 2 cookies on tin sheet at 375 F. for 7-8 minutes, or until golden brown on top and bottom. Using length of time found satisfactory, bake 6 cookies on each sheet for this same length of time. Compare results. Formulate rule for use of cookie sheets made of different materials.

7. To compare evenness of heat in ovens of different ranges:
Prepare cookies as in Experiment 6. Use cookie sheets all of same material. Place oven shelf in approximately same position in each oven. Bake cookies for same length of time in each oven. Compare results.

8. To demonstrate uses of broiler (using different types of ranges when available):
   a. To compare spread of heat over broiler pan:
      Cover broiler grid with slices of two-day-old white bread (sandwich loaf recommended). Place broiler pan in center of broiler compartment. Turn on unit or burner. Toast until center slices are golden brown. Compare.
   b. To broil slices of bacon:
      Place slices of bacon on grid. Broil and turn when desired crispness is obtained. Remove and note how fat drips through openings in grid to pan below and smoke is eliminated.
   c. To cook "S'mores" on broiler:
      Use soda or graham crackers. Place in center of each cracker $\frac{1}{2}$-inch-thin square of sweet chocolate and cover with $\frac{1}{2}$ marshmallow (cut with scissors). Place in broiler compartment sufficiently below source of heat that chocolate will be melted before marshmallow is too brown. Note that heat for broiling is usually controlled by distance of broiler grid from heat source.

9. To compare ranges other than those in laboratory:
   If the utility company or a dealer is willing to give a range demonstration, especially on an electronic range, ask the teacher if your class may go.

QUESTIONS

1. What type of unit is commonly found on the surface of the electric range? Why does it heat rapidly?
2. Compare the use of pilot lights on the gas range and signal lights on the electric range.
3. Trace the flow of gas from the meter to a burner on which a saucepan of apples is cooking.
4. What features are found on the back splasher of the electric range? Of the gas range?
5. What do nontipping shelves in the oven eliminate?
6. How do you obtain even browning when you bake three or four layer cakes at one time in the oven?
7. How do you control the heat for broiling? How often do you clean your oven and broiler?
8. What limitations are there in the use of the automatic clock and timing device?
9. If the surface units of a range will heat and the electric oven will not heat, what two things may be the cause?
10. A wedding present might be money for a range. List the features of the range that you would consider essential, giving reasons for your choice.

Chapter Three

REFRIGERATORS AND FREEZERS

Food spoils fairly rapidly when temperature rises above 50 F. At 32 F. most foods will begin to freeze, but the process is rather slow so that large crystals are formed which tend to rupture the cell walls, giving an undesirable, mushy product when the food is thawed. For most satisfactory preservation, therefore, food to be consumed within a few days should be kept at a temperature between 32 and 50 F., and the closer to the freezing temperature, the greater improvement in freshness and flavor. Food to be kept a longer period of time should be quick frozen and kept in that state at a temperature of 0 F. or below.

Taking the United States as a whole, there is an average of only 19 days when the temperature remains within the 32- to 50-degree range during the 24-hour period. It is evident, then, that some type of refrigeration is essential.

REFRIGERATORS

Although ice refrigerators are still used, house-to-house delivery of ice is almost unknown. Automatic gas and electric refrigerators have become accepted appliances for the home.

There are two types of automatic refrigerators, one operated by a motor and hence electric, known as the compression system; and the other operated by heat, usually from a gas flame, but an oil flame or an electric element may also be used. This is known as the absorption system, and although the mechanism is more complicated than in the compression system, the basic parts and cooling action of each are similar.

Refrigerators vary in capacity from 6 to 17 or more cubic feet. It is desirable to purchase as large a size as one can afford or as space will permit, as even small families find they never have too much refrigerator storage space. A 1966 summary of the sales of conventional refrigerators by size indicates that 51 per cent of new purchases are of 14 to 16 cu. ft., 28 per cent are of 11 to 14 cu. ft., and only 10 per cent are of 8 to 10 cu. ft. The size of motors also varies: $1/5$ and $1/8$ horsepower sizes are used in the conventional refrigerators, $1/4$ and $1/3$ horsepower in the no-frost and cyclic defrost models.

CONSTRUCTION

Heat always travels from a warmer to a colder area, so it is necessary for the refrigerator to accomplish two purposes: to create within the cabinet a temperature cold enough to preserve foods in a desirable state and to keep room heat from penetrating the interior of the cabinet. The freezing compartment of the standard refrigerator must maintain a temperature to preserve already frozen foods and to freeze ice cubes and certain desserts. Most fruits and vegetables will tolerate temperatures between 32 and 34 F. if accompanied by high humidity; fresh meat is improved under temperatures as low as 31 F.; dried and cured meats, which have a lower freezing point, as low as 29 F. Some companies have developed new features to obtain these desired temperatures, the Center Drawer (Fig. 3.1a and b) or the Air-Wrap compartment (Fig. 3.2). Maintaining these specialties may add slightly to the cost of operation, but this may be compensated for in the improved flavor and the length of preservation.

To prevent exterior "sweating" during adverse weather conditions, all modern refrigerators utilize built-in electrical compensators; but the refrigerator in Figure 3.2 has a Power Saver to reduce electrical output of these devices during normal weather without loss of efficiency.

To accomplish the two purposes mentioned above, the cabinet is constructed of a welded, double-steel shell, with insulation between.

Insulation

About 80 per cent of the heat that gets into the interior comes through the walls, in spite of good insulation, causing the mechanism to operate even when the doors have not been opened for hours. Therefore the quality of insulation is very important. Fiberglas, a widely used insulation, is a satisfactory material. (See Figs. 15.8a and b). It tends to stay in place without sagging and is odor and moisture proof, the last an essential characteristic, since moisture is a good conductor of heat. The manufacturer makes

FIG. 3.1. One of two methods of obtaining a lower temperature for improved food preservation: the center drawer with 2 cold zones, one for vegetables (above), the other for meats. Opened less frequently than the rest of the refrigerator, foods are not exposed to so much warm air. Frost-free always.—Frigidaire.

the Fiberglas even more moisture repellent by treating it with a tarlike substance. Research goes on continuously for new insulation materials. New thin-wall refrigerators may use high-density Fiberglas, sometimes combined with Freon-12 gas in a special envelope. Freon-12 is also used to form a rigid, closed-cell urethane foam that is generated in the cavity between the refrigerator walls.

FIG. 3.2. This refrigerator provides Instant Cold for faster recovery when door is opened, more condensing capacity, and greater horsepower. The large coil area allows warm foods to chill more quickly. Three sliding storage drawers with see-thru fronts, one of which may be converted by flicking a switch to an "Air Wrap" meat keeper.—Philco.

The foam expands to fill every bit of the space and bonds to all surfaces, leaving no possible path for heat leakage (Fig. 3.3).

The breaker strip connecting the outer and inner walls at the door opening is commonly of plastic to prevent transfer of heat from one wall to the other. The door frequently is lined with plastic, too, and has a gasket of vinyl plastic to provide a tight closing against heat or moisture leakage. Doors are often closed by a magnetic latch, or there may be a continuous magnetic seal imbedded in the gasket on all four sides of the door. In some models the magnet is not placed on the hinge side. Many doors have an inside release that may glow in the dark and open at a touch to make impossible those tragic accidents of children being shut into discarded refrigerators where they smother. The law now requires that the door be opened from the inside by a pushing force of not over 15 pounds.

The U.S. Public Health Service has issued a bulletin on entrapment hazards and how to correct them.[1]

---

[1] U.S. Public Health Service, "Preventing Child Entrapment in Household Refrigerators," Publ. No. 1258, 1964. For sale (5 cents) by Supt. of Documents, U.S.G.P.O., Washington, D.C., 20402.

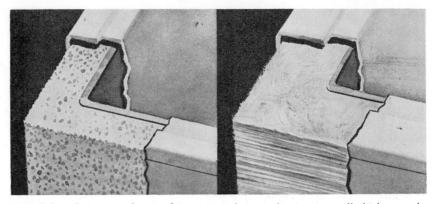

FIG. 3.3. Cutaways from refrigerators show reduction in wall thickness obtained by new thin-wall, no-frost refrigerators made possible by urethane foam insulation.—Norge.

The refrigerator should stand level to seal the door correctly and to prevent vibration which might cause wear on the motor. Leveling screws are usually found at the lower front corners.

The latch and hinge combination should hold the door tightly closed. The adequacy of the seal may be checked by shutting a dollar bill or paper of similar texture at different places between the door and frame. It should not be possible to pull the paper out; if it can be, warm air can filter into the food chamber and the latch should be adjusted to maintain the seal.

Shelves and Drawers

Shelves in the food chamber should be of corrosion-resistant metal bars or rods, closely spaced to hold small containers without tipping. Stainless steel, chromium-plated steel, and aluminum are all used for shelf material, and some manufacturers are again using glass shelves throughout, in addition to those commonly found over the crisper drawers. It is an advantage if some of the shelves are sliding so that food containers at the back may be reached easily. A rail at the rear prevents dishes from falling off when the shelf is pulled out. Swing-out shelves or those adjustable to more than one level increase the flexibility of food arrangement. One refrigerator has reversible shelves that provide two levels. Depending upon the side that is up, the height may be three inches above or below that of the other side. Divided shelves make possible the storage of large products or containers and step shelves serve a similar purpose (Fig. 3.4). Narrow shelves recessed in the door take care of many smaller articles not easily accommodated on the regular shelves—cheese, butter, eggs, bottled drinks, milk, etc., often in their own special compartments.

Many manufacturers in their specifications now indicate that NEMA (National Electrical Manufacturers Association) has certified their ratings for total capacity of refrigerator in cubic feet, refrigerator volume in cubic feet, freezer volume in cubic feet, freezer capacity in pounds, and shelf area in square feet.

Drawers especially designed for crisping will preserve the freshness of succulent vegetables. These drawers are usually placed at the bottom of the food compartment but in a few models are on the door. Although storage drawers are a convenience, they are not as essential as they once were, since most vegetables are marketed in plastic bags. In fact, if only a small amount is to be stored, less moisture is lost from food if it is stored in a plastic bag.

Finish

The inside of the refrigerator is finished in porcelain enamel, occasionally in titanium porcelain enamel, the outside commonly in synthetic enamel. The refrigerator, along with sinks, ranges, and kitchen cabinets, has often discarded its white uniform and now appears in many colors—yellow, blue, pink, or green. And where the whole refrigerator isn't colored, it has a front decorative panel in color, often a panel that can be easily changed when the homemaker wishes to adopt a different color scheme. The first interest in color was confined to the inside of the refrigerator and

FIG. 3.4. A step-shelf provides for high storage containers.—Hotpoint.

freezer and is still used there by certain manufacturers, especially on breaker strips and door linings. The inside color was seen only now and again—probably one reason for bringing the color outside.

Freezing Units

In either of the conventional systems of refrigeration—the compression (electric-motor-operated) or the absorption (heat-operated)—the mechanism is enclosed, and a substance known as a refrigerant circulates, undergoing certain changes of state as it does so. When a solid changes to a liquid, as in the ice refrigerator, or when a liquid refrigerant changes to a gas in the automatic refrigerator, heat is absorbed and, therefore, cooling takes place. Since the food chamber is the area that needs to be cooled, the refrigerant is changed from a liquid to a gas in the freezing unit that is within this compartment. The freezing unit, called the evaporator, may be in the form of coils, separate or stamped into the walls of the evaporator, or it may be a flat plate placed against the back wall or forming a part of the roof of the food chamber. The latter type of construction is frequently used when a freezer is combined with the refrigerator.

Condensers

Since the refrigerant changes from a liquid to a gas in one part of the system, it must change back from a gas to a liquid in another part, as shown in Figure 3.5.

A few electric refrigerators use a rotary compressor (Fig. 3.6a) instead of the one just described. The refrigerant enters the chamber on one side, is compressed by the rotating movement of the crankshaft, and is discharged from the other side (Fig. 3.6b). A movable blade is always in contact with the rotating cylinder and separates the chamber into two sections. When in operation the movement is continuous and not intermittent as in the system shown in Figure 3.5. In the compression system when the motor operates, the gaseous refrigerant is drawn from the freezing unit into the compressor, then forced into the condenser, where the change to a liquid takes place. In this change, heat is given off which must be discharged outside the refrigerator. The condenser tubes are frequently supported on a chimney or screen at the back of the refrigerator so that air can circulate over them and carry the heat away. It is essential to leave sufficient space at the rear and sides of the free-standing refrigerator to allow this heat to dissipate easily; otherwise, it will tend to pass through the insulation and cause the motor to operate a larger percentage of the time. Several manufacturers eliminate these rear condenser coils so that the refrigerator may be a straight-line model, so popular at present. Air is circulated by forced draft through a ventilation

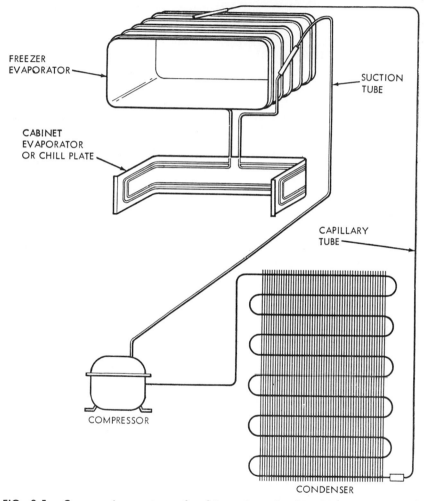

FREEZER EVAPORATOR

CABINET EVAPORATOR OR CHILL PLATE

SUCTION TUBE

CAPILLARY TUBE

COMPRESSOR

CONDENSER

FIG. 3.5. Compression system of refrigeration. Combined motor and compressor (lower left) suck gaseous refrigerant from the evaporator (top), force it into the condenser (lower right) where it is changed to a liquid; capillary action draws it through the capillary tube into the evaporator where it changes to a gas; this process absorbs heat, thus cooling the area surrounding it.

FIG. 3.6a. The Power Capsule, a rotary compressor, made of satellite-type materials, has only 3 moving parts, no piston, gasket, connecting rod, or oil pump found in the usual reciprocating type compressor. Depending on size, packs up to 78 per cent more power per cubic inch than past Frigidaire units, provides new power for the larger refrigerators now demanded by the homemaker, yet is whisper quiet in operation.—Frigidaire.

FIG. 3.6b. An inside view of the Power Capsule, showing the circulation of the refrigerant from where it enters the chamber at the bottom to its discharge through the pipe at the top.—Frigidaire.

grill in the lower part of the front panel. From the condenser the liquid refrigerant flows back to the evaporator through a capillary tube.

Refrigerants

Refrigerants selected for automatic refrigerators should be able to undergo frequent changes from a liquid to a gas and back again without deterioration and also should compress and evaporate at a pressure and temperature readily obtainable.

Freon-12. Freon-12 is the refrigerant commonly used in the compression system. It is nontoxic, nonflammable, and nonexplosive—desirable characteristics should a leak occur. The possibility of a leak is fairly remote since, in modern household refrigerators, the motor and compressor are under a single housing.

Ammonia. Ammonia is the refrigerant used in the absorption system. Since liquid ammonia does not readily change to a gas under the pressure maintained in the system, hydrogen, the lightest gas, is introduced into the evaporator to help bring about the change.

Ammonia combines with water when the water is cold, and is

just as readily separated from water when a small amount of heat is applied. The ammonia and hydrogen gas pass from the evaporator to the absorber where water combines with the ammonia to form ammonium hydroxide. The hydrogen gas, practically insoluble in water, goes back to the evaporator. The ammonium hydroxide flows to the generator where heat is applied to separate the ammonia from the water. Final separation takes place in the separator; the ammonia vapor rises to the condenser where it is changed to a liquid and the water goes back to the absorber. A study of Figure 3.7 will make clearer the relationship of the different parts.

Ammonia is toxic, flammable, and explosive, but not usually so under home conditions, and it does have a characteristic odor to warn of a leak. The steel parts of the system are welded together and leaks almost never occur.

Each system has advantages and disadvantages. The absorption system has no moving parts so there is little wear on the mechanism and it is noiseless. It may be cheaper to operate if the cost ratio of gas and electricity is more favorable to gas. However, since it must be attached to a fuel line, it is difficult to move from one location to another. The compressor-type refrigerator is easy to move and may be attached to any electric wall outlet. Noise caused by operation of the motor and compressor of the conventional compression system is slight, perhaps increasing somewhat as the refrigerator becomes older. The larger motor-compressor needed for large refrigerators tends to increase noise. Fans used in the no-frost models also add to noise, and the foamed-in-place insulation makes the cabinet more rigid, which may cause vibration. Sound-absorbing materials and dampening operations are employed by most manufacturers in an effort to reduce noise to a minimum.

Thermoelectric Refrigeration

A new type of refrigeration is now available—thermoelectric— which incorporates the thermocouple principle that an electric current passed through two wires of dissimilar metals which are joined together at their ends, will create cold at one junction and heat at the other. The refrigerators, only about 3 or 4 cubic feet in size, are adapted primarily for special purposes, and several might be used in different areas of the house, were they not somewhat expensive in proportion to their size. They have no moving parts except a small fan and, therefore, noise is almost completely eliminated. Since no refrigerant need circulate, the construction is so simple that servicing is rarely if ever required.

STORAGE OF FOODS

Although a possible temperature from 32 to 50 F. has been indicated, most automatic refrigerators maintain a temperature

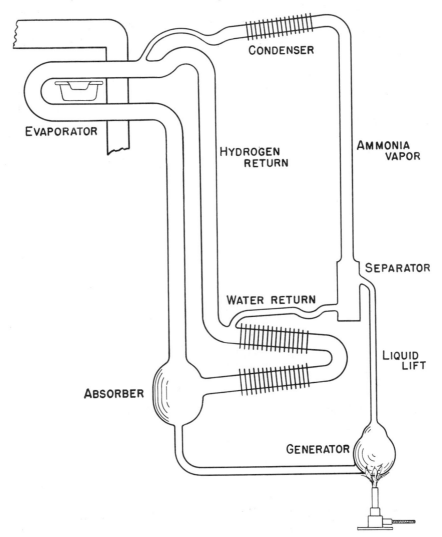

FIG. 3.7. Absorption system of refrigeration. Heat, instead of a motor, forces the refrigerant through the processes of vaporizing, condensing, and evaporating (cooling).—Servel.

between 36 and 42 F. There is usually little variation throughout the food compartment, but the space directly beneath the freezing unit, in the first down-drop of cold air, is somewhat colder and is recommended for storage of protein foods, meat and milk, and gravies, sauces, and puddings made from them. In one refrigerator the meat keeper is held at 33 F., in others a special construction surrounds the meat in a circulating blanket of chilled air. Protein foods are more susceptible to spoilage than other foods. Ground meats and ready-to-serve varieties should be frozen if they are not used within 24 hours after purchase. Raw meats should be unwrapped and placed in a ventilated container or, when stored in an open dish, wrapped loosely in wax paper with the ends left

FIG. 3.8. On-the-door pantry compartment of this refrigerator-freezer is bathed in moisture and cold to keep the contents fresh and at peak flavor. Transparent door enclosing "vapor zone" tilts down to become loading shelf.—Frigidaire.

open for circulation of air. All cooked products should be tightly covered.

New refrigerator models feature "cold-in-motion" (Fig. 3.9a). Evaporator coils are placed in the walls of the refrigerator or refrigerator-freezer combination, and by means of a fan the cold air is circulated uniformly and continuously to all sections of the food chamber. This method of cooling is said to keep foods colder and, therefore, fresher for a longer time and most manufacturers

FIG. 3.9a.   A sensible refrigerator for the family with a freezer. It's all fresh-food storage except for the locker that is just the right size for ice cubes and a day's supply of frozen foods. Cold air is fan-circulated throughout, even to the door shelves. The stacked crispers have special humidity seals front and back to help keep over ⅔ bushel of fruits and vegetables fresh. Defrosts automatically. NEMA certified capacity.—Whirlpool.

FIG. 3.9b. The Cube 'N Food Locker has two lever-ejecting trays holding 36 cubes. A Million-Magnet door—a "million" permanently magnetized particles sealed in a continuous vinyl gasket—forms a tight seal all around door.—Whirlpool.

now market at least one model in which frost is entirely eliminated.

Succulent vegetables and fruits are placed in the crisper drawers after all waste such as tops and damaged leaves have been discarded. A new feature is a "vapor zone" compartment to preserve peak flavor (Fig. 3.8). Do not store foods that do not need refrigeration—e.g., peanut butter, vinegar, prepared mustard, and many salad dressings. Strong-flavored vegetables and fruits such as cabbage, cauliflower, and melons tend to taint the air and always should be stored in plastic bags or other tightly covered containers. Leftovers are best stored tightly covered. It is not necessary to empty the contents of opened tin cans, but cover the top with aluminum foil. It is well to leave the paper label on, for the can then cools more rapidly since the paper absorbs the cold, while the shiny metal tends to reflect it.

Freezing Compartment

The conventional freezing section of the food compartment is used for freezing of ice cubes and desserts, for short-time storage of frozen supplies, and for freezing of foods to be used within a few days. When the homemaker has a separate freezer, this freezing compartment need be only large enough to freeze ice cubes and to store small quantities of frozen foods (Figs. 3.9a and b).

Frozen food may be stored for a week or longer only when the refrigerator is a dual-temperature model with a separate freezer section that maintains constant temperature of approximately zero degrees.

Freezing Ice Cubes

Ice cube trays, with dividers providing a variety of shapes—square, rectangular, round, hollow tubes, and thin slices—are usually of aluminum and may be coated with silicone for increased ease of removal. Many trays also have a release for freeing the cubes, or the tray may be slipped into a special section and a lever pushed to allow all the cubes to fall into a container. The freezing operation may be speeded by setting the control at the coldest reading of the thermostat dial and pouring a little water onto the shelf beneath the tray so that it makes close contact with the shelf. Some refrigerators have a sensitive signal arm device for freezing cubes automatically, eliminating the need for trays. Connection to the water supply is essential. Cubes made by this method remain dry and, therefore, do not stick together (Fig. 3.10).

Freezing Desserts

Desserts always are frozen as rapidly as possible to prevent the formation of large crystals. To obtain a fine texture, the mixture should be stirred or beaten when partially frozen, or certain ingredients may be added to hinder the growth of the crystals.

FIG. 3.10.   Automatic ice cube freezer in refrigerator.—Whirlpool.

These substances, known as interfering agents, tend to coat the crystals and inhibit their growth. They include eggs, cream, cornstarch, gelatin, tapioca, and marshmallows. It is better to use a small amount of two interfering agents rather than such a large amount of one that the product resembles a gelatin or cornstarch pudding rather than a frozen ice cream. Always completely dissolve sugar before starting to freeze, since it is crystalline in form and may serve as a nucleus around which a larger crystal may grow. In recipes calling for whipped cream, coffee cream, 2 or 3 days old, is often preferable to whipping cream, as the consistency should be soft enough to flow when the bowl is tipped. Be sure that the inside of the tray is dry before adding the mix. On the other hand, wiping the outside bottom of the tray with a damp cloth will cause it to adhere to the evaporator sleeve and so hasten the freezing process.

LOCATION OF REFRIGERATOR

It has already been noted that in certain cases space should be left behind and at the sides of a refrigerator. Free space, 4 to 10 inches of it, should be left above, too. This space is especially important when a gas refrigerator is installed. If adequate space is not available and cannot be secured by the removal of an overhead cabinet, a flue should be constructed at the back of the cabinet. Because heat is always trying to get into a refrigerator, the refrigerator should be placed in a cool location, away from cooking areas or a furnace register or radiator, and where sunshine will not touch it.

CARE OF REFRIGERATOR

Location as well as type and age of the refrigerator will determine the frequency and kind of care necessary to keep operations at an efficient level and foods in the desired conditions. Regularity in defrosting and cleaning will do much to eliminate waste of both foods and energy.

Rollers allow some refrigerators to be moved out easily from the wall for cleaning under and behind.

Defrosting

Frost acts as an insulator and causes the refrigerating mechanism to operate more of the time. Frost also tends to retain odors and to impart them to certain foods susceptible to absorbing

foreign odors. Accumulation of frost is hastened by frequent opening of the door, especially when the room atmosphere is high
in humidity, so it is preferable to plan removal of food so the door
will be opened as infrequently as possible. Keeping stored food
well covered also decreases deposit of frost.

Automatic Defrosting

An automatic-defrosting refrigerator is a favorite choice of
the homemaker, but may lead her to neglect the necessary cleaning. There are several methods of automatic defrosting; the
simplest, perhaps, is the one in which the freezing unit reaches a
temperature of 36 to 38 F. during each off-cycle, so that any frost
formed will melt and the water drip into a trough below the evaporator. The water is carried away through a tube into a container
on the shelf of the food compartment, or into a shallow tray behind the panel at the bottom of the refrigerator cabinet. The
depth of water in the inside container can be noted and so will be
emptied fairly regularly. At such times the dish should be washed.
When the receptacle is below the cabinet, the heat from the motor
and compressor causes the water to evaporate, but at the same time
the warmth and moisture supply an excellent breeding place for
molds and bacteria. If the tray is not removed at regular intervals
and thoroughly cleaned, undesirable odors will develop.

Manual Defrosting

Manual defrosting should be done before the frost is ¼
inch thick. The unit is defrosted by turning the control switch to
the "defrost" position, or by turning off the current, and then filling the ice-cube trays with warm water and placing them inside
the evaporator sleeve. At the present time several commercial defrost aids are on the market. One such aid is an aerosol spray
which removes the frost coating, and will prevent further heavy
buildup of frost if repeated weekly. Another aid is an electric coil
on an extension cord; after the refrigerator is disconnected from
the outlet, the coil may be placed inside the freezing unit, and connected to an outlet and the heated coil melts the frost. Special care
must be taken to keep the heat away from plastic parts. If your refrigerator or freezer door is lined with plastic or if the breaker
strips are of plastic, you should cover the plastic with aluminum

foil before turning on the coil. Empty the catch basin as needed—many of these are shallow and difficult to manage when full.

Cleaning Refrigerator

All refrigerator interiors should be cleaned frequently. This task combines easily with manual defrosting, but should be done just as regularly in the automatic-defrosting refrigerators. Wipe the freezing unit and walls with baking soda solution—one tablespoon of baking soda to a quart of water—and then with a dry towel. Shelves, crisper drawers, and ice cube trays are washed in warm soapy water, then rinsed and dried. The gasket around the door also is washed in warm soapy water, wiped off with fresh water, and dried.

Manufacturers now usually make one or more no-frost models; i.e., frost is never deposited inside the freezer or food chamber but collects on coils in the walls. The coils are automatically defrosted once in 24 hours, the water flowing to a tray below the refrigerator where it is evaporated by heat from the motor and compressor. In some cases, moving currents of cold air will vaporize the slight frost deposit without its passing through the liquid stage. This vapor supplies desirable humidity to the food compartment. In a 1966 survey of sales, 56 per cent of refrigerators sold are of the "never frost" type.

Condenser coils should be dusted occasionally to allow free circulation of air. When the coils are below the cabinet, the refrigerator should first be disconnected. The outside of the refrigerator may be wiped and waxed with any of the special waxes on the market.

COST OF OPERATION

The 8- to 12-cubic foot conventional refrigerator consumes from 30 to 45 kilowatt-hours of electricity a month under normal operating conditions. But operation of newer models may be expected to cost more for several reasons. Families tend to purchase larger refrigerators, often with a big freezer compartment maintained at zero temperature. The no-frost types have a higher horsepower motor ($\frac{1}{3}$hp instead of $\frac{1}{8}$) to run the fans that keep the frost out of the food and freezing sections. And the refrigerator holds such a variety of tempting articles—ice cream, soft drinks, snacks—that the door is opened more frequently by the family, causing the mechanism to operate more continuously. But if it renders more service, it is doubtless worth the extra cost.

With a minimum flame, gas refrigerators use approximately 750 Btu per hour, regardless of size. At the maximum setting the consumption may vary between 1800 and 2900 Btu per hour.

FREEZERS

A separate freezer is an economy in some families, and the combination refrigerator-freezer is increasingly popular with home-makers who purchase frozen foods, but only occasionally do any freezing of products themselves. In a number of the combinations the freezer is placed below the refrigerator section (Fig. 3.2). Since food is removed from the freezer less frequently than from

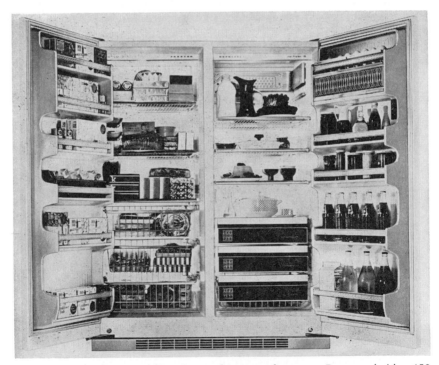

FIG. 3.11. No-frost combination refrigerator-freezer. Freezer holds 450 pounds of food, has 3 shelves and 3 glide-out baskets, aluminum shelf guards on door. Refrigerator side features 2 full-width storage drawers for meats and produce, and a glide-out basket for fruits and vegetables. Net volume and shelf area conform to NEMA standards.—Hotpoint.

the refrigerator, some stooping is eliminated. The steadily expanding use of frozen foods in the home has led manufacturers to enlarge the freezer section until in several models it is of the same or even greater area than the refrigerator compartment. In one case twin models are provided (Fig. 3.11). The refrigerator half of this combination has the cooling coils in the walls and has no freezing section, even for ice cubes.

A new trend is to install a refrigerator and freezer side by side into space previously occupied by kitchen cabinets. Sometimes they are in place of wall cabinets, but low-built models may replace base cabinets with the tops serving as a work surface. They are not so easy to get into when they are down below, but when they are placed high enough not to interfere with use of counter space (often a scarce commodity in a small kitchen), short people may have difficulty reaching the upper shelves.

The freezer should maintain a fairly constant temperature at zero degrees or slightly below because a fluctuating temperature tends to draw moisture from frozen foods. In the conventional freezing unit the temperature fluctuates, often 20 degrees or more during the off and on periods of the cycle.

TYPES OF FREEZERS

Free-standing freezers are of two general types, chest and upright. The chest may have a single compartment or be divided, with a separate, fast-freezing section. Coils are placed in the walls and may also extend across the bottom of the box (Fig. 3.12). In

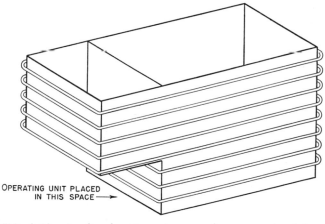

OPERATING UNIT PLACED
IN THIS SPACE ——→

FIG. 3.12. In the chest-type freezer, the evaporator tubes are wrapped around the food compartment.

the upright freezer it is common practice to fasten the coils below each shelf so that all surfaces are refrigerated. This arrangement tends to increase speed of freezing since more food comes into direct contact with the unit (Fig. 3.13). Some upright freezers have additional storage space on the door, occasionally in the form of package dispensers (Fig. 3.14).

The size of freezer required has been estimated as 2.3 to 4.0 cubic feet per person, depending on the amount of the daily menu supplied from the freezer. One cubic foot will store 35 pounds of frozen food.

Construction

In general construction features the freezer is similar to the refrigerator, although the interior may be finished in aluminum or synthetic enamel as well as porcelain enamel. It is true that there is a growing tendency to use aluminum in certain parts of the interiors of refrigerators also. The insulation must be thicker in the freezer, since there is a greater difference between inside and outside temperatures. This temperature difference has tended to cause sweating on the exterior surface of the freezer in humid areas, a condition which some manufacturers have tried to overcome by placing the condenser coils against the outside walls. Breaker strips of plastic help to prevent the heat from penetrating to the inside of the freezer, and occasionally the whole lid or door is lined with plastic. The lid on the chest freezer should be counterbalanced and an interior light is an advantage. Wire baskets aid in the storage and removal of food, especially in the chest type. Some form of alarm is desirable, should the flow of electricity be interrupted and the temperature start to rise. Freon-12 is the refrigerant commonly used.

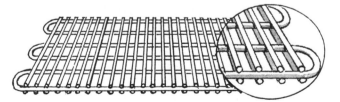

FIG. 3.13. Freezing coils form the shelves and enable you to freeze on each shelf. There is also a coil at the top for extra cold.—Admiral.

EFFICIENCY OF USE

To use a freezer most economically it should be kept filled with food at all times. It is poor practice, for example, to load the freezer with asparagus, peas, beans, strawberries, raspberries peaches, and perhaps a quarter of beef and a dozen or so chickens

FIG. 3.14. Upright freezer with grill fronts that hold in food but tilt down for loading and unloading. Basket in bottom rolls out.—Frigidaire.

during the summer and early fall months and then use these products throughout the year without putting in other foods. Stews, casserole dishes, and many baked products can replace the original foods as they are removed. The more rapid the turnover, the less the cost of operation per pound stored.

Packaging Materials

A variety of packaging materials is available—plastic boxes or waxed cartons with pliofilm liners, polyethylene bags, aluminum foil, Saran wrap, or glass jars. Sheet wrappings should be pliable enough to cling closely to the product to eliminate air, and all materials should be odorless and moisture-vapor proof to prevent the desiccation of the food. To obtain optimum products food should be selected while it is fresh and at the peak of maturity, and only the amount that can be frozen within 24 hours should be placed in the freezer at one time, usually not more than 1/15 of the capacity of your freezer. You can determine this desirable amount by multiplying the cubic foot rating of your freezer by 35 and dividing the answer by 15. For example, if your freezer is an 18-cubic foot model, at 35 pounds per cubic foot, the total capacity in pounds is 630 pounds; 630 divided by 15 equals 42 pounds that may be frozen safely in a 24-hour period. However, if your freezer is only a 10-cubic foot model, then you should freeze only about 24 pounds at one time.

Fluctuations in temperature, caused by placing too large a new load of food to be frozen in an already partially filled cabinet, may draw moisture from the stored food. This is especially true when such a practice is followed several days in succession. Follow the manufacturer's instructions. Pamphlets on freezing may usually be obtained from the bulletin office of the state agricultural college. The freezer unit should operate continuously during the freezing operation, but only about 50 per cent of the time during storage.

Defrosting

The accumulation of frost in a freezer does not greatly affect operating efficiency, but if too thick, may interfere with space for storage. When it does, the excess deposit may be removed from the walls with a wooden or plastic scraper. Complete defrosting may be done once a year, when the amount of food stored is at a minimum, so that it can be placed temporarily in the freezing unit of the refrigerator or wrapped in sufficient layers of paper to prevent thawing. Spreading a bath towel or two in the bottom of the freezer to catch scraped-off frost and moisture will greatly facilitate their removal. Models which provide for drainage through a hose are desirable for utility rooms or basements with floor drains (Fig. 3.15). After defrosting, wipe the interior of the cabinet with a cloth wet with baking-soda water; then dry cabinet thoroughly. Baskets and racks may be washed in warm soapy water. Placing the freezer in a cool, dry area and wrapping all foods carefully will tend to reduce the frost deposit.

FIG. 3.15. An aid in defrosting. A drain provided in this freezer has an attachable hose by which the water may be drawn off.—Whirlpool.

EXPERIMENTS AND PROJECTS

1. Make a table to record the following data on refrigerators and freezers (additional models may be available in foods laboratories or in appliance stores):
    Ease of operating door latches
    Thickness of insulation (i.e., distance between outside and inside walls)
    Material of breaker strip
    Type and arrangement of shelves
    Type of freezing unit, method of defrosting, position of container to collect defrost water
    Position of condenser, construction to allow circulation of air
    How to distinguish between a refrigerator, a combination refrigerator and freezer, and a freezer
2. To demonstrate optimum method of storage:
    Try different locations in the refrigerator for meat, milk, celery, cauliflower, butter, cheese, and cornstarch pudding. Decide which arrangement is the most desirable.
3. To compare methods of freezing:
    Turn temperature control on refrigerator to coldest setting. Make lemon sherbet: Mix together until sugar is entirely dissolved ⅔ cup lemon juice, grated rind of one lemon, 1½ cups sugar, one quart of coffee cream or half-and-half. Divide into two portions. Freeze one part in tray of refrigerator, stirring thoroughly with wooden spoon once or twice during freezing period. When this half reaches the mushy stage, freeze second half in freezer equipped with dasher (turned by electricity or by hand). Compare two products as to texture, flavor, color, desirability. Explain cause of differences. Turn refrigerator temperature control back to normal setting.
4. To make fruit ice of desirable consistency:
    Turn refrigerator temperature control to coldest setting. Cook one quart cranberries in 2 cups water. Put through sieve. Add 1¼ cups sugar and stir until dissolved. Add juice of one lemon, juice of one orange. Freeze. When half frozen, remove to chilled bowl and beat with chilled beater. Return to tray and finish freezing. Turn refrigerator temperature control back to normal setting. (When cranberries are not available, any fresh fruit ice recipe may be used.)
5. To demonstrate freezing ice cubes:
    If ice cube trays of different shapes are available, freeze cubes in them. Suggest uses for each shape.
6. To demonstrate defrosting and cleaning a refrigerator:
    If two or more refrigerators are available, have one or two members of the class demonstrate defrosting and cleaning simultaneously, comparing them for ease and efficiency. The switch should be set at "defrost" several hours before demonstration is to begin.

QUESTIONS

1. Why are refrigerators necessary?
2. In what different ways is heat transferred in a refrigerator?
3. Where is the coldest area in the refrigerator? What foods should be stored in this area? Why?
4. What various methods of food storage should the homemaker use?
5. What two parts do gas and electric refrigerators have in common?
6. Where is the heat that is removed from the food in the refrigerator given off? In what part of the mechanism is the heat removed?
7. If a refrigerator does not defrost automatically, when should it be defrosted? What cleaning will you give it at this time? If the refrigerator does defrost automatically, what care does it still require?
8. What features indicate whether your refrigerator is a combination refrigerator freezer or not?
9. You have an asparagus bed and a strawberry patch and freeze your surplus supply of these foods. What three essentials must you pay attention to if you are to obtain top-quality frozen products?
10. Mrs. Wilson bought hamburger for Wednesday dinner and then the family was invited out for the meal. She found that she could not use the hamburger until Saturday. How should she store it? Why?

Chapter Four

ELECTRIC HOUSEWARES

O NCE A HOUSEHOLD was considered well supplied if it had an electric toaster and coffee maker. Now there are so many small electric appliances that at times the range seems almost an unnecessary piece of equipment. Moreover the appliances themselves have become so completely automatic that their operation requires a minimum of the homemaker's attention. They do, however, demand storage space. If the appliance will be used frequently and, therefore, meets a real need, or if its use simplifies the job to be done and so saves the homemaker's time and energy, even if used only occasionally, then it justifies the space it occupies; otherwise not. Such points should be evaluated before making a purchase.

Most of the changes made in electric appliances from year to year are in finish or styling. But fundamentally they are the same; a frypan still fries and a toaster toasts. The most noteworthy recent improvements probably have been the more sensitive and accurate thermostat controls and the sealing of the electric units so that the appliances can be immersed entirely for washing.

In selecting any electrically operated appliance the purchaser should look always for the Underwriters' Laboratories Seal of Approval, often the initials "UL," surrounded by a circle (Fig. 2.22). The seal may be stamped into the metal of the appliance or be attached as a separate label. It indicates that the equipment has passed certain rigid tests for safety against fire and shock hazard. Cords usually have a yellow or blue band or circle surrounding them, but such a label on the cord indicates that only the *cord* has been tested—the appliance must have its own label.

COFFEE MAKERS

The electrically operated coffee maker may be either a percolator or a vacuum type (Figs. 4.1, 4.2, and 4.3). Both usually are made of steel, chromium plated on the outside, with the inside of stainless steel, chromium plate, or aluminum. They are available

FIG. 4.1. Automatic percolator, 2- to 9-cup capacity marked on inside. Special features: a brew selector to assure desired strength; will reheat without percolating; and a no-drip spout. Note specially balanced design, a desirable safety feature in families with small children. —General Electric.

in various sizes, from 2 to 8 or 10 cups. The cup used in measuring is equivalent to ¾ of the standard measuring cup.

Percolator

In the percolator the coffee is placed in a perforated receptacle that is fitted over a tube which extends to the bottom of the pot just above the heating element. The valve type, in which percolation starts almost as soon as heat is applied, can be identi-

FIG. 4.2. Here is a departure from the conventional design of an automatic coffee maker. By eliminating the traditional spout where oils collect and rancidity develops, engineers believe they have made cleaning easier and assured consistent taste. The water-pumping system has no moving parts or valves. Brew control offers any strength from mild to strong. A guide in the lid directs the flow into the cup in a thin stream without any drip.—Westinghouse.

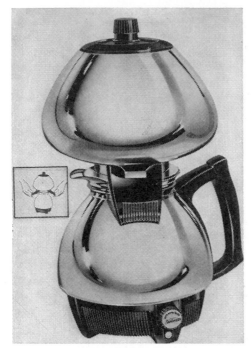

FIG. 4.3. The vacuum-type automatic coffee maker utilizes steam condensation to complete the brewing process. The lever switches to low heat to keep the coffee warm until it is served. To remove the brew-top, raise both locking levers, as shown.—Sunbeam.

fied by the divided openings at the lower end of the tube. Only a small amount of the heated water is forced at one time up the tube and so it remains slightly below boiling point, the best temperature for extracting the maximum flavor from the coffee, while leaving behind the oils that tend to give a bitter taste.

The cover of the percolator is centered with a glass or plastic spreader that deflects the hot water over the coffee in the container, through which it then filters back into the pot. Usually there is a perforated cover over the container to regulate the rate at which the water reaches the coffee. The transparent spreader allows the operator to note the color and hence the strength of the coffee; moderate strength is obtained in about 6 minutes, if one rounded tablespoon of regular- or medium-grind coffee is used to a cup. More coffee rather than a longer percolation period is recommended if a stronger coffee is desired, since a long period tends to extract more of the oils and caffein. As a rule coffee makers brew the best beverage if used to capacity. Purchase a size, therefore, that provides the number of servings you use regularly.

The base and handle of the percolator should be of heat-resistant material. The lip of the spout should be sharp and narrow to prevent dripping. Tall, slender percolators are attractive in appearance, but short, broad ones have less tendency to tip and should be selected when there are small children in the home.

The automatic percolator eliminates watching. An indicator may be set to give the strength of coffee desired, a signal light may show when the percolating is finished, and a temperature control will turn the heat to "warm" until time for serving. A fuse or circuit breaker should protect the percolator against damage if the water is all evaporated. Additional fuses should be kept in supply.

Vacuum-type Coffee Maker

The vacuum-type coffee maker has two bowls, fitted tightly together with a rubber gasket. The heating element is in the bottom of the lower bowl. From the upper bowl a tube extends almost to the bottom of the lower bowl. The top of this tube is covered with a fine wire screen or a circle of cloth over a porous plate. On this the coffee is placed. Water is measured into the lower bowl and the two bowls pressed together. As the water heats it forms steam, which, together with the air in the bowl, exerts pressure and forces the water up the tube into the upper bowl, where it mixes with the coffee. The mixture should agitate for about three minutes. When the heat is removed—or reduced in the automatic type—the steam in the lower bowl condenses, leaving a partial vacuum. This induces the brewed coffee to flow back into the lower bowl. The top bowl containing the grounds is removed and the coffee served.

Although drip grind coffee is often recommended for use in the vacuum-type maker, experience seems to indicate that this grind may clog the meshes of the very fine wire screen, preventing some of the brew from returning to the lower bowl. Regular grind is considered preferable.

Care of Coffee Makers

To make good coffee, always use fresh coffee and fresh cold water and keep the coffee maker, whatever the type, spotlessly clean. Electric units may not be put into water, but the percolator and the lower bowl of the vacuum type may be washed out with warm soapy water and occasionally operated just with water, to which soap or baking soda has been added. This practice will remove the residue of coffee oil that tends to deposit in the crevices. Do not use baking soda when the coffee maker is lined with aluminum, since it will darken the aluminum. At present at least one percolator is completely immersible. If a cloth is used in the vacuum-type maker, wash it after each use in clear water—never use soap—and boil it about once a week. It is a good procedure to leave the pot uncovered between times of use.

TOASTERS

Most toasters on the market today are of the well type, usually automatic, but the nonautomatic, side-slice toaster is still available. The latter is less expensive, and is entirely satisfactory, but does require more constant watching during the toasting operation if burned toast is to be avoided. It is assumed that the side-slice toaster produces slightly drier toast, since only one side of the bread is toasted at a time and the other side has a chance to dry. The difference, however, is probably too small to influence choice. Both sides of the bread are browned at the same time in the well toaster. This is faster, and automatic equipment usually tends to save time for the homemaker, and reduces wastage (Fig. 4.4).

Various devices lower the bread into the well; it may go down and come up by itself without a sound, or a lever may be depressed and the toast pop up at the end, with or without a signal by a bell or light. Most models are constructed to raise small slices of bread high enough from the well to be easily removed. Never use a fork for this purpose; it may damage the electric unit and could cause a shock if the toaster is connected to an outlet. The toaster has a hand-operated release for use when the automatic device fails to function.

The thickness of the wire guards that support the bread de-

FIG. 4.4. Gives choice of 1, 2, 3, or 4 slices of toast. "Selectronic" color guide assures same golden brown toast with any kind of bread, even frozen. Reheats cold toast without changing color.—Proctor.

termines the evenness of browning. If the wires are heavy, the bread will have light streaks between the browner areas. Toasters frequently have an indicator that may be set for different degrees of browning. Nonautomatic toasters are usually rated from 600 to 800 watts; the automatic types from 1000 to 1200.

Oven-type toasters are also available. They open on the side like an oven with the heating element in the top and have a sliding shelf to hold the bread. Their chief advantage is undoubtedly the ease with which they accommodate buns, rolls, and other unusual sizes and shapes of bread. They are very satisfactory for the preparation of open-face toasted cheese sandwiches, cinnamon toast, and similar foods (Fig. 4.5). One manufacturer now makes a combination well- and oven-type toaster.

Crumbs should be removed frequently. Most automatic toasters have a hinged or separate tray beneath the well for ease in cleaning. Base and handles are of insulating material, but when the toaster is used fairly long at one time, the metal parts may become uncomfortably hot.

WAFFLE BAKERS

The modern waffle baker is commonly square in shape and will cook four rather large square waffles (Fig. 4.6). It is finished in chromium on the outside and has cast aluminum grids, which

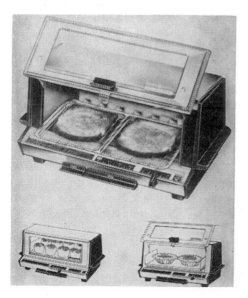

FIG. 4.5. Toast-R-Oven may be used for both toasting and baking. The bake guide indicates temperatures from 200 to 500 F. The electric coils located at the top and bottom of the oven are enclosed in glass tubes, eliminating shock hazard.—General Electric.

FIG. 4.6. This waffle baker with high knobs close together will produce 4 large sections of crisp waffle.—Sunbeam.

are treated with silicone by most manufacturers to hinder sticking. If the grids have not been pretreated, they should be brushed with unsalted fat and heated to a fairly high temperature; this seals the pores in the aluminum, thus preventing sticking. This process is recommended as an added precaution even when the grids have been pretreated. The first waffle baked after this procedure may be discarded if it has absorbed too much fat. If sufficient shortening is added to the waffle recipe, no future sticking should occur, but recipes of high sugar content should have the amount of fat increased. Always leave the lid open at the end of the baking process until the grids have cooled; otherwise moisture may collect between the grids and break the seal. Care must be taken, moreover, not to wash the grids, just wipe them off with a slightly damp cloth.

Construction Features

The crispness of the waffle is influenced in part by the recipe, but also by construction of the grid. Knobs shallow and spaced somewhat far apart will tend to produce a soft, moist waffle; those taller and nearer together, a crisp one. The hinge should allow the rising batter to lift the upper grid so that steam may escape and so prevent a soggy waffle. It is an advantage to have the temperature of the baker automatically controlled. Sometimes there is only a heat indicator that shows when the grids are preheated. In this case the waffle is usually done when steam ceases to escape from between the grids. When there is no heat-indicating mechanism, a piece of white paper may be placed in the baker until it acquires the desired shade of brown.

A variety of waffles may be made, as suggested in the experiments at the end of the chapter. Waffle bakers differ in size, but approximately one-fourth of a cup of batter to a section is a good measure for a trial run. Increase or decrease the amount as needed to assure sufficient batter so that it will rise and fill the upper grid; otherwise the top of the waffle will not brown adequately.

GRIDDLES

The griddle is made of heavy-gauge aluminum, a good, even conductor of heat. It may need to be pretreated to seal the pores in the aluminum. Handles at each end to aid in moving and an automatic heat control are desirable features (Fig. 4.7).

Since the griddle may also be employed as a grill and consequently washed, the seal will be destroyed. If used in this way frequently, it may be preferable to omit the pre-treatment of the surface and simply apply a thin film of fat when pancakes are to be cooked.

WAFFLE - GRILL COMBINATIONS

Some waffle bakers are supplied with grill plates that may be put in place of the grids. The grill may be used for making cheese sandwiches, and when the upper grid is supported in an open position, for pancakes, bacon and eggs, hamburgers, etc. It is always an advantage when one appliance may be used for a variety of cooking operations. When used as a grill, a container

FIG. 4.7. A family of appliances operated with the same detachable heat control. — Hamilton Beach.

FIG. 4.8. A "Teflon"-coated waffle baker and grill combination. Foods do not stick to this surface, making cleaning easy. Run-off spout drains excess grease, and expandable hinge adjusts to food thickness.—Kelvinator-American Motors.

into which excess fat may drip and from which the hot fat is easily emptied is a desirable feature (Fig. 4.8).

ROASTERS

The electric roaster may often substitute for the range oven. The roaster comes in several sizes and shapes, round, oval, and rectangular, holding from 3 to 20 quarts. The larger models are more versatile.

Construction of Roaster

Roasters are of welded steel, finished in baked enamel on the outside, porcelain enamel within. They are fitted with an inset pan into which a rack is placed to hold the dishes of glass or pottery used for cooking a meal, or to support the shelves on which pie, cake, or muffin pans or cookie sheets may be put (Fig. 4.9). The rack also holds the separate grill attachment when it is used. The combined wattage rating of the roaster oven and grill is too high (approximately 3,000 watts) for them to be used simultaneously without blowing a fuse. To prevent such an attempt, the terminal studs on the two sections are spaced farther apart than in the standard appliance plug and only one plug is provided by the manufacturer. The oven is thermostatically con-

FIG. 4.9. Roaster with automatic control may be used for cooking a whole meal with a minimum of attention. Note window and vent in lid.—Nesco.

trolled and supplies a series of heats comparable to those of the range oven. The roaster must always be connected to a wall outlet.

The roaster oven is covered with a lid, commonly of aluminum, with a vent, preferably adjustable, for the escape of excess steam, and a glass panel so the homemaker may observe progress of the baking. Since heat rises, much heat is lost when the cover is lifted unnecessarily. The cover may be hinged or separate; when separate, a support frequently is provided on either end of the roaster body to hold the cover at an angle to prevent dripping.

The inset pan has a rim that extends over the edge of the roaster oven and so prevents condensed steam or fat from dripping into the oven. This pan can be removed and washed like any dish, as can the grill plate which is removable from the broiler-grill unit. The roaster body, with the electric unit between the walls, should never be put into water, but may be wiped with a damp cloth.

The roaster is especially adaptable for a young couple or a single person doing "light housekeeping," and also provides extra cooking facilities for a large family or one that does much entertaining. It requires a fairly large amount of storage space. Special stands for the roaster and cabinets for the storage of the grill and baking dishes may be purchased. A smaller edition of the roaster is the electric oven that opens on the side. It is similar to the toaster oven and is thermostatically controlled, but is somewhat limited in the amount of food it will bake at one time.

FRYPANS

Another small electric appliance also capable of taking over many range operations is the automatic electric frypan. It is of cast aluminum, square or round in shape, of various depths, and may be furnished with a flat or dome-shaped cover of metal or glass. The feet and handle are of insulating material so that the frypan may be used on the buffet or dining-table. Handles on either side facilitate the ease of moving the frypan from place to place.

Use and Care of Frypans

In several models the heat-control dial and indicator light are on the handle, and also a temperature chart for foods most frequently cooked in the frypan—bacon, eggs, hamburgers, pancakes, ham, potatoes, fish, fried chicken, and others. The use of the frypan is by no means limited to such a list, however; various vegetables may be sautéd in it and, with the cover, it may double as a stewpan or casserole, as a corn popper, or may bake cake, apples and cup-custards, and at the low settings keep foods warm until served. The glass cover, available from at least one

FIG. 4.10. This frypan has the nonsticking "Teflon" coating on the inside. It is always used with a wooden or plastic spatula to prevent scratching.—Club Aluminum.

manufacturer, is useful for watching the progress of the cooking.

An outstanding feature of certain frypans is the sealed heating unit which makes washing easy for it is possible to immerse the entire pan in water as far as the dial or light on the handle. Some pans have the control thermostat on a separate cord and the frypan then may be entirely immersed (Figs. 4.10 and 4.11), but it *must not be immersed until it has cooled.* When the temperature regulator is on the body of the pan, this method of cleaning cannot be used. The pan should not be scraped with sharp, metallic objects; if soaking fails to loosen particles of the cooked food, the pan may be gently scoured with fine steel wool. Even distribution of heat across the bottom of the pan tends to reduce any sticking, and much research has been carried on to improve the distribution, in some cases by making the aluminum as dense as possible and by applying a coating of silver or silicone to the interior surface of the pan.

The frypan has an average rating of about 1200 watts and provides a range of temperature from 140 F., or slightly below, to 420 F. It should not be stored in the range oven and preferably not in the range storage drawer. If subjected to heat—even low heat—fairly continuously, the plastic handle and control unit may be damaged.

A variation of the electric frypan is the Electromatic Skillet (Fig. 4.12). It consists of two parts, the skillet of Pyroceram, and

FIG. 4.11. A multi-cooker frypan with a cover that tilts into six positions for cooking different foods or for holding the cover out of the way when turning or basting. The frypan has a special "Tilt-Leg" that allows excess fat to drain off automatically.—Sunbeam.

FIG. 4.12. The Corning Ware Electromatic skillet and percoator are made of Pyroceram (p. 289), the missile material. The percolator is attached to an electric outlet by inserting the plug into the underside of the handle. The skillet is placed on a thermostatically controlled heater base which may be used at the table to keep foods warm. A detachable handle aids in manipulation of the skillet.—Corning.

a separate base heater, rated at 1400 watts, with thermostatic control that supplies automatic cooking. A signal light on the base indicates when the current is on. At the end of the preheat period the light goes out, then, by flashing on and off during cooking, shows that a steady heat is maintained. The base is insulated with Fiberglas and may be used on the table to keep food warm. It may be wiped off with a damp cloth, but must not be immersed in water.

The skillet may be used separately for any top-of-range cookery, in the oven, and under the broiler, or as a container for freezing foods, just as other Pyroceram utensils.

BROILERS

A portable electric broiler is now on the market. The broiler unit of 700 watts is in the domed cover. The cover is easily detached from the base, which then may be washed as any utensil. When the cover is in the open position, it rests securely on a large plastic support. Two additional plastic handles on the base facilitate portability. This appliance broils food uniformly and quickly and eliminates cleaning the larger broiler compartment in the range.

FRYERS

Deep-fat frying may be done in a pot or kettle on the surface of the range, but the electric fryer, by providing very exact temperature control, has increased the ease with which this method of cookery may be carried on, and has improved the product. The fryer of chromium-plated steel with an aluminum lining may be round, rectangular, or bowl shaped, and when the lower area of the well is somewhat below the heating unit, the bottom remains cooler and there is less tendency for crumbs to overcook and discolor the fat. A fill line indicates the depth of fat that should be used to prevent any bubbling over the edge. Fryers are rated from 1100 to 1450 watts and indicate temperatures to 450 F. A signal light is an advantage.

A fryer may be used for baking, stewing, roasting, and other cooking operations, but because of its shape is usually not as versatile as the electric frypan.

SAUCEPANS, CASSEROLES, PRESSURE PANS

These appliances are similar in use to their nonelectric doubles, but the automatic controls eliminate watching and guesswork. They should be well balanced, broad rather than tall, and the controls placed to allow partial or complete immersion. Indicator lights are desirable features. They need the same care as electric frypans.

ROTISSERIES

The rotisserie (Fig. 4.13a), with or without a grill attachment, has been so popular that it has been incorporated in a number of ranges, in the oven or broiler or even on the surface of the range.

FIG. 4.13a. A combination rotisserie-broiler features "Open-air" broiling by means of a constant flow of fresh air through the appliance. It is chrome plated outside and in, has a glass door that hinges down for easy access and may be removed for washing.—General Electric.

FIG. 4.13b. The Carousel Rotisserie. Broiler has a polished aluminum cover unit with heat-resistant glass top, removable for loading. Powerful motor turns the stainless steel spit at correct speed for perfect cooking results.— Sunbeam.

It is a form of broiling that has been used for many years in certain foreign countries. The motor-operated revolving spit may be positioned either horizontally or vertically. As it turns, the food is cooked uniformly on all sides. The vertical rotisserie (Fig. 4.13b) occupies less counter space than a dinner plate, and is said to give faster cooking results than the horizontal. This model also has a wire basket for cooking vegetables or warming breads. Many kinds of foods may be prepared in this way—chickens, roasts, frankfurters, or kabobs with onions and tomatoes, to mention only a few. An automatic timer is a convenience.

Should the rotisserie seem to produce an undesirable amount of noise, this is directly related to the position of the bird or meat on the spit. The food should be so centered that it will balance properly as it turns.

The separate rotisserie is connected to an appliance outlet. If used outdoors (not usually recommended), place it on a slab of insulating material to prevent current leakage to the ground. The operator should stand on a block of wood or on a rubber mat. The rotisserie is generally only slightly insulated or not at all, and care must be taken not to touch the hot metal sides.

To clean, disconnect it, and if possible remove the heating unit. As soon as it is cool enough to handle, but still warm, wipe off all spatters of fat with a paper towel. Then wipe with a cloth dipped into warm, soapy water and dry. Any deposit left on the interior surfaces will be baked on during a following use and then can be removed only with difficulty.

MIXERS

Many of the operations in food preparation involve stirring, beating, mixing, whipping, and creaming. If they may be performed by a mixer, energy and time are saved; hence the electric mixer is a worthwhile appliance for the household. It should be stored in a readily accessible place, either on the work counter or in a cabinet from which it may be rolled out or raised into position automatically (Fig. 4.14). A plastic cover will keep it clean, free from dust. Keep the mixer away from the sink unless it is grounded, for it sometimes develops current leakage and there have been reports of fatal accidents to children who climbed up beside the sink and at the same time touched the metal on the mixer (p. 274). For the same reason do not wash attached beaters under the sink faucets.

FIG. 4.14. Mixer housed in a cupboard on a platform which pulls out and up, elevating mixer to proper work level.—St. Charles Kitchens.

Types of Mixers

Mixers are operated by a motor. They come in various sizes, and may be portable with no supporting stands (Fig. 4.15) or stationary with controls for regulating the speed of the beaters and rotation of the bowls so that all of the food may be brought into contact with the blades. One manufacturer makes the bowl stationary while the beaters revolve around the bowl at the same time that they rotate (Fig. 4.16). Frequently the mixer head may be removed from the stand so it may be used as easily as a portable model, although it is somewhat heavier to handle. Attachments that perform a variety of tasks—grating, slicing, grinding, knife sharpening, and juice extracting—are sometimes available, but usually a power adapter must be inserted between the attachment and the motor. Bowls are usually of glass, occasionally of metal.

Use and Care of Mixer

Mixers have certain limitations in what they can do. When some mixers are used to stir heavy-textured products, the beaters

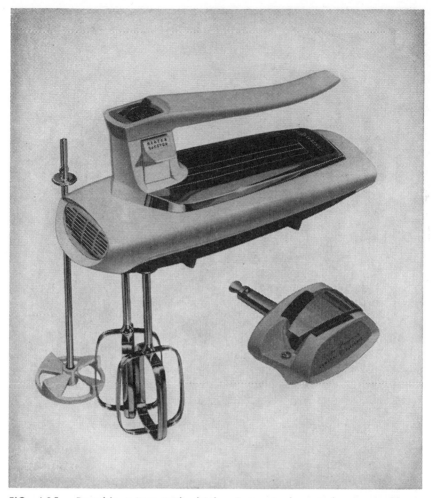

FIG. 4.15. Portable mixer with drink mixer attachment, hangs up like a saucepan, sits down like a hand iron, has beater ejector. Beaters without center posts mix faster and are easier to clean. Knife sharpener accessory plugs into back of mixer. All controls—switch, speed selector, and the ejector button for beaters—are located on the handle within thumb reach.—General Electric.

gradually slow and may stop altogether. The motor then becomes hot and may even smoke, so the operation must be stopped or the motor will be burned out. Small, inexpensive mixers often have very limited use—only to beat eggs or cream or similar thin mixes. At the best they are not a satisfactory buy. There are a few mixing difficulties that may be overcome by the homemaker her-

FIG. 4.16. The bowl on this beater is stationary and the beater has double action—it rotates on its own axis and at the same time revolves around the bowl; this is known as planetary motion.—KitchenAid.

self. For example, if potatoes are cooked until they fall apart, they are whipped much more easily. The amount of flour used in a hand-stirred recipe may be somewhat reduced when the mixer is used, without altering the quality of the product.

Remove the beaters for washing. Wipe off the motor case and stand with a damp cloth. Oil the motor according to the manufacturer's directions on type of oil and frequency of application. Too much oil may be as harmful as too little.

BLENDERS

A type of mixer that has become popular is the electric blender. In place of beaters the blender has a unit of 3 or 4 small, sharp steel blades set into the bottom of a glass or plastic jarlike container, which in turn is clamped to a base containing the motor (Fig. 4.17). Present-day blenders are featuring pushbuttons and automatic timers with pilot lights; one has a heating element in the base, another, with a container that is wide at the bottom and narrow at the top, has large, dull blades instead of the small, sharp ones and is especially effective in blending viscous mixes, but not so good for liquefying solids and for grinding dry ingredients. Most containers carry cup and ounce graduations; they should not extend to the brim to avoid spillovers. When blending frothy mixtures, the blender should be filled only about half. If liquid splashes over, current leakage may occur, an electric hazard. A

FIG. 4.17. A food and beverage blender with a special solid-state control.—Westinghouse.

container that may be opened at both ends aids in the removal of nonpouring ingredients and allows easy access to the steel cutters for cleaning. The blender is used primarily for chopping, grinding, and shredding vegetables, fruits, and nuts, for blending frozen juices, puréeing, and for preparing children's food and special diets. It may also be used for creaming fat and sugar together and stirring the eggs into a batter; the flour is usually stirred in by hand. Recipes that come with the blender suggest a wide variety of uses.

The manufacturer of the Osterizer (Fig. 4.18) suggests a few Do's and Don'ts for the use of the blender:

Do: Put liquid portions of recipes into container first unless otherwise specified.

Cut all kinds of cheese, firm fruits and vegetables, cooked meats, fish, and seafoods into 1-inch pieces.

Start the motor on low, then turn to high, if indicated.

Rest hand lightly on handle when starting motor.

Use low for processing liquid ingredients.

FIG. 4.18. This blender allows a choice of 8 operating speeds, all at the touch of a button. Glass container opens at both ends for easy cleaning.—Oster.

Use a rubber spatula if necessary when blending heavy ingredients. Move the spatula up and down rapidly, tight against the sides of the container to avoid the blades.

Remove heavy dips through the bottom opening.

Don't: Process mixture too long. The blender performs in seconds, not minutes.

Overtax the motor with extra heavy loads such as stiff doughs.

At the end of the operation, clean the cutters thoroughly. When the container cannot be removed from the blades, add warm water and a detergent and agitate; if necessary, turn off the motor from time to time and use a fairly stiff brush to clean around and under the blades.

CAN OPENERS

In the course of a year most families open a large number of cans. The electric can opener consequently will save much energy. It may be attached to a stand used on the counter or mounted on the wall. A built-in magnet holds the cut-out lid and prevents it from falling into the food (Fig. 4.19).

OTHER ELECTRIC APPLIANCES

If the family lives in a rural home and has dairy cattle, an electric churn and home pasteurizer are usually worthwhile investments. Raw milk may cause diseases, especially undulant fever, and pasteurization of milk by heating it in a container on the surface of the range is not satisfactory because of the difficulty of controlling the temperature at the standard 143 F.

There are other small electric appliances on the market—the corn popper, meat grinder, carving knife, hot trays, table oven, saucepan, egg cooker, pressure cooker (Fig. 4.20), and knife sharpener (Fig. 4.21). They help take the guesswork out of the operations they perform; but those included in this chapter are most widely used.

Several companies now manufacture a "family" of electric appliances for use with a single cord and plug equipped with a thermostat control. Included are a griddle (Fig. 4.7), skillet, saucepan, and pressure cooker, all of which may usually be immersed for washing.

Another combination is the 5-in-1 appliance, called a Gourmet Center, featured by one manufacturer. A meat grinder, ice crusher, and salad maker that shreds, slices, grates, and chops fruit, vegetables, and cheese may be attached for operation on one

FIG. 4.19. The electric can opener will cut the top from any shaped can—round, oval, or square—without leaving a jagged edge. Note the magnet that grasps the lid, preventing it from sinking into the contents of the can.—Sunbeam.

FIG. 4.20. An electric pressure pan automatically maintains correct pressure without being watched.—Presto®.

end of the appliance, a can opener and knife sharpener on the other end. Push buttons on the top of the unit release the several attachments; the cord is stored in the base.

The nameplate (p. 276) on any appliance and specification sheets and booklets put out by the manufacturer will give additional information and should be read carefully whenever a purchase is contemplated.

EXPERIMENTS AND PROJECTS

The mixer and frypan may have been used in experiments under ranges. The mixer may be used again in preparing waffles.
1. To test waffle baker:
   Almost any mix, such as gingerbread, baking powder biscuits, spice cake, etc., may be cooked in the waffle baker—some to be used for dessert with whipped cream, ice cream, or a sauce, others, like baking powder biscuits, as the foundation for creamed salmon or tuna or chicken or for strawberry shortcakes. Plain waffles may be varied by adding canned blueberries, grated apples, marmalade, nuts, grated cheese, or cooked chopped bacon (use the bacon fat for the measured fat in the recipe). If the recipe has a high sugar content, it must be baked at a somewhat lower temperature than plain waffles. Two recipes are suggested:
   a. Brownie waffles (enough for 4 large sections)
      Melt together 2 full squares of unsweetened chocolate and ⅓ cup shortening. Beat ½ cup sugar into 2 eggs, and add to chocolate-shortening mix. Add ½ teaspoon of vanilla and 1 cup sifted flour. Stir well. The mixture will be rather thick. Bake at medium heat.
   b. French toast (4 to 6 slices)
      Trim top and bottom crusts from bread. Mix 2 beaten eggs, ¼ cup milk, 1 tablespoon vegetable oil or melted margarine, and ¼ teaspoon of salt. Dip bread completely in mix and place one

FIG. 4.21. A single appliance that will sharpen knives, scissors, or pencils quickly and safely. A pencil shavings catcher increases ease of cleaning.—General Electric.

slice in each section of waffle baker. Slices of sandwich bread are a desirable size. This method of making French toast gives an attractive surface to the toast and eliminates much of the smoke usually occurring when French toast is fried on a griddle.

2. To demonstrate blender:
   Carrot and Pineapple Ambrosia (5 to 6 servings of 6 oz. each). Add pieces of sliced carrot and 1 to 2 cups of pineapple juice to blender and operate until carrots are well shredded—5 minutes or more. Then add ½ pint of vanilla ice cream or a cup of crushed ice. Continue to operate until mixture is well blended. Serve in 3-ounce paper cups or punch cups.

3. To compare coffee makers:
   Make coffee for class in percolator and vacuum-type coffee maker, following manufacturers' directions. Place samples of each in glass cups. Compare clearness, i.e., absence of sediment, and sparkle of brew; also desirability of flavor, although for anyone but an expert this is largely a matter of personal taste. Compare ease of cleaning coffee makers.

4. To compare toasters:
   Toast bread from same loaf in different toasters. Compare evenness of browning, giving explanation for any differences observed, and crispness of product. If oven-type is available, compare toast made in it with toast made in well-type, noting time for operation of each. Compare ease of cleaning toasters.

5. To test roaster grill:
   Discuss uses of roaster oven.
   Use roaster grill to cook cheese sandwiches. Cut off crusts from bread. Butter each slice on both sides. Place slice of American cheddar cheese between two slices of the buttered bread. Preheat grill ½ minute and cook sandwiches, turning once. It is recommended that the reflector pan beneath the grill unit be removed so that the temperature of the grill will rise more slowly. The cheese will then melt before the bread is overbrowned.

6. To compare griddle and frypan:
   Using a packaged mix, make plain or blueberry griddle cakes; cook on griddle and in frypan. Compare ease of operation, desirability of product, and ease of cleaning appliances.

QUESTIONS

1. What determines the evenness with which toast is browned?
2. Explain the action in the vacuum-type coffee maker; i.e., what makes the water go into the upper bowl, and the coffee return to the lower bowl?
3. If you prefer soft waffles, what type of waffle grid will you select?
4. Show how a waffle baker may be used for any meal in a day and for any course in a meal. How may you avoid having the waffles stick?
5. What is the advantage of having a waffle baker in which the grids may be reversed to give you an electric grill? Any disadvantages?
6. What special features of an electric frypan make it easy to care for?
7. Why can't you use the roaster oven and roaster grill at the same time? Why is the window in the roaster lid especially desirable?
8. How do different companies provide for thorough mixing of a cake batter in an electric mixer?
9. When would you feel that an electric blender justified its cost?
10. When a girl marries, relatives and friends give the following electric housewares: coffee maker, toaster, grill-waffle combination, frypan, egg cooker, and corn popper. In choosing an apartment in which to live what must she watch out for?

Chapter Five

NONELECTRIC HOUSEWARES

Nonelectric housewares are used in operations performed by hand. Before purchase every utensil should be evaluated on construction, efficiency, and care required. It should be of a material suited to the purpose for which it will be used, simple in design, durable, of desirable shape and size. It should accomplish the job for which it was manufactured without excessive expenditure of effort and in a reasonable length of time. The work needed to clean the utensil also must be taken into consideration.

As is noted in the chapter on Materials (pp. 287–90), surface utensils should be of materials that are good conductors of heat in order that a minimum of water may be used, thus saving minerals and vitamins. Aluminum, iron, stainless steel with bottom surfaces or cores added to improve conductivity, porcelain enameledware, and heat-proof glass are commonly used (Figs. 5.1a, b, and c).

SURFACE UTENSILS

The surface utensils most commonly used in the home are the saucepan, pot, kettle, frypan, and pressure pan. Some families also have a Dutch oven and ovenette and perhaps a steamer.

Saucepans

The saucepan, pot, and kettle are used for similar cooking operations and are distinguished from one another by the type of handle, that is, the saucepan has one handle, the pot two, one on each side, and the kettle a bail handle. Methods of fastening the handle to the utensil are discussed under Materials (p. 291). When a pouring lip is provided, it should have a sharp edge and be shaped to prevent spilling down the outside of the utensil. Pans with straight, seamless sides and flat bottoms that fit the unit or burner are desirable. A well-rounded union between bottom and sides simplifies cleaning. The material should be thick enough to hold its shape.

FIG. 5.1a. This saucepan combines aluminum with a "Stainless Inner-Clad" to assure even distribution of heat and an easy-to-clean interior. The cover is black aluminum, but a shiny cover is also available. These utensils are designed to cook foods in their natural juices without added water.—Wearever Aluminum.

FIG. 5.1b. Flat bottom and straight sides, with an easy-over cover that features an off-center handle to minimize burned fingers.—Mirro Aluminum.

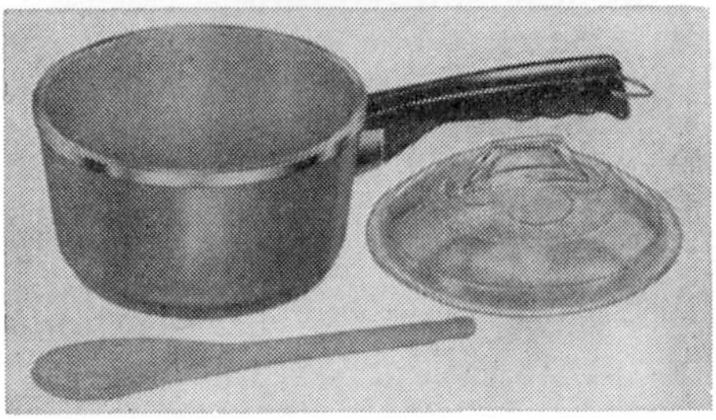

FIG. 5.1c. "Teflon"-coated saucepan with a glass cover and a handle molded to fit the hand and supplied with a ring for hanging.—Club Aluminum.

The pressure pan shortens the cooking process by preventing the escape of steam and so increasing the pressure and hence the temperature inside the pan. The cover locks into grooves on the outside of the pan and a rubber gasket completes the seal. A vent tube on the cover permits air and steam to escape and a gauge or a weight placed over the vent indicates the internal pressure, 5, 10, or 15 pounds (Fig. 5.2). When the specified pressure is reached, made known by a hissing sound or perhaps a visual indicator, the pressure is held constant by adjusting the heat. Cooking time is counted from the time the desired pressure is reached; for most processes this is very brief, so that care must be taken not to overcook the food. The saucepan must never be opened until the pressure indicator has returned to the zero setting and the weight has been removed. In certain cases cooling may be hastened by placing the pan in cold water. A safety plug in the cover prevents the build-up of excessive pressure. The vent tube must be kept

FIG. 5.2. The temperature control in the saucepan above is a weight that provides for 5, 10, or 15 pounds pressure, depending on the position in which the weight is placed over the vent. The control in the lower saucepan allows for 15 pounds pressure only. Pressure is maintained in each pan by adjustment of the heat.—Mirro Aluminum.

clean by running a tiny brush or a pipe cleaner through it frequently. Foods which tend to foam may clog the vent, so it is a wise precaution to cook at one time only small amounts of these foods. (Rice, stews, and apple-sauce are often mentioned specifically by the manufacturer as needing cautious handling.) The rubber gasket must be washed carefully and replaced if it no longer makes a tight seal. The pressure pan should carry the Underwriters' Laboratories seal (Fig. 2.22).

Frypans

Frypans have characteristics similar to saucepans, but usually are of heavier construction, often of cast iron or cast aluminum. Some cast-iron utensils have been greatly improved in appearance by a coat of porcelain enamel that is guaranteed not to chip, peel, or crack. Aluminum pans may be coated with porcelain enamel also. One aluminum company uses for this purpose a special ceramic porcelain, developed by DuPont, that is fused into the

FIG. 5.3. This frypan is finished in turquoise-colored aluminum on the outside and gray "Teflon" on the inner surface.—Club Aluminum.

metal. This same company finishes the inside surfaces of certain utensils with "Teflon" (Figs. 5.1c, 5.3 and 5.4), to which foods will not stick, so no fats are needed in cooking. Metal spoons will scratch this finish and only wooden or plastic tools are recommended. Avoid metallic scouring pads, scrapers, powders, and spatulas.

One aluminum company is featuring a collection of gourmet cookware imported from Ireland. Of iron, the pans are finished on the exterior surfaces with white porcelain enamel, on the inside with black porcelain enamel and lined with Durabond, a highly scratch-resistant finish which retains "Teflon's" nonstick qualities. The finish is fused and bonded to the metal, becoming a part of

FIG. 5.4. A griddle with a cooking surface sealed in non-stick "Teflon" is designed for frying, grilling, or baking. The finish permits cooking without the addition of fats.—Mirro Aluminum.

the pan, and regular household tools may be used in cooking and serving without danger of chipping or marring. The pans do not stain and are easily cleaned with hot suds. The bottoms of the pans are ribbed which lift them slightly, allowing better heat distribution and eliminating hot spots. Another design feature is the handle from Siamese teak, a naturally fire-resistant wood.

Dutch Ovens

The Dutch oven (Fig. 5.5) and ovenette provide methods of cooking over a single unit or burner instead of heating the oven. They are especially economical when small quantities of food are to be prepared.

A number of manufacturers stress as a selling point that their surface utensils may be used without water (Fig. 5.1a). Even when no water is added, a small amount may be supplied from the washing of the vegetables; otherwise moisture is extracted in the cooking process from the food itself, since most vegetables and fruits contain a fairly high percentage of water.

Utensils for waterless cooking must be very good conductors to spread the heat evenly, and must have tight-fitting lids to hold in the steam once it is formed. As soon as the boiling point is reached, heat must be reduced just to maintain boiling. The pan should be as nearly full of food as possible—at least two-thirds full—to reduce to a minimum the amount of air above the food.

As previously pointed out, the use of a small amount of water tends to preserve the mineral and vitamin content of the food.

When green-colored vegetables are cooked in a tightly covered

FIG. 5.5. Two types of Dutch ovens, one with plastic handles and the easy-over cover, the other with handles cast in one with the pan and finished in black "Teflon."—Mirro Aluminum.

saucepan, however, the volatile vegetable acids change the bright green color to a dull olive green or even a brownish shade that is most unattractive. This change may be prevented usually by lifting the lid several times during the first minutes of cooking, to allow the volatile products to escape. The same method should be used when cooking strong-flavored vegetables such as turnips, cauliflower, and onions, or they may be cooked entirely uncovered. More water is used in this instance.

Pie, cake, muffin, and roasting pans, baking sheets, and casseroles are oven utensils (Figs. 5.6a, b, and c). They should be of a

FIG. 5.6a.—Aluminum layer pans allow the cake batter to rise to optimum volume. Note that the pans are staggered on the oven shelves to allow even circulation of heat.— Frigidaire.

FIG. 5.6b. Corning Ware, made of Pyroceram glass ceramic, may be used in the oven, under the broiler, on top of the range, and on the table.—Corning.

FIG. 5.6c. The aluminum pan may be used for baking and roasting. The cover with the transparent polystyrene window keeps the food fresh and allows the pan to be carried to picnics, suppers, etc.—Mirro Aluminum.

material that is a good heat absorber (p. 288), although aluminum is also used for cake and muffin pans and cookie sheets. As is noted (p. 290), aluminum permits a longer cooking period and consequently allows foods that rise or expand to increase in volume. Baking cookies is a short process, and the aluminum sheet allows an extension of the time in the oven without the scorching that may occur when sheets of dark metal are used (Fig. 5.7). Corning, manufacturers of Pyrex, recommend for their cake pans a temperature 25 F. lower than that used for other materials. By removing the detachable handle, top-of-the-range saucepans of Pyroceram (Fig. 5.6b), also made by Corning, may be used for baking dishes and casseroles in the oven or under the broiler. Although Pyroceram withstands high temperatures without the slightest damage, a temperature 25 degrees lower than that used with a shiny metal pan is recommended for oven cookery because the ware is so efficient that it requires less heat. Dishes of this material are attractive and may be used for serving at the table. Moreover, if you wish to warm leftovers later, you can put the casserole right on top of a surface burner. Baked-on food not removed by soaking and gray marks left by metal stirring spoons are removed easily with a plastic cleaning pad or with scouring powder on a damp cloth.

Roasting of meat without cover has been found to result in reduced volatile and dripping losses, but many homemakers prefer

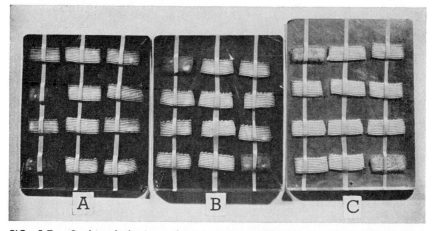

FIG. 5.7. Cookies baked on sheets of three different materials: (A) Russian iron; (B) darkened tin; and (C) aluminum. All were baked in the same oven at the same heat for the same length of time. When a dark material is being used, the oven temperature should be lowered or the baking time reduced.

the moist heat of covered roasters for the cooking of poultry. Earthenware, china, and oven-glass casseroles are good absorbers and tend to give crusty surfaces to foods cooked in them. *Casseroles of these materials are never used for surface cookery.*

Any oven utensil should be simple in design with rounded corners and unions for ease in cleaning. Soaking rather than scouring is recommended for removal of burned-on food. Glass utensils, however, should not be placed in cold water while they are hot. Handles or a broad edge that may be grasped when taking warm food from the oven are an advantage.

Pans frequently are stamped with measurements which have been approved by the American Standards Association. Recipes in cookbooks and on packaged mixes may specify the most desirable size of pan to use. Experiments have shown that too small an amount of food in a pan may give a coarse texture or cause excessive browning.

ACCESSORY UTENSILS (often called tools)

Many small hand utensils are used in preparing food for some cooking process or directly for the dining table. Those most widely used include cutlery, graters, slicers, sifters, strainers, scrapers, can openers, measuring cups and spoons, and hand beaters.

Cutlery
Knives

The most desirable knife is of hollow-ground vanadium or high-carbon steel, hammer forged to develop a fine grain in the steel (Fig. 5.8). Stainless steel knives that also are of high-carbon content are now available, but the usual stainless steel knife will not keep a sharp edge because some of the carbon has been re-

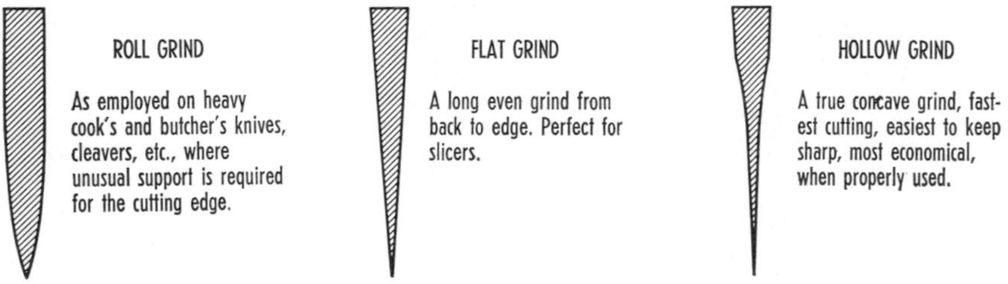

ROLL GRIND

As employed on heavy cook's and butcher's knives, cleavers, etc., where unusual support is required for the cutting edge.

FLAT GRIND

A long even grind from back to edge. Perfect for slicers.

HOLLOW GRIND

A true concave grind, fastest cutting, easiest to keep sharp, most economical, when properly used.

FIG. 5.8.   Cross-sections of knife edges, showing kinds suited to different purposes.—Russell-Harrington Cutlery.

placed by chromium. The shank of the knife blade, called the tang, should extend at least half the length into the handle and be firmly fastened by two or more compression rivets to prevent loosening. If the handle is of plastic material, it may be molded onto the tang. Handles are commonly of plastic or of stain- and moisture-resistant hardwood.

The names of most knives indicate the use for which they were made—paring knife, carver, slicer, butcher, and bread knife. The bread knife has a scalloped or serrated edge that is self sharpening, for the points of the edge receive most of the wear. Then there is the utility knife, about twice as long as the paring knife, used for operations for which the paring knife would be too short; the grapefruit knife with a curved and frequently serrated edge to separate the fruit from the membranes and skin; the French cook knife, with the back of the blade and handle in a straight line, leaving room for the hand in front, used to chop celery, nuts, etc.

FIG. 5.9. Knives adapted to a variety of uses. From left to right: butcher, carver, French cook, bread, slicer, utility, paring (two types), and grapefruit. Several are hollow ground, noticeably the carver and the French cook knives.

rapidly into any desired size. Not all of these knives may be needed for every home so they should be chosen for the specific task (Fig. 5.9).

Once purchased, knives should receive good care. Store them separately in a rack to prevent nicking and dulling of their edges. Cut food on a board. Do not use a knife to cut paper, metal, or string. Never leave a knife lying in hot water; the temper of the steel which enables it to take and keep a sharp edge may be reduced. Hot water may injure the handle, too, particularly if it is made of certain plastics. Sharpen good knives, especially hollow-ground ones, on an oil stone; however, a sharpener of carbide, the hardest material made, is also acceptable. One company grinds a special line of knives at 100 degrees below zero. These knives, known as "Frozen Heat" knives, are guaranteed to hold an edge without need for resharpening for at least three years.

Forks, Spoons, Spatulas, Scrapers, and Shears

Forks, with two or more tines, are of the same material as knives and should receive similar care. They are used for removing food from the cooking utensil or to hold it for paring.

Spoons for stirring and mixing are of various metals, of plastic, and of wood and may be solid or slotted. Metal spoons tend to scratch the bowl or saucepan, so wooden or plastic spoons are preferred by many; these may warp or wear down on the edge, so will need to be replaced occasionally. Flat-ended metal or plastic spoons, either solid or slotted, are especially efficient for stirring viscous foods.

Spatulas are of different sizes, depending on their use. The narrow, flexible spatula is used to level cups of dry ingredients, or scrape a bowl free from batter, to fold in egg whites, or to frost a cake; the more rigid, broad one will remove cookies from a baking sheet, place squares of cake on a serving plate, or turn pancakes (Fig. 5.10). It is an advantage to have an angle in the shank of spatulas to be used in utensils with sides.

The plastic or rubber scraper is used to remove the last of ingredients from pans or bowls. Most of these food products contain fat, and fat causes the rubber scraper to deteriorate fairly rapidly and acquire a sticky edge. It should, therefore, be washed in soapy water as soon as possible after use and not be allowed to lie at the side of the sink until the next regular time for dishwashing.

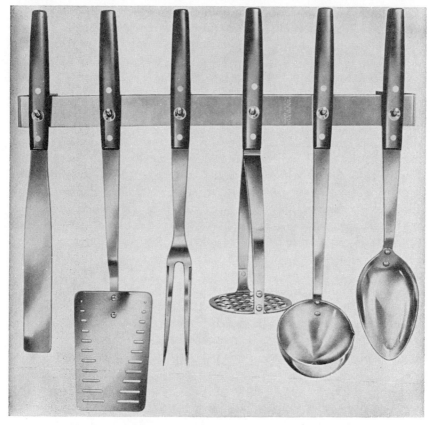

FIG. 5.10. Extra-long, stainless steel tools with tapered handles. Hang-up holes are placed low on the handles for ease in grasping.—Ecko Products.

Kitchen shears are practical for many jobs: snipping chives, parsley, and celery leaves, cutting dried fruits and marshmallows, shredding poultry, separating bunches of grapes into servings, dividing bread dough into rolls.

Graters, Sifters, and Strainers

Graters, slicers, sifters, and strainers are made of stainless steel, aluminum, and tinned steel. Steel and tinned steel usually are preferred to aluminum because they can be used in thinner sheets which give sharper cutting edges, and the quality of the product often depends upon how finely it can be cut.

Holes in a grater are punched or drilled. The drilled holes, round or oval in shape, produce distinct slivers of food and a fairly large volume. Food grated on the punched holes is mushy and often juicy in texture, and much of it sticks in the holes so that the volume is small. This type is also much more difficult to clean (Fig. 5.11).

Slicers are either flat plates, which may be held in the hand, or the rotary type, similar in general appearance to a meat grinder and operated by a handle. Either kind may have adjustable knife blades.

Sifters and strainers are made of tinned-steel wire mesh of varying sizes fitted to the homemaker's needs. The mesh is fastened into a metal collar and will have less tendency to pull loose if two pieces of heavy metal ribbon support the bowl from below. These supporting ribbons are especially desirable when the strainer is used with a spoon in preparing puréed fruits and vegetables. A sifter that can be held and operated with one hand is a good choice, for it leaves the other hand free for stirring the food product.

Sieves and colanders and fruit and vegetable presses are made from metal sheets and have drilled holes. Tinned steel, graniteware, and aluminum may be used, but the holes in the tinned steel will have sharper edges. The presses are of several different types; one is of conical shape, over which a tapered wooden bar is

FIG. 5.11.   Graters: the one on the left has punched holes, the other, drilled.

rotated, another a metal seamless bowl with a crank-operated re-volving spiral blade, in a third a flat disk is pressed into a hollow perforated cylinder. All these utensils should be carefully washed and completely dried in a warm place to prevent rusting.

Can Openers

A can opener should have a sharp knife edge and should cut the top from any shaped can—oval, round, or square—without leaving a rough edge or causing fine slivers of the tin to fall onto the food. An opener fastened to the wall or to the edge of the table and that clamps the can into position is recommended so that only one hand is used for the cutting operation. For opening cans of liquids such as fruit juices, a lever that punches a 3-sided hole in the cover is very efficient.

Measuring Utensils

Accurate measuring cups and spoons are needed in the prep-aration of any recipes. Cups of aluminum, stainless steel, glass, or plastic should conform to the specifications set up by the National Bureau of Standards, i.e., the cup must have a capacity of 8 fluid ounces, or 16 tablespoons. Divisions are graduated in thirds on one side, in fourths on the other, and marked "one cup" at the top. Cups may measure a cup level with the top or at a short distance below the edge, the first for dry ingredients, the second better for liquids. Divisions usually are indented from the inside of the metal cups, making them more difficult to clean.

Divisions frequently are marked with red on the outside of glass cups, leaving the inside smooth and easy to clean. The trans-parency of the glass aids in the accurate measure of portions of a cup. Plastic cups are light in weight but may be brittle and they tend to warp out of shape in very hot water.

A third type of measuring cup is the set of single-capacity cups, the full cup, and the separate half, quarter, and third (Fig. 5.12). These single measuring cups are very desirable for use with dry ingredients.

Also available is a set of Pyrex mix and measure bowls, with clearly visible molded measuring marks on the sides, easy-to-hold handles, and no-spill pouring spouts (Fig. 5.13). They come in three sizes, 1 cup, 1½ pints, and 2 quarts.

Four measuring spoons are in common use: the tablespoon, teaspoon, half-teaspoon, and quarter-teaspoon (Fig. 5.14). They

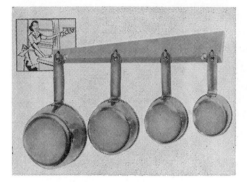

FIG. 5.12. These stainless steel measuring cups are obtainable in the full-cup size, divided by the usual quantity marks, and in the single-capacity portion of the full cup. They may be hung up for convenient storage, and are designed to prevent tipping.— Foley.

are made of plastic, aluminum, or stainless steel and may be purchased in a cluster or individually in a rack that may be fastened inside a cupboard door or on a wall above the kitchen preparation center. The capacity of the tablespoon is ¹⁄₁₆ of the standard cup; the teaspoon is $\frac{1}{3}$ tablespoon. Accurate spoons are frequently stamped "U.S. Standard."

Hand Beaters

Beaters, either rotary or whisk, are used for the many mixing operations performed in the home. The rotary beater (Fig. 5.15) has four circular or elliptical agitators of stainless steel, each two attached around a heavy metal shaft that is fastened to the main framework. A large, cogged drive wheel, turned by a handle, makes contact with two pinion wheels that operate the shafts and beater blades. The ratio of the cogs in the drive and pinion wheels is 4 or 5 to one, so that for every revolution of the drive wheel the pinion wheels make 4 or 5 turns and consequently the operator does only one-fourth or one-fifth of the work. Nylon bearings in the drive wheel add to the ease of operation. The top handle by

FIG. 5.13. Pyrex Mix and Measure bowl set, 1-cup, 1½-pint, and 2-quart sizes. Convenient handles and pouring spouts, molded measuring marks, heat resistant. Can be used in oven to melt shortening or chocolate. —Corning.

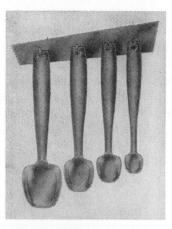

FIG. 5.14. A set of sturdy, stainless steel measuring spoons in a rack fastened to the cupboard door or to the wall above the mix center are instantly available when needed. The long handles increase the ease of reaching into tall containers.—Foley.

which the beater is held in position should be large enough to prevent cramping the fingers.

Whisk beaters are often spoon-shaped, the framing edge of heavy wire, and the center a criss-cross of many fine wires. Sometimes the edge is also encircled with a coil of fine wire or, in the case of the French whip, the whole beater is made of many fine wires, the long hoops fastened together at the top to form a handle. In the use of the whisk beater the operator does all of the lifting

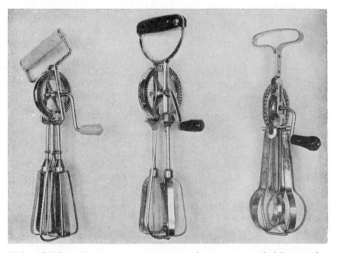

FIG. 5.15. Representative rotary beaters available on the market. Simplicity of design makes for ease in cleaning. A slanting handle is a good choice when the work counter is too high—a delight for short women or little girls learning to cook.

action and therefore the handle should be comfortable in the hand. Depending upon the number and fineness of the wires, the whisk beater produces a large volume but a rather coarse texture. The rotary beater gives a finer texture but somewhat less volume.

The bowl used with the beater should be suitable in size for the amount of food to be beaten, appropriate in shape for ease of manipulation, and should be of a material that will not chip or scratch. For the rotary beater it should be heavy enough to stay in position without needing to be held (Fig. 5.13).

Mention may be made of certain small tools: butter curlers, cooking tongs, egg and tomato slicers, perforated and lipped turners and ladles, molds, and cutters for all kinds and shapes of fancy cookies, cakes, and garnishes. The same principles of selection apply to these utensils as to the larger pieces. Tools should justify the storage space they occupy. If used rarely, they doubtless should be discarded to avoid cluttering the kitchen.

EXPERIMENTS AND PROJECTS

1. To test saucepans for heat conduction:
   a. Use saucepans of same capacity of aluminum, porcelain enameled-ware, stainless steel, copper-bottomed steel, aluminum-bottomed steel, heat-proof glass and Pyroceram. Add 1 or 2 cups of water to each pan. Use water of same temperature, obtained by drawing dishpan of water 1 hour before laboratory period. Using one pan after another, bring water to boiling point over same unit or burner at constant heat setting, noting time required. Keeping time may be assigned to various members of the class.
   b. Use saucepans as in "a." Oil each pan lightly and dust with flour. Use one pan after another over constant heat setting using the length of time required to brown flour in aluminum pan. Compare resulting shades of brownness in the different pans.
2. To demonstrate use of a Presto pressure saucepan to cook cup custards:
   Beat 1 egg slightly; add 2 tablespoons of sugar, ⅛ teaspoon salt, 1 cup lukewarm milk, ¼ teaspoon vanilla. Stir, strain, and divide into 3 custard cups. Sprinkle ground nutmeg over top of custards. Cover each cup with aluminum foil. Place cups on rack of pressure pan and add ½ cup of boiling water. Fasten lid on pan. Place pan over giant burner and turn burner to high heat. When steam issues from vent in steady stream, place weight over vent, and heat until 15 pounds of pressure is indicated on weight. Turn gas to simmer position to maintain pressure at 15 pounds and cook 2 minutes, 15 seconds. Remove pan from heat and reduce heat rapidly in cold water. Remove weight and lid—always in this

order—and take out custards. Remove aluminum foil and allow to cool.

3. To demonstrate use of ovenette for cooking over surface burner:
    Use muffin mix—blueberry or corn or other. Mix according to directions on package. Meanwhile preheat ovenette over standard gas burner to No. 4 (approximately 8 minutes), and preheat gas oven to 400 F. Grease the four muffin cups supplied with the ovenette and four similar ones to use in the oven. Fill cups with mix. Bake muffins in ovenette, about 6 minutes or until a toothpick inserted in a muffin comes out clean. Bake muffins in oven 20 to 25 minutes and test with a toothpick. Compare moistness and texture of muffins, baking time, and approximate cost for fuel. Under what conditions would one method of baking be chosen rather than the other?

4. To compare ovenware materials:
    Mix at one time sufficient cake mixture to make four loaf cakes. If available, an institutional size Hobart mixer may be used. Pour into pans of comparatively same size of porcelain enameledware, aluminum, tin, and oven glass; bake in the same oven, staggering pans to allow even circulation of heat. Remove each cake when baked, comparing time required. If oven with window is available, oven door need be opened only very briefly. Compare appearance, evenness of rising and browning, moistness, and texture.

5. To compare results using aluminum pans of various shapes:
    Mix at one time sufficient cake mix to use the following aluminum pans: loaf pan, angel food pan, one layer cake pan, shallow sheet pan, muffin pans. Bake in same oven or similar ovens, at same temperature. Compare evenness of browning, texture, moistness.

6. Review results of using tin, aluminum, and Russian iron for cookie sheets in experiments for Chapter 2 (p. 36).

7. To compare various types of small equipment for resulting products and ease of cleaning:

    a. Beat a whole egg with new and old style rotary beaters. Allow egg to dry on beaters. Compare product obtained and ease of cleaning beaters.

    b. Grate carrot on graters with punched and drilled holes. Compare product obtained and ease of cleaning graters.

    c. Chop a piece of celery with a French cook knife and a paring or utility knife, cutting on wooden board. Note ease and speed of operation in each case and product obtained.

    d. Use grapefruit knife to section ½ grapefruit or orange.

    e. Compare individual and all-in-one measuring cups of glass and metal for measuring ½ and ¼ cups of sugar or flour. Repeat experiment, measuring ½ and ¼ cups of water. Note desirable features of each.

QUESTIONS

1. Why do you want your saucepan to be of a material that is a good conductor?

2. You have always used a darkened tin cookie sheet. You buy a new cookie sheet of aluminum. What change will you make in your method of baking?

3. Why does a rotary beater require less effort on the part of the operator than the whisk beater?

4. If a knife is to maintain a good cutting edge, of what material must it be made? What additional characteristics would you look for in a knife? Name four or five knives you would want in your kitchen. How would you wash and store them to keep them sharp?

5. You are making a salad of raw cabbage and carrots. What type of grater will you use? Give reason for choice.

6. To what requirements must measuring cups and spoons conform? What types will you choose for your kitchen?

7. Explain why the use of a pressure saucepan shortens cooking time. What precautions must you observe in the use of a pressure saucepan, at the beginning of a cooking period? At the end? What foods should you usually not cook in the pressure pan? Why?

8. List five general fundamentals of selection you would consider in the purchase of any nonelectric houseware.

9. To start housekeeping you have $50.00 for the purchase of kitchen utensils and tools. List what you would buy, giving reasons for your choice.

10. What common characteristic do most tools have?

Chapter Six

BRINGING EQUIPMENT

TOGETHER IN THE KITCHEN

T HE RANGE, THE REFRIGERATOR, and the sink are the three major appliances in the kitchen. All are essential for the satisfactory preparation of food, and their location in relationship to each other may have an important influence on time and motion saving. When these three appliances are joined by continuous counters with cabinets above and below, the arrangement is usually considered optimum. However, the homemaker frequently has to adjust arrangements to such permanently placed fixtures as doors, plumbing, and radiators.

WORK CENTERS

Work in the kitchen is concentrated around three centers: the mix center, range center, and sink center. Serving may be considered a separate center or grouped with the range. It also may be possible to include a planning center, making five altogether.

Mix Center

Food preparation at the mix center involves the use of certain foods, such as milk, eggs, and butter or margarine from the refrigerator, and also the raw ingredients that go into salads. The sink is used for water and the peeling of fruits and vegetables. Counter space is essential, and cabinet space for staples—flour, sugar, baking powder, and flavorings—and for bowls, pie and cake pans, cookie sheets, casseroles, and the many small utensils used in this area first (Fig. 6.1). Small electric appliances, especially the mixer, are stored here, too.

Sink Center

Since the sink is used primarily for dishwashing, the center has a counter for the stacking of dishes and a receptacle for waste, if a food disposer is not a part of the sink.

FIG. 6.1.   An easily accessible shelf for storage of casseroles and other utensils used at the mix center.—St. Charles Kitchens.

It may have ventilated storage bins (Fig. 6.2) for potatoes,
onions, apples, and other fruits and vegetables not requiring refrigeration, that are prepared here. Paring knives and slicers will
be stored in a slotted wall or counter rack or in a drawer where
they are easily accessible. Dishcloths and towels, scouring pads
and powders occupy an adjacent drawer or shelf (Fig. 6.3). When
a dishwasher is a part of the equipment, a minimum of dishcloths

FIG. 6.2.   This sink cabinet has ventilated storage space for nonrefrigerated fruits and vegetables.—St. Charles Kitchens.

and towels are required. Even when dishes are washed by hand, fewer dishtowels will be needed if the homemaker acquires the very desirable habit of allowing the rinsed dishes to dry in a rack. They may be covered with a clean towel and not handled until time for the next meal. Silver and utensils that tend to rust or spot should be dried by hand.

Range Center

The range center also would include the refrigerator since raw foods—meats, fish, eggs—are taken directly to the range for roasting, broiling, and frying. Water is needed from the sink for

FIG. 6.3.   Sliding trays may be used to store dishtowels, aprons, and table mats and napkins used in the breakfast area.—St. Charles Kitchens.

most surface cookery operations. Saucepans, pots, frypans, and serving spoons, forks and ladles, with the necessary hot pan holders, and serving dishes for the cooked food should be stored close to the range. Certain nonperishable foods used in this area may be placed on a shelf nearby (Figs. 6.4 and 6.5).

ARRANGEMENT OF WORK CENTERS

The three major kitchen appliances closely associated in most food preparations should, therefore, be placed in near proximity to each other. Depending upon the location of permanent fixtures, four general arrangements are possible: one-wall, L-shaped, corridor (or two-wall), and U-shaped (Fig. 6.6).

Clearance Space

A clearance space of not more than 5 or 6 feet between equipment on opposite sides of a room is considered desirable. This distance is more readily obtained in a large kitchen if the shape is rectangular rather than square. When the clearance is too great,

Bri

〈

Ran

Refrig.

Cor

FIG. 6.6.

are i
whei

men
rarel

pan
from
this l
used

forta
belov

FIG. 6.4.   Foods and utensils can be stored near the cooking center on shelves that pivot out of the wall.—Frigidaire.

the sink or range may be placed in an island or on a peninsula to reduce the distance. (See Fig. 6.22b.) A connecting distance of 15 to 16 feet between major work centers (indicated on Figs. 6.21b and 6.22b) is considered optimum and this walking distance should never exceed 22 feet.

Since the sink is used with equal frequency from both the range and the mix center, it should be reasonably near to both— never in a corner accessible from only one side.

FIG. 6.7. An L-shaped kitchen with breakfast area. Note counter space beside refrigerator, hood and light over built-in range, and light over sink.— Youngstown Kitchens.

inches above the floor as to reach to 42 inches above, and two times as much to reach to 56 inches. Bending to bottom shelves in base cabinets requires 19 times more energy than to reach supplies stored at elbow height.

Cabinets should be adapted to the supplies, utensils, and dishes they are to store. If small articles, frequently used, are to be clearly visible and removable with a minimum of effort, narrow shelves must be provided for them (Fig. 6.8). These may be built between the wider ones, or a special cabinet, 6 or 7 inches deep, may be constructed in a convenient place.

Space between two shelves or a drawer in a base cabinet may be divided by vertical partitions into a file arrangement for individual storage of pans of various sizes (Fig. 6.9). A similar arrangement may be built between the counter and the floor to store trays and taller flat items. Deep drawers may be divided by inch-high strips to hold bowls, jars, and casseroles in place; shallow ones similarly divided keep in place the many small utensils of common use.

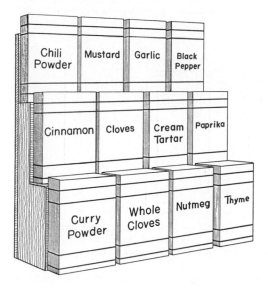

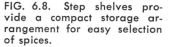

FIG. 6.8. Step shelves provide a compact storage arrangement for easy selection of spices.

Knives, long-handled forks, spatulas, and pancake turners are slipped into a slotted board (Fig. 6.10). The man of the family can usually build in such partitions, each space adapted in size to the article it is to hold.

If corner wall and base cabinets do not have sliding shelves, they are more easily usable if fitted with revolving shelves—Lazy Susans, as they are frequently called.

Beside the refrigerator is a good location for a shallow drawer to hold plastic bags and covers, aluminum foil, and wax paper or Saran Wrap, used in the storage of leftovers. A pegboard over or beside the range is a very satisfactory place to hang saucepans and other articles. The location of the hooks is adapted to the sizes of the various utensils.

Counter Area

Work space should be as continuous as practicable and should be provided beside each major appliance.

Height and width of work space must be adapted to the individual if she is to work with enjoyment. Continuous use of small muscles causes strain and leads to unnecessary fatigue, so a counter height that will allow most work to be performed with the shoulders level or slightly dropped will ensure use of the large muscles and prove less tiring to the homemaker. It has been

FIG. 6.9. A file between shelves or in a drawer is recommended for storage of pie, cake, and muffin pans. A similar arrangement will hold lids for pots and kettles.

customary to build all counters 36 inches from the floor, but this will not be comfortable for the very tall or the very short person, and when it is not possible to alter existing conditions, other adjustments may be developed (Fig. 6.11). Counter widths of 24 to 25 inches are satisfactory for most women.

Undoubtedly it is desirable to sit for many tasks, and a lower counter or table or a pull-out board (Fig. 6.12a) makes this feasible. A recessed area for the kitchen stool (Fig. 6.12b) adds to comfort and convenience without cluttering up floor space.

Streamlining the modern kitchen by building the range sur-

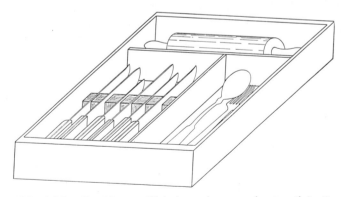

FIG. 6.10. Partitions will help to keep each utensil in its own place. A slotted rack for knives prevents nicked and dulled edges.

FIG. 6.11.   A U-shaped kitchen with breakfast bar which may be used for mixing center, should work counters be too high for the homemaker. Mid-way storage cabinets are under wall cabinets at right and left of range surface units.—Youngstown Kitchens.

face into the counter and the oven and refrigerator-freezer units into the wall tends to suggest ease of movement, but special care must be taken to provide sufficient counter area beside each major appliance, a requirement that is sometimes overlooked. If the appliances occupy some of the wall and base cabinet space formerly used for storage of supplies and utensils, additional cabinets may need to be built in another part of the kitchen, a practice that may result in a crowded kitchen, or the need to have a larger kitchen with greater walking distances between centers. Or it may mean that some storage space must be higher up, with the resultant necessity of stretching or climbing. Such factors should certainly be given consideration in planning.

Light and Ventilation

Kitchen windows generally are placed above work surfaces, especially the sink but preferably not the range because of the

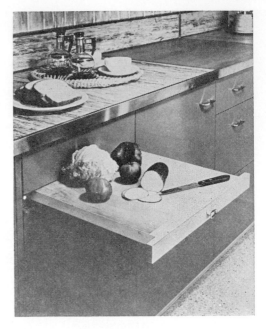

FIG. 6.12a. A sliding shelf adapts itself to many tasks that can be performed while seated.—St. Charles Kitchens.

FIG. 6.12b. Space should be provided for storage of the kitchen stool when not in use. This is strongly recommended to eliminate accidents and reduce walking distances for the homemaker.—St. Charles Kitchens.

danger of window curtains coming into contact with heated areas. Also, in the case of gas ranges, a breeze may blow the burner flame—causing the heat to fluctuate. Two windows are desirable, but a glass in the service door will supply needed daylight. Fans frequently are installed to remove heat and moisture, volatile fats given off in the cooking process, and undesirable odors. They are more efficient than ventilating by window and door and may be used in cold weather without reducing the kitchen temperature too great an amount.

A type of hood that requires no outside venting may be installed over the range. It electronically removes smoke, cooking odors, and grease, which are deposited on filter plates. These plates may be washed in warm soapy water without causing any deterioration in the filter.

Adequate light for work carried on after dark is very important, since it lessens the possibility of accidents, of which all too many occur in kitchens. General illumination is provided by a central fixture installed close to the ceiling, with local lights over mix center, range, and sink. Working in her own shadow increases the homemaker's fatigue and reduces her efficiency. Lamp bulbs should be of high enough wattage for ease in seeing. The bulbs should be surrounded by a translucent globe or be placed above a translucent panel to diffuse the light evenly and eliminate shadows.

Sink Area

The need for a readily accessible sink cannot be overemphasized. The sink, of one or two compartments, may be built into the counter, or be a separate unit with a single drainboard or one on either side. It is commonly of iron, finished with acid-resistant porcelain enamel in white or color, and is also available in stainless steel and Monel metal. A mixing faucet that swings to either side is recommended.

A newer type of faucet, the Mono-Tap, also swings from one side to the other. It does not have two separate faucet handles to turn on the hot and cold water, but a water control as a part of its own construction. The spout is raised to start the water flowing as soon as the position of the lever indicates the water temperature desired (Fig. 6.13). Modern sinks frequently have a spray attachment for rinsing the dishes. Unless a food disposer is installed, grease drippings and coffee grounds should not be poured down the drain.

Abrasives should not be used to clean porcelain enamel, since they mar the surface, and once the sink is scratched, it is difficult

FIG. 6.13. The single-handle type of faucet has a control as part of its construction. The position of the lever regulates the temperature of water and raising the spout starts the flow.— Youngstown Kitchens.

to keep clean. If warm, soapy water is not effective, baking soda may be used.

Food-Waste Disposer

In the sink center there are often found two additional appliances, the food-waste disposer and the dishwasher. The disposer of one to two quarts capacity, operated by a $\frac{1}{3}$ or $\frac{1}{2}$ horsepower motor, is attached beneath the sink (Fig. 6.14). The drain leading into it is closed either with a slit rubber disk, allowing continuous-feed operation whenever a switch is thrown to "on," or is covered with a perforated plate that must be locked into position before the action will start. This second arrangement tends to prevent flatware or other objects from falling into the chamber. There are no cutting knives in food-waste disposers. When a switch is operated, a circular table whirls around at a speed of about 1,725 revolutions per minute; the food wastes on this table are thrown against the sides of the chamber where a shredding ring of high-grade stainless steel alloy is located. The force of the waste striking against the shredders cuts the food into particles fine enough to be washed into the drain. Small projections or lugs on the revolving table keep the food moving. In some models the shredders are reversible which tends to make them wear evenly. A full stream of cold water should be turned on before you start the disposer and water should be allowed to continue to flow for a few seconds after the disposer has been turned off, to be sure all waste has been flushed into the drain. Cold water hardens any grease that otherwise may cause stoppage of waste pipes inaccessible for cleaning. A disposer uses about 6 gallons of cold water a day and approximately 3 cents of electricity per day. The disposer should be grounded.

Drain-cleaning chemicals *should never be used in the disposer* as they may corrode the shredders. One manufacturer offers additional protection against corrosion by using glass-filled polyester for the drain housing and also embedding the stationary part of the motor in "space-age" epoxy material which is impervious to moisture.

Food must be dropped in gradually and never packed into the disposer. Fibrous wastes—celery, pea pods, corn husks—require a longer operating time before they are shredded and flushed away. Viscous food such as cooked oatmeal and raw bread dough tend to clog the shredder mechanism and should be added

FIG. 6.14. A disposer designed from modern materials—stainless steel hopper and shredder, Carboloy ® cutter, polyester drain housing, jam-resistant impeller, cushioned mounting in synthetic rubber, and shroud filled with insulating material, cutting down noise and vibration. This model carries a lifetime guarantee.—General Electric.

alternately with fruit or vegetable peelings or dry crusts of bread. Certain materials are never placed in the disposer: glass, china, metal, plastics, paper, string, clam and oyster shells, and cigarettes, especially filter-tipped cigarettes, because the filters will mat over the shredding ring.

Should the disposer become jammed, shut off the electricity and examine the chamber to be sure no forbidden material has accidentally fallen into the unit—remember there are no knife edges in the disposer. Some disposers are supplied with a self-service wrench which can be inserted into a socket at or under the bottom of the disposer; this wrench can be worked back and forth until the table again revolves freely. If no wrench is furnished it is possible to insert a broom handle through the top opening of the disposer and press it against one of the lugs on the table, then exert force first in one direction, then in the other until the wheel is rotating. If this action fails to loosen the jam, a serviceman must be called.

New models are extra quiet in operation. Thick, rubber-cushioned mounting cuts down on vibration and muffles sound. In certain designs the mechanism is encased in efficient insulating material.

In some localities food disposers may be used in connection with a septic tank, although the waste may increase the tank load by as much as a third. In other rural areas installation may be prohibited. Limitation on water supply also may prevent its use.

Automatic Dishwasher

Dishwashers are made from heavy-gauge bonderized sheet steel, with white or colored baked-on enamel or porcelain enamel on the exterior surfaces, although occasionally stainless steel or copper is used in deluxe models. The top and front panel may be of wood or finished in a plastic material. The interior is preferably of porcelain enamel. The power rating is $\frac{1}{4}$ to $\frac{1}{8}$ horsepower.

Dishwashers may be installed permanently at the right or left of the sink, or may be portable. Top-opening models from which the racks are lifted out for loading or lift up with the lid and side-opening types with sliding racks are available (Figs. 6.15 and 6.16). Each load of dishes uses an average of only 10 to 15 gallons of water, but the cleansing effect is intensified by the water-distributing system which sprays and resprays the water over the tableware. A first rinse without a detergent is desirable since it removes cool water from the intake line, warms the dishwasher, and flushes away any loose soil.

Much attention has been given to the design of the spraying device so that the water may reach all of the dishes and wash them equally well. Three types are commonly used today: a blade impeller installed in the center bottom of the tub, a revolving wash arm, also usually attached in the center at the bottom, and the revolving tube located near the top of the tub. A few models have double rotating arms, providing sprays at both top and bottom.

FIG. 6.15. Dishwasher with two-cycle selection for heavy or light soil, rotating top tray, and capacity for once-a-day operation.—Youngstown Kitchens.

The impeller may rotate first in one direction, then in the other, to distribute the water; two wash arms may rotate in opposite directions; or the mechanism may throw a horizontal or vertical pattern of spray (Figs. 6.17 a and b). Other recent designs give multilevel water action at the sides as well as top and bottom. Some dishwashers feature a cycle selector for prewash, pots and pans, and the full cycle. Sometimes the upper tray itself may rotate and occasionally this tray may be adjusted up or down to permit the loading of taller tableware or those of odd shapes in it or in the lower tray. New large capacity models allow 12 to 18 table settings to be washed at one time. A special basket, in addition to the silver container, is often provided for small articles that tend to fall through the racks. A number of washers require no prerinsing of the dishes, only the removal of bones and large pieces of food. The action cuts up or liquefies soft food particles so that

FIG. 6.16. Gas dishwasher that uses super-hot rinse.
Plastic coated interior and racks deaden sound and protect
dishes. Racks are interchangeable and are especially constructed to prevent dishes from nesting together and dis-
torting the water distribution pattern.—Preway.

FIG. 6.17a. Four-way washing action eliminates prerinsing. Revolving spray arm at bottom discharges water through 13 openings while rotating vertical spray column in center blasts water in 5 directions from jet vents. At top, swirling blades of spray impeller direct water downward.—Frigidaire.

FIG. 6.17b. Effective triple-washing action. Power Shower at top sprays water downward; Power Tower in center jets water upward; Power Arm underneath has swirl-around action, all combining to deluge dishes completely.—General Electric.

they may be flushed down the drain, eliminating the cleaning of clogged strainers. In a few models a screen filters the circulating water and prevents any redepositing of food soil on the dishes. A rinse cycle may be provided for dishes to be left in the dishwasher until dishes from a future meal are added. This rinse removes surface soil that might otherwise dry on.

For optimum results, a water temperature between 150 and 160 F. is recommended, but a gas dishwasher has two thermostats that automatically control preset water temperature. The gas heater raises the temperature of the wash water and first rinse water to 160 F., the second rinse to 180 F. This high temperature kills harmful bacteria and is claimed not to damage even the finest china (Fig. 6.16). Several dishwashers feature a short cycle for fine crystal and china. This is desirable since alkaline solutions attack overglaze china at high temperatures.

One or two models are supplied with a small water tank and heater that provides only the needed amount of water heated to the required temperature. This eliminates the necessity of maintaining the large tank at this high temperature. Side-opening types have a tubular unit of 600 to 750 watts in the washer to keep the water hot and to dry the dishes at the end of the cycle. Most dishwashers have been provided with fairly heavy Fiberglas insulation to prevent loss of heat and for quieter operation. A cuplike container in the lid holds the detergent. Several different brands of detergents are available, but it is well to select the one recommended by the manufacturer of the dishwasher and to be careful to use the specified amount. A wetting agent may be added, manually or automatically, to the final rinse to prevent water spotting.

In circumstances where it is not feasible to have a built-in dishwasher, the portable type is a good choice (Figs. 6.18a, b, and c). Its mobility is an attractive feature. In order to connect the portable dishwasher to your sink faucet, an adapter is screwed to the faucet, then the collar on the coupler is retracted, the coupler slipped over the adapter and the collar released. The coupler may be joined to a double hose assembly, one hose for filling, the other for emptying the dishwasher, or only the filling hose may be attached to the coupler collar and a separate drain hose provided to be placed over the edge of the sink. The electric cord should be plugged into a grounded outlet. Usually two detergent cups are provided; they should be filled with a detergent made

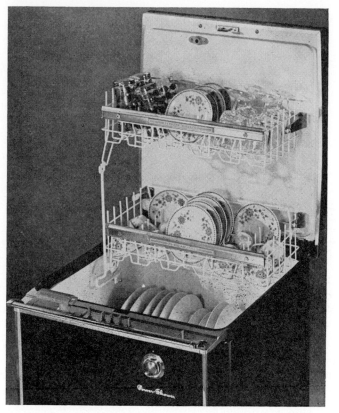

FIG. 6.18a. Portable dishwasher with twin vinyl-coated racks attached to the cover, eliminating the need of lifting out upper rack when loading the one below, saving both time and energy. Top of cabinet is finished in "Grass-cloth" Textolite, providing a durable and convenient work counter, one that can be rolled wherever needed. Rinse agent, to prevent water spotting may be injected during rinse-cycle at push of a button.—General Electric.

especially for dishwashers, such as Cascade, Calgonite, Dishwasher All, Finish, or Jet Dry; directions state how much detergent to use, depending on the hardness of the water. The covers on the detergent cups should be closed firmly, first brushing off any powder from the magnetic strips around the cups; otherwise the cups may not close securely. If hot water is needed while the dishwasher is in operation, a button on the side of the coupler may be pressed and water will flow from the opening at the bottom of the collar. Both drain hose and electric cord may be stored out of sight in a special receptacle on the side of the washer. Some investigators

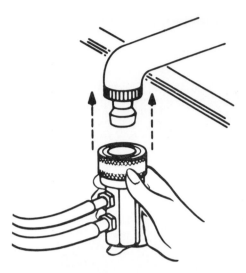

FIG. 6.18b. The portable-dish-washer is attached to the faucet by retracting the collar on the coupler assembly and slipping it over the faucet adapter.—Whirlpool.

report that effectiveness in cleaning the tableware depends on the action of the detergent and the force of the water, but research at the U.S. Department of Agriculture in Washington indicated the basic cycle as most important.[1] Dishwashers that included two wash cycles separated by a rinse cycle were always in the group of best performing machines.

The National Electrical Code (p. 269) requires a 15-ampere

---

[1] N. D. Poole, R. K. Taube, and B. B. Aulenbach, "Mechanical Dishwashers for the Home: Their Performance Characteristics," *Jour. of Home Ec.*, March 1966, p. 194.

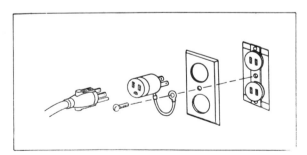

FIG. 6.18c. Electrical connections for a portable dish-washer. The grounding adapter is attached to the outlet by removing the plate screw of the outlet cover and rescrewing it through the adapter eyelet, as shown. Outlet box must be grounded. Check with your electrician to be sure this is completed.—Whirlpool

circuit for either a disposer or a dishwasher, and when the two are connected into the same circuit, a 20-ampere circuit is specified.

A hand-operated dishwasher attached to the hot-and-cold-water mixing faucet is fitted with a detergent cup and a nylon brush. By means of a control valve, sudsy water may be sprayed over the dishes, followed by a clear rinse (Fig. 6.19).

Incinerators

The incinerator is another means of disposing of garbage, both wet and dry, and of all combustible trash, but not metal or glass. Most models, holding 1½ to 2 bushels, are operated by gas, automatically controlled, with a safety shut-off in case the flame accidentally goes out. A special filter prevents clogging of the pilot.

The incinerator may be placed in the kitchen, basement, or enclosed porch. Connection by a chimney to outdoors is *mandatory*. The appliance is insulated with Fiberglas and has special devices to eliminate odors and smoke. Any ash falls into a removable drawer, which should be emptied frequently to allow optimum performance. The gas incinerator should carry the AGA Seal of Approval.

ADDITIONAL DESIRABLE CENTERS
Eating Area

An eating space in the kitchen is a convenience desired by many families. The space may be a bar, built-in table and benches, or a movable setup. The area required varies, depending upon the kind of construction and the number of people to be accommodated. Table and benches need 6 square feet of space as a mini-

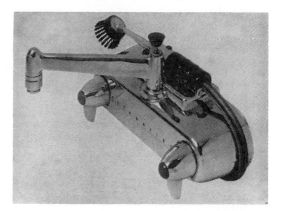

FIG. 6.19. Hand operated dishwashing attachment installed in combination with sink faucets.—Gerity-Michigan.

mum, the bar is at least 16 inches from front to back although 18 inches is preferable. When the chairs and table are movable the area should be from 7 to 8 feet square.

Planning Center

The business end of homemaking can be taken care of more efficiently if all of the essential materials are kept readily accessible so these tasks may be combined with others that keep the home-maker in the kitchen. If the room is not large enough to accommodate a desk, the breakfast bar, table, or a pull-out board can substitute. In a nearby drawer or section of a cabinet are stored all necessary supplies: bills, receipts, account books, checkbooks, manufacturers' guarantees and booklets of instruction, note pads, stationery, pen and pencils, jar labels, clippings, recipe files, cook-books, and general miscellany dear to every homemaker's heart. If the telephone or an extension can be installed here, much time and energy can be conserved.

Automatic Appliance Center

Counter space and storage area also are needed if the new automatic appliance center (Fig. 6.20) is installed in the kitchen.

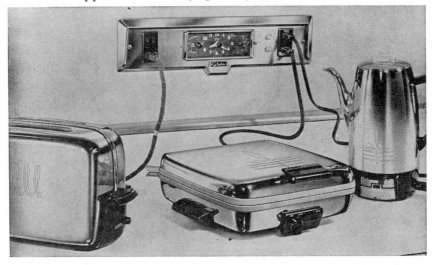

FIG. 6.20. Electropanel center permits the homemaker to use four electric appliances at one time without overloading circuits or blowing fuses. Converts 220-volt current to 110-volt service, protected by circuit breakers. One outlet (on right) connected to clock for timed cooking. May be installed in kitchen, recreation room, porch, patio, or terrace.—**Forecast for Home Economists.**

Such a center recognizes the present extensive use of small electric appliances, the fryer, egg cooker, toaster, waffle baker, frypan, etc., and provides a space for them where they can be connected easily or left permanently attached for instant use. The center may include retractable pull-out cords, ample outlets of sufficient rating to eliminate drop in voltage, circuit breakers for protection, and an automatic timer. This area would be a desirable location for the 300-watt, 6-speed motor that is installed flush with the counter, to which may be attached various motor-driven appliances such as the mixer, blender, meat grinder, juicer, or knife sharpener. This list of appliances, to which others will be added as new items appear on the market, certainly requires fairly ample counter and storage space, if the area is to be used efficiently.

MATERIALS

Many innovations have been introduced into the field of materials usable in kitchens—in construction and in finish of the kitchen itself and the equipment used there.

Use of Color

A welcome development in kitchen design is the extensive use of color, not only on walls and in counter and floor coverings, but in the appliances themselves. Wood finishes frequently are used, either the natural finish of wood or simulated wood colors and detail in enamels. Enamel, both the baked-on and porcelain types, is obtainable in a variety of colors, yellow, blue, pink, green, peach, and others—any currently popular color—from which the homemaker may choose a single one for cabinets, sink, range, and refrigerator, or she may combine several to suit her fancy. Many of the resulting kitchens are very lovely, a far cry from the drab or cold-looking rooms of 20 or 30 years ago when everything was white. Unless money is no object so the color scheme may be changed at will, be sure the color chosen is one that may be lived with indefinitely without its palling or, even worse, causing irritation. Manufacturers themselves frankly state that they expect color to shorten the life period of an appliance before real obsolescence occurs.

Wall Finishes

The modern kitchen, bright with color, becomes a second living room where family and friends enjoy good times together.

Walls usually are painted, but moisture-proof paper, tile, and a variety of composition tile boards may be used. Any finish should be washable and impervious to stain. Cabinets are of wood or metal and usually are finished to harmonize or complement the color schemes of the room; wood may be finished naturally and either material may be painted or enameled.

Curtains usually are considered a part of wall decoration. Kitchen curtains should be reduced to the minimum of size and weight so they will not interfere with light and ventilation. Since these curtains will need to be washed frequently, they should be chosen to require little care in laundering. By selecting inexpensive materials, the homemaker will not hesitate to change them more often than any other features in the kitchen, thus they may serve as a means of changing or freshening the color emphasis.

Counters and Floors

Linoleum has long been used for counter tops. It is quiet in use because of its resiliency, a characteristic that also reduces damage to china and glassware. It is marketed in a wide variety of colors that are durable and easily cleaned. Recently Formica, vinyl, and Melamine plastic coatings over laminated bases have become popular. They are resistant to discoloration and wear. Any material chosen should be corrosion, scratch, and heat resistant, should not absorb water, grease, or the common household fruit and vegetable juices, and should require a minimum of effort to be kept in good condition.

A section of wood counter near the sink and the range for the cutting of meats, vegetables, and other food products is an advantage. Hard maple is especially resistant to grease, but beech and birch also are used, although they must be treated to increase their resistance. Cutting boards (Fig. 6.12a) may be used for these purposes.

Materials used for floor coverings have qualities similar to those used for counter tops. Since the homemaker may be on her feet for fairly long periods at a time, resiliency is of primary importance, but the finish should also be stain resistant and durable. Again linoleum and vinyl plastic are commonly selected. According to the manufacturers, vinyl plastic need not be waxed, but both it and linoleum seem to maintain a good appearance longer when they are waxed. Self-polishing, water-emulsion waxes are easy to use and satisfactory. Two or three thin coats, applied 30

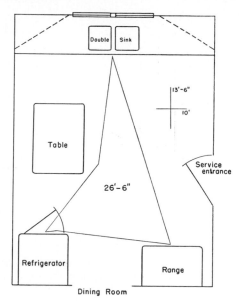

FIG. 6.21a. This kitchen has many faults: the range and refrigerator are in corners with no counter space beside them; the distances connecting work centers are too great; cabinet space is too limited; and there is cross traffic passing the range.

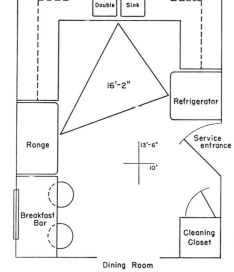

FIG. 6.21b. By relocating the range and refrigerator, logical sequence of work has been obtained, distance between work centers has been shortened, and much additional cabinet space gained, even a closet for cleaning equipment and supplies.

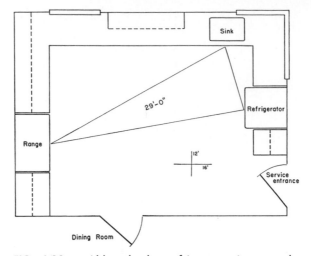

FIG. 6.22a. Although the refrigerator is near the service entrance and the range near the dining room, the kitchen is so large that many steps must be taken between work centers.

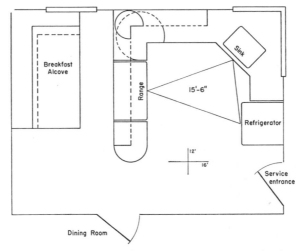

FIG. 6.22b. Placing the range on a peninsula has reduced distances between work centers and provided space for an eating area near the range. Cabinets above the range are suspended from the ceiling, leaving a pass-through to the table.

minutes to an hour apart, will give a long-lasting finish, which can be dry mopped or wiped with cold water between applications. Of course if there are a number of small children or pets who play out in all kinds of weather, a thorough cleaning may be needed more frequently.

EXPERIMENTS AND PROJECTS

1. To plan motion-saving arrangements of kitchen equipment:
   a. Select from any available house plans (frequently found in magazines) three or more kitchen plans, with no equipment indicated. Copy them, enlarged to scale, on sheets of lightweight cardboard.* Do the same with three or more plans in which the equipment is shown. For easy use, cardboard plans may be hung from picture molding or thumb-tacked to supports.
   b. Study Figures 6.21a, 6.21b, 6.22a, 6.22b for ideas on improving kitchen arrangements.
   c. Assign floor plans from the group with no equipment. Each student will copy the plan to scale on cross-sectioned paper (paper divided into ¼-inch squares is a good choice; 2 squares to a foot is a suggested scale). Following the recommendations for optimum kitchen planning, draw in the appliances, cabinets, etc., indicating the three centers on the plan. Have each student evaluate the finished plan.
   d. Assign floor plans from the group including equipment. Have students evaluate their plans, draw a remodeled plan and again evaluate. If necessary, windows and doors may be moved, provided new ones are on same walls as originals. If kitchen kits are available, set up plan to determine whether further changes are needed.
   e. Have students draw plans of their own home kitchens; evaluate and remodel if necessary, indicating distances saved.
2. To demonstrate need for different heights of working areas:
   a. Have students study and report on the following references:
      Space Design for Household Storage, by Helen E. McCullough (Univ. of Ill. Agr. Exper. Sta. Bul. 557, 1952. Price, $1.25), pp. 30–33 and 46–50.
      Kitchen Cupboards That Simplify Storage, by Mary K. Heiner and Helen E. McCullough (Cornell Extension Bul. 703, July, 1959. Price, $.05).
      Management in the Home, by Lillian M. Gilbreth, Orpha Mae Thomas, and Eleanor Clymer, 2nd edition (Dodd, Mead, & Co., N. Y., 1959), pp. 59–122.
   b. Arrange a low counter or table with different working heights. This may be done with flat fruit boxes or similar ones obtained

---

* Plans should be drawn to scale, but it is better not to spend time in drawing double walls, cross-hatching the space between, or other practices of professional architects. Emphasis is on arranging equipment, *not* on drawing plans.

at grocery stores. Build up or cut down boxes so the heights will be increased one or two inches each. Boys in this class or a shop class can help with this. Two or three students of noticeably different heights can demonstrate the need for various working heights when using an egg beater with a bowl, rolling out baking powder biscuits, and washing dishes in a dishpan.

3. To apply motion- and energy-saving plans to supplies in cabinets: Arrange supplies and utensils in disorder in cabinets. Assign students to rearrange them so they may be put in and taken out with the least expenditure of motion and energy.

4. To compare efficiency in methods of washing dishes: Compare time needed to wash, rinse, and dry dishes by hand with time needed to wash, rinse, and cover for drying in dish drainer. Discuss advantages and disadvantages of the two methods.

QUESTIONS

1. List four possible work centers in the kitchen and four things that should be stored at each center.
2. What is a good rule to follow in storing utensils and supplies?
3. What is a desirable location for range and eating areas? Why is this often difficult to obtain?
4. How should work in a kitchen move?
5. What are the optimum distances between range, refrigerator, and sink? Why should the sink never be located in a corner?
6. What is the most desirable height for work surfaces? Are work surfaces the same height for all tasks? All people? Explain.
7. What kind of covering material will you select for floors, walls, and counters? Give reasons for choice.
8. If you have only one window in your kitchen, how may you obtain the necessary light and ventilation?
9. Would you consider a food-waste disposer essential? Give reasons for and against.
10. Have you had experience in using a dishwasher? Does it have any limitations? If you do not have a dishwasher, how can you avoid wiping the dishes?

Chapter Seven

SAFETY IN THE KITCHEN

In the course of a year there are four times the accidents in the home as in auto mishaps. According to a recent yearly report over four million people were injured in the home; of this number about 27,500 were killed. Not all occur in the kitchen, of course, but the kitchen is a good place in which to start to remove hazards. Many of the suggestions for improving safety are incorporated in the illustrations in previous chapters.

STORAGE AREAS
Cabinets

Consider first the cabinets. One modern feature that improves safety is building the ceiling down so that wall cabinets are not so high (see Fig. 6.11) but, unless a person is really tall, the top shelf still cannot be reached without climbing. Less frequently used equipment and dishes are stored on the top shelf, and nine times out of ten they are of breakable materials. So when climbing is necessary, as it often is, be sure that a step-stool is available, one with a broad solid foundation that will not tip when the homemaker stretches for a glass salad bowl at the back of the top shelf. Otherwise, if she uses just any kind of a stool or even a chair, she may lose her balance and fall, with serious damage to herself and the dish.

Deep storage areas are both inefficient and bothersome. To avoid storing utensils and dishes two or three layers deep, use half shelves between the wide ones, or cut away the centers of shelves and attach a rack to the door to compensate for the lost space. Have a file built between two shelves in one of the wall cabinets where each baking pan and dish may be slipped into its own individual space and several pans need not be lifted to find the one wanted. Or have sliding shelves in the base cabinets, that can be pulled out so the needed utensil can be selected easily. To have to hunt for articles increases fatigue, and accidents are much more apt to happen when one is tired or frustrated. In planning or selecting upper cabinets make sure the doors, when open, do not extend beyond the work counter. It is easy to forget to close a door and, when rising from a stooping position, you may contact the sharp corner of the open door with painful results.

Sharp-edged Equipment

Knives dumped together in a drawer endanger the hand of the person trying to pick out a special one, and also tend to nick and dull the finest edge, so keep knives in a slotted rack (see Fig. 6.10). Fingers may be cut, too, if sharp knives are put into the dishpan or sink and lie hidden in the soapy water. Wash and dry each knife separately. To slice or chop, put a chopping board on the side of the sink, the bowl or saucepan in the sink, then slice or chop any desired size, letting the pieces fall by gravity into the receptacle.

A can opener is another utensil that may cause injuries. The opener itself as well as the can cover may cut the hand. Invest in a can opener that is fastened to the wall. It is easier to use and much the safest method as it cuts the cover off clean, leaving no jagged edges.

RANGES AND COOKING

Locate the range so there is no possibility of a window curtain coming into contact with an open flame or a hot electric unit. When this is impossible, eliminate curtains or select ones short enough to avoid danger. If the range is an electric one, be sure that it is grounded. Otherwise, if insulation wears off from a wire and the wire accidentally touches the range frame, there is a chance of shock from current leakage. If the range uses gas, select a model with self-locking valve handles. Then small, exploring fingers cannot unintentionally turn on the gas. Always turn the handles of pots and pans away from the edges of cooking surfaces, so that there is no chance for them to be knocked about, causing spillage of hot liquid over the floor and, even worse, over yourself or a child. Don't use pans with loose handles; repair them or discard them for new ones. Keep pot holders near at hand and have them thick enough to prevent any likelihood of burns. Make a habit of using pot holders and not the corner of your apron, then a pan that proves too hot to be held will not be dropped. Quilted mitts protect the entire hand and are recommended, especially for removing foods from the oven. Wipe up spills immediately so that no one will slip on the spot and perhaps fall.

Store matches, often used to light the gas oven, out of the reach of children. Avoid using the gas oven to heat the kitchen, unless the room is well ventilated. Burning gas not connected to an outside vent will tend to use up the supply of oxygen in the kitchen and make the homemaker feel dull and headachey.

SMALL APPLIANCES

Many small electric appliances used in the kitchen—the toaster, coffee maker, mixer, perhaps a roaster—as well as hand irons, have cords that need to be watched for damage, fraying of the insulation, etc. Sooner or later they will cause a short circuit, if not a fire. Place all cords where they cannot be tripped over and out of the reach of small children. If a cord accidentally becomes wet, be sure it is thoroughly dry before it is used again. Install safety wall outlets into which a plug is inserted by rotating the center of the outlet through an arc. Such an outlet prevents small children from sticking a piece of metal into the outlet and receiving a bad burn or a shock.

As has been noted, always select electric appliances and cords that carry the UL seal of approval (page 33 and Fig. 2.22), indicating that they have been tested for safety against fire and shock hazard. Gas appliances should have the AGA Blue Star seal (p. 33 and Fig. 2.20).

Never use electric appliances near the sink; never wash off the blades of an electric beater while it is still connected to a circuit. As has been previously noted, the sink is grounded through the water pipes, and if the appliance should prove defective, a bad shock or even death may result.

WORK HABITS

Then there is the matter of slipping when in a hurry. First, plan your work so there will be no flustered, last-minute dashing around; also equip your kitchen with nonskid, sponge-rubber mats by sink, range, and mix center. They not only reduce the tendency to slide, but also make the feet and back muscles less weary, when one must stand for a long time. Acquire the habit of sitting, however, to do every job possible—it is a safe and restful habit.

Make the kitchen safe, *keep* it safe. Get the cooperation of the entire family, and so reduce or, better still, eliminate the terrible toll of home accidents. The life you save may be your own.

EXPERIMENTS AND PROJECTS

1. To reduce or eliminate kitchen accidents:
   a. Have students make a list of hazards in laboratory kitchen. Suggest methods for eliminating the hazards.
   b. Have students list hazards in own home kitchens. Suggest what may be done to eliminate them with a minimum of expense and without remodeling the kitchen.

QUESTIONS

1. When you are cooking potatoes in a saucepan on the range, how do you prevent them from accidentally spilling onto the floor?
2. If some salad dressing should drip from your work counter to the linoleum floor, what should you do immediately? Why?
3. Why use holders in removing a casserole from the oven instead of the edge of your apron?
4. Why store knives separately in a rack instead of loose in a drawer?
5. Where do you place appliances and utensils that you use frequently? Why?
6. How can you avoid fatigue in doing your kitchen tasks? Why should you?

Chapter Eight

EQUIPMENT FOR

THE LAUNDRY

Development of automatic washers and dryers that require little or no attention during their period of operation has done much to save human energy and release time for other duties or for recreation. The more recent combination of the two has made it practical to locate the laundry areas, if not in the kitchen itself, at least adjacent to it. This is often a multipurpose room where ironing, sewing, and perhaps preparation of food for the freezer may be carried on. The bathroom, if sufficiently large, is also a good location, utilizing the plumbing that is close at hand. Here the combination washer-dryer is a desirable choice.

When building a new home the laundry area may be placed next to the bathroom, where one may press a needed dress or blouse while in the process of dressing. An added advantage is the ease with which newly pressed clothes may be hung immediately in nearby closets, avoiding the wrinkling sometimes occasioned when being carried from another part of the house. Ironing of course may be done in any room; the bedroom is often a good choice, but it is a gain when a room is available where the ironing center may remain ready for instant use at all times. Such a room also may be supplied with storage facilities for towels, sheets, and other requirements for adjacent bedrooms and bath.

Obviously the basement is still frequently used. Here both time and steps may be saved when a bell or buzzer calls attention to the end of a cycle. Even the nonautomatic washer, the wringer or spinner types, may be equipped with a device that makes this known (Fig. 8.1). Dryers have largely eliminated the necessity of carrying heavy baskets of damp clothes over the stairs.

Counter space and bins on wheels should be provided for sorting and transporting the linens and wearing apparel. Shelves are needed for storage of detergents, starches, bleaches, softeners, and the utensils used with them. The floors and walls should be

FIG. 8.1. The timer clock may be set from 1 to 8 minutes, according to type of fabric, to stop agitator and ring a bell.—Speed Queen.

moisture resistant and easily cleaned. Daylight and artificial illumination should be at a level high enough to allow the homemaker to see with ease and work without strain. Light-colored walls and counter tops will increase the reflected light available.

WASHERS

There are two types of washers—the revolving drum, and those with a central agitating mechanism, usually supported on a central shaft (Fig. 8.2). The agitator washer circulates water through the clothes, the tumbler washer with the rotating drum circulates the clothes through the water. The finned agitator, with or without perforations or corrugations to aid in water action, is the most common (Figs. 8.3a and b), but one model has a pulsator (Fig. 8.3c) and another uses an agitator without any fins (Fig. 8.3d). Water action is obtained by the rocking and rolling of the mechanism, which sends out high-speed waves 600 times a minute. A ball-joint balance eliminates vibration (Fig. 8.3e).

The efficiency of a washer in removing dirt probably is related directly to the ratio of water to amount of clothes. One authority states that there should be not less than 1¾ gallons of

FIG. 8.2. The tub of the washer is bowl shaped, which adds a rolling action to the usual cleaning process. A stainless steel tub and aluminum wringer frame prevent corrosion. When release bar is pushed, it stops rotation of the wringer rolls and separates them several inches.—Speed Queen.

water to each pound of clothes if the water and detergent are to flex the clothes and if the water is to be flushed through the clothes sufficiently. The washer with the vertical mechanism usually has a ratio of 1½ to 2 gallons of water to a pound of clothes.

Washers fill at the turn of a control. The time-fill control

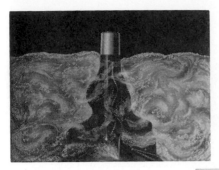

FIG. 8.3a. Surgilator agitator.—
Whirlpool.

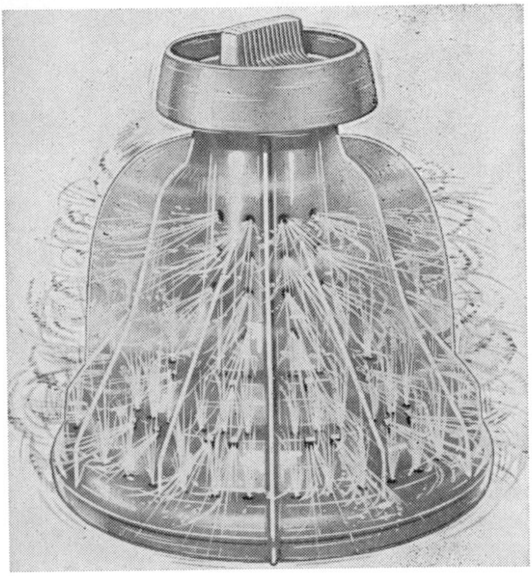

FIG. 8.3b. Agitator moves in
one direction only, while 12
large vanes create vigorous
water action, and 180 scientifi-
cally placed holes jet sudsy
water through the clothes.—
Kelvinator.

FIG. 8.3c. Cutaway view of tri-coned
agitator. Vertical motion of cones creates powerful jet currents of water.
Note bleach cup in agitator column.—
Frigidaire.

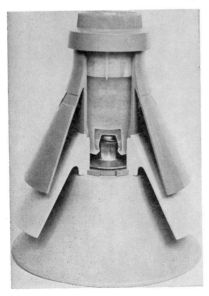

FIG. 8.3d. Blade-free agitator.—Philco.

FIG. 8.3e. The agitator jets out high-speed
water waves 600 times a minute, moving the
clothes up, down, and all around the tub.
—Philco.

is not very satisfactory if the water pressure is low; it may not
allow a sufficient amount of water to enter the tub before the agitation starts. The metered-fill, however, is uniform, and action
begins only after the desired amount is in the tub, an amount
which usually can be selected by the homemaker on the basis of
size of load.

CONSTRUCTION OF WASHERS
Body

The wash tub may be of aluminum or stainless steel or may
be finished in porcelain enamel. The exterior is commonly coated
with baked-on enamel, a finish that resists knocks and blows, but
would not withstand the constant friction of clothes rubbing
against it if it were used in the interior. When the top is to be
used as a work surface it should be of porcelain enamel to withstand abrasion. The agitator is of aluminum, stainless steel, or
plastic material, with the fins, 3 or 4 in number, varying in shape
and size. Several wringer washers now have built-in lint collectors
on the agitator shaft, similar to those found in the automatics;
they may be used also as detergent dispensers as shown in Figure
8.2. Wringer rolls are of semisoft rubber, with or without a pressure selector. They should have a safety release that will separate
the rolls completely and at the same time cause them to stop rotating (Figs. 8.2 and 8.4). For versatility in use, the wringer swings

FIG. 8.4. New open-top wring-er for maximum visibility and safety. Adjusts automatically to any type of material and gives even pressure over full width of rolls.—Norge.

and locks into several different positions, and rolls may be rotated in either direction. One wringer-type washer provides a Deep-Power rinse, eliminating need for separate wash tubs. During the rinse cycle the agitator supplies vigorous action that circulates fresh water to rinse each article mechanically. The drain pump empties the tub in less than two minutes.

In the nonautomatic spinner washer the water is extracted in a separate, perforated cylinder that revolves at a high rate of speed. When the cylinder is constructed with a central cone pierc-ed by many tiny openings through which a fine spray of water can be forced, rinsing may be done in the cylinder without the necessity of removing the clothes to another tub.

In the automatic washer the water usually is removed by the spinning of the tub in which the clothes are washed. Rinses are of three different kinds: the spray rinse removes some of the loose soil and detergent residue; the deep rinse is similar to the wash cycle in agitating and flexing the clothes; the overflow rinse tends to float off any remaining scum and lint freed by the agitated rinse. Deep and overflow rinses are often combined (Figs. 8.5a, b, and c).

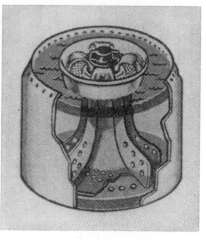

FIG. 8.5a. Triple-filtering action; filter on central shaft catches lint; openings around tub at water level skim off floating scum and other particles; grit and sand settle to bottom of tub and pass out of holes under agitator. —Hamilton.

FIG. 8.5b. At end of wash cycle, fresh water is added so that inner tub overflows, causing lint and dirt to float over top and down drain.—Speed Queen.

FIG. 8.5c. Sand and grit settling to bottom of tub are forced out through ejector tube ("Sediment E-jector") when tub spins, so tub is free of sediment at start of final rinse.—Speed Queen.

The water may be ejected through holes in the side and bottom of the tub or openings at the top just below the trim, the latter method the better, probably, in preventing the lint and extracted soil from redepositing on the clothes. Certain washers are supplied with a special lint filter. One type cleans itself—no soggy lint to handle. The filter is composed of two parts that fit together to form a flat, pancake-shaped device. Water is drawn through it continuously during washing and rinsing at all water levels, and the lint is trapped in channels from which it is flushed away with the wash and rinse waters during draining. It is quiet in operation and comparatively service free.

The nonautomatic washers are top opening. The automatic agitator types also have a top opening lid, but revolving drum washers open on the side as do the washer-dryer combinations.

Improvements in new models put out by the various manufacturers include: (1) new types of construction and use of materials for elimination of noise and ease of servicing, (2) no-drip tops and reduction in vibration, (4) fluid drive preventing starting shock and wear on mechanism, (5) infinite water-level selection, (6) aerated water inlet, causing detergent to disperse more rapidly, increasing laundering efficiency, (7) provision for larger loads, (8) a soak cycle, (9) additional rinses—one washer supplies three deep rinses, (10) automatic load balance during spin cycle, (11) more easily cleaned lint filters, (12) device in pump to prevent clogging by buttons, pins, etc., (13) 3-wire grounding-type cord, and (14) more understandable owner's manual.

Controls

Controls on all washers should be centrally located and clearly marked. Some nonautomatic washers have a device marked in suggested time periods for washing the different fabrics; when the time is up, the motor stops (Fig. 8.1). All automatic washers control the complete cycle of washing, rinsing, and spin drying. Certain models have a "suds saver" that automatically pumps the hot sudsy water into a separate tub and, after the rinse cycle is completed, pumps it back to be used again in the washer. To prevent redeposition of soil on the following load, the suds saver should not be used when the water is very dirty. Usually more hot water must be added to maintain the desired temperature, and frequently extra detergent is needed.

Water is an important factor in laundering, both for washing and rinsing. A generally accepted rule for washing white and colorfast linens and cottons is "the hotter the water, the whiter and more sparkling the wash." A minimum temperature of 140 F. is recommended.

Recent automatic washers feature special cycles for synthetic and delicate fabrics, and for "wash-and-wear" garments; the cycles have a shorter wash period, with cooler water and gentle spinning. Cold water washes and rinses also are more widely available. Several de luxe washers use the Fabric Formula or Programming method: the homemaker simply pushes a button indicating the type of load and everything else follows automatically, the temperature of wash and rinse waters and the length and speed of agitation and spin cycles. A number of washers have automatic dispensers to add the detergent, bleach, or rinse conditioner at the proper time in the cycle (Fig. 8.3c).

A few compact washers are on the market, most of them only partially automatic. These do not take the place of the standard washer, but may be used to wash a few small items from time to time. In general the compact washer is not as efficient as the full-sized machine, for usually the homemaker must fill and/or drain the tub and extract the water from the clothes by means of a hand-operated wringer. Often an impeller in the side of the tub takes the place of an agitator. Low-sudsing detergents are recommended.

INTERRELATION OF HARD WATER AND DETERGENTS

Satisfactory washing results are influenced by a number of factors in addition to the type of washer. Two major ones are the degree of water hardness, and the kind of detergent used. These two factors are closely interrelated.

Eighty per cent or more of the areas of the United States have hard water of varying degrees because of the presence of insoluble calcium and magnesium salts. These salts react with soaps to form a curd or scum which settles in the meshes of the fabric, is rinsed out with great difficulty, and causes "tattle-tale gray." An increase in the deposit from week to week is not only very detrimental to the appearance of table and bed linens and wearing apparel, but also makes the material feel stiff and rough and tends to shorten its life. Synthetic detergents, often called simply detergents, in contrast to soaps, form no precipitate and for this reason are more and more widely used. Homemakers of America spend

TABLE 8.1

A PARTIAL LIST OF COMMONLY AVAILABLE SOAPS AND SYNTHETIC DETERGENTS†

SOAPS	
Mild	All purpose
Cold-water Woolite*—also in dry form Chiffon Ivory Flakes Ivory Snow Lux Flakes Kirkman Flakes	Chipso Duz Fels Naphtha Rinso, green package White King

SYNTHETIC DETERGENTS		
Light Duty	All purpose	
	High Sudsing	Low Sudsing
Cold Power* Cold-water All* Dreft Glim* Ivory* Joy* Lux* Nylast* Swerl* Trend*—also in dry form Vel*—also in dry form Wool N Wash*	American Family Detergent Blue Cheer Felso Fun Oxydol Sun Super Suds Surf Tide White King D Wisk*	AD All—also in liquid Ajax Bold Breeze Dash Dreft Duz Fab Rinso Spin Trend Vim
	Premeasured	Premeasured
	Answer Rinso Measurematic Swerl Tide Redi Paks	AD Packs AD Tabs Dash Redi-Paks Handy Pack All Hum Quick-Solvo Solvo Vim

NOTE: The following detergents are marketed in plastic containers: Chiffon, Ivory Liquid, Lux Liquid, Swan, Texy, Trend, Vel.

  * Liquid

  † New products appear frequently on the market, and old brands change their formulas, so any listing must of necessity be recognized as authentic when published, although subject to correction as conditions change.

one and one-half billion dollars a year for synthetic detergents, more and more the light-duty type. Low-sudsing detergents also are favored. A number of the products are packaged in squeeze-type plastic containers with a squirt top or a cap for the measure. Comparatively new on the market are the premeasured detergents, sold as tablets or in packets made from soluble polyvinyl.

Both soaps and detergents may be either mild or built. The

mild products have very little or no free alkali and are used for the washing of silks, woolens, most of the man-made fibers, and all delicate fabrics, regardless of their composition. Built detergents (detergent in the true meaning of the word is a general name and includes both soaps and synthetics) contain free or added alkaline substances that are effective in removing dirt and grease from badly soiled garments such as overalls and children's play clothes. Table 8.1 gives a partial list of soaps and synthetic detergents. All are not marketed in every part of the country and new products are added frequently. Many recent items are liquid in form for ease in handling.

Low-sudsing Synthetic Detergents

Note that certain detergents are classified as low-sudsing or controlled sudsing. A number of manufacturers of automatic washers recommend the use of low-sudsing detergents in their machines. Too much suds will tend to decrease the action of the washer, prevent the complete removal of dirt, and in some cases cause corrosion when the foam gets into areas of the washer not easily reached for cleaning. Low-sudsing detergents are always specified for the tumbler washer. The action of this washer tends to increase the volume of suds. Certain detergents contain an optical bleach or fluorescent-type bluing which imparts a bluish appearance to the fabric by reflecting blue light, making the materials appear whiter. Occasionally CMC (carboxymethyl cellulose) is added to hinder the removed dirt from redepositing on the cloth.

The impression that the free alkali in all-purpose soaps and synthetic detergents may cause irritation to the skin of the hands apparently has been disproved by tests with women who had normal hands and those who had hand eczema. The results showed, in fact, that some cases of eczema were benefited by using the alkaline products.

Water Softeners

If the water is hard and the homemaker prefers to use soap, it is desirable to add a water softener first or, even better, to soften all the water by passing it through a resin or zeolite tank as it comes into the house. The tank may be regenerated manually, or it may be fully automatic, controlled by an electric time switch which, according to the need, causes the regenerating solution to flow into the conditioning tank at the proper frequency.

Some packaged softeners on the market, such as washing soda, form a precipitate with the hard water minerals, a precipitate that must be removed or it will settle on the fibers of the material just as the soap curd did. There are at present, however, a number of softeners—Calgon, Noctil, Quadrofos, Tex, sold by the package, that hold the calcium and magnesium in solution. They are easier to use and undoubtedly more satisfactory than the precipitating types. Soft water can reduce from $\frac{1}{2}$ to $\frac{2}{3}$ the amount of money spent each year for soaps and detergents.

Fabric Softeners

A new laundry additive is the fabric softener—Sta-Puf, Final Touch, Nu-soft, Downy, Texize Laundry Fluff, are examples. These are organic ammonium salts in a solution of water and alcohol. The chemicals are positively charged and therefore are attracted to most fibers which have a negative charge. The softeners form a lubricating type of coating on the fibers, helping them to retain a certain amount of moisture. They soften all types of fabrics, even heavy denims, making them easier and quicker to iron. They also tend to eliminate from lingerie and other clothing static electricity and the tendency to cling. Softeners minimize wrinkling and make woolens fluffy. They should be added at the end of the final rinse water after water softeners, detergents, and bleaches have been removed entirely from the clothes since the fabric softener tends to form a scum with detergents, but they should be added before starching. Directions of the manufacturer should be followed carefully, since constant use of too large an amount may cause the fabric to become water repellent. It is suggested that the homemaker skip the use of a softener every fifth time to avoid undesirable build-up.

Softeners show a tendency to discolor fabrics, giving a yellowed or gray appearance to the fibers, but manufacturers of Texize Laundry Fluff claim that this softener prevents yellowing of the material, deodorizes it, and does not cause water-proofing. Deodorants such as Borateem, Diaper Pure, and Diaper Sweet are recommended for use with the detergent in washing diapers and outfits heavy with perspiration. Some deodorants prevent bacterial infections. Many softeners now contain optical brighteners, since the brighteners contained in detergents are partly destroyed by the softener.

In general, all laundry additives should be measured as accurately as ingredients are for baking.

DIRT REMOVAL

Dirt is of two kinds; that from the earth—dust or mud, depending upon weather conditions—and that from other sources, usually grouped together and frequently referred to as stains. Mud and dust tend to cling to the surface of the soap bubbles, an action known as adsorption. Fats and greases, on the other hand, are emulsified, that is, they are surrounded by the soapy solution and held in suspension during the washing process.

Surface Tension

The purpose of washing is to get rid of dirt. If the dirt is to be removed adequately, lowering of surface tension is essential. Surface tension is the force that will cause any liquid to take the form of drops, a form that gives the least surface area in proportion to volume. Adding a detergent lowers the surface tension of the water, causing it to spread out in a film and wet the fabric, instead of staying in the form of drops.

Stain Removal

Stains always should be removed before the material is laundered. It is essential that water of the correct temperature be applied to each stain. Some man-made fibers may be damaged by hot water; but fortunately most of these fibers do not absorb stain. When it is not possible to test a sample for stain removing, the garment should be sent to professional cleaners.

Stains requiring boiling water are: red and blue fruit, tea, and coffee. All other stains, including milk and grease, should be rinsed or soaked in cool water before they are put in the washer. A cool-water soak period of 15 to 20 minutes for all laundry tends to loosen the dirt, hastening its removal in the washer. The United States government publishes a bulletin on stain removal (see reference on p. 312) giving directions for treatment of individual stains.

Bleaching and Bluing

Bluing and bleaching usually are not necessary if hot, soft water is available. The detergents with the fluorescent-type bluing give a blue-white appearance to clothing. If the homemaker, however, prefers to use bluing, she should add the flake or bead form to the wash water and the liquid bluing to the rinse.

Bleaching of pillow cases, dish towels, and small children's panties sometimes will be desirable. Bleaches currently on the

TABLE 8.2

A PARTIAL LIST OF COMMONLY AVAILABLE BLEACHES

Perborate	Monopersulfate	Chlorine
Dexol	Dribrite	Action
Kitchen Klatter	Durite	Beads-o'-Bleach
Lestare		Clorox*
Snowy Bleach		Des Moines*
(all available in		Fleecy White
premeasured packets)		Hilex
		McCoy
		Purex*
		Roman*
		Star Dust
		Texize*

* Available in plastic containers.

market are listed in Table 8.2. A chlorine bleach, containing
sodium or calcium hypochlorite, is used on linens and cottons,
always in hot water and always with a heavy-duty detergent that
contains no fluorescent dye. The combination of chlorine and dye
may yellow the material. The suds buffer the action of the bleach
and so protect the fabric. Do not use a chlorine bleach in rusty
water. The chlorine tends to make iron stains worse. Do not add
it to hard water containing soap. Chlorine reacts with soap to form
more curds. Always dilute the bleach with at least eight parts
of water before pouring into a loaded washer. Always rinse fabrics two and preferably three times following the use of chlorine
bleach. Chlorine reacts with water to form hydrochloric acid and
oxygen. The acid will damage fabrics unless kept well diluted.
The perborate bleaches, in contrast, are harmless and may be used
on practically any material. The bleaching action is caused by
oxygen set free from the perborate when hot water is used. In general these bleaches are not as effective as the chlorine bleaches.
Some fairly recently developed bleaches are said to combine the
safety of the perborates and the efficiency of the chlorines. A com-
pound known as DDH is one example. Two others are Durite
and Dribrite, oxygen-type bleaches made from Oxone, a Du Pont
product. Oxone is potassium monopersulfate, an odorless com-
pound that has proved effective in removing stains. Moreover
these bleaches may be used safely on all fabrics, even on man-
made fibers and resin-treated cottons. All bleaching should be
followed by careful and thorough rinsing. Bleaches are marketed frequently in premeasured and/or plastic containers.

Occasionally, if there is sickness in the family or if a public
washer is used continuously, disinfectants should be added to the

laundry load, to prevent spreading disease-causing bacteria. Quaternary and phenolic disinfectants are recommended. Add the quaternary to the rinse water, the phenolic to either wash or rinse. Chlorine bleaches, where they can be used on the fabrics, are also effective. The following names are a partial list of available disinfectants:

Quaternary
>   Co-op Sanitizer (obtainable in Co-op Stores)
>   Roccal (obtainable at dairy and janitors' supply houses)

Phenolic
>   Fast
>   Sea-Air-Pine-Sol (both obtainable in grocery stores)

Starching

Starching often improves the appearance of dresses, aprons, blouses, and shirts and prevents soil from clinging to the fabric. Two types of starches are available, the vegetable and the plastic. Vegetable starch, liquid or dry in form, made with either boiling or cold water, tends to coat the surface of the material. Plastic starches, from resins, will penetrate into the fibers, so that one treatment is adequate for a number of washings. When brown textiles are to be starched, tea often is added to prevent a streaked appearance; similarly bluing or a dye is put into starch used on dark blue garments.

A new method of starching is application of the starch as a spray from a pump-type or pressurized container. It enables the homemaker to starch only what she wishes to starch when she reaches the article in the ironing process. She must be careful, however, to spread the starch evenly, and not to starch accidentally garments not needing it. Some spray starches tend to coat the iron and all are still fairly expensive to use. The starches Sta-Flo, Easy-on, and Glamorene are sold as sprays.

Prewashing Requirements

Water. Hot water between 140 and 160 F. should be used. If hard, it should be softened by adding a nonprecipitating softener to prevent formation of a curd that will settle in the fibers and give them a grayed appearance. This gray curd is *not* removed by bleaching.

Detergent. Dissolve the correct amount of soap or synthetic in the water. If using a high-sudsing detergent, a standing suds of two to three inches on the surface of the water is desirable. Too much detergent slows down agitation and results in unsatisfactory cleaning action, but too little detergent is even more deleterious, and results in grayness and often in yellowing. The two major causes of a gray tinge on clothes are: hard water and not enough detergent; of yellowing: again not enough detergent and water not hot enough. If the water has not been softened, it is usually better to use a detergent that will not cause a scum or curd. When recommended by the manufacturer, use a low-sudsing detergent in the automatic washer.

Preparation of clothing and household linens for laundering. Empty pockets; remove shoulder pads, belts, pins, and buckles; close zippers; brush out cuffs and pockets; mend tears, sew on loose buttons; treat spots and stains; bleach if necessary; sort into groups similar in color, construction, and amount of soil; and test for color fastness. The Gas Appliance Manufacturers Association suggests that a bit of doubtful material be soaked and then blotted between the folds of an old, white bath towel. If there is even the slightest indication of stain, the material should be washed by itself quickly in lukewarm water, rinsed carefully, and hung to dry immediately.

Washing Procedure

Soak for 15 to 20 minutes in cool water to prevent the setting of any stains that may have been overlooked and to loosen meshes of material making it more pliable. Instead of a soak cycle, the homemaker can stop the agitator after five minutes of action and let the clothes soak 15 to 20 minutes, then complete the cycle. This method makes use of less water and equipment, but more detergent should be added to the wash.

Wash white nylons by themselves first, since they tend to pick up any dirt or dye in the wash water, even from supposedly dye-fast fabrics. Nylons remain white longer if washed in hot water. Certain nylon weaves may wrinkle in very hot water, but not if the wash period is only two or three minutes long. Use the short cycle when it is provided in an automatic washer. Putting nylons through the wringer may cause wrinkling, but a short fluff period in the dryer usually removes wrinkles (Fig. 8.6).

If a nonautomatic spinner or wringer washer is used, change the wash water frequently enough to prevent redepositing the soil on the materials. When wringing clothes, double buttons inside, and fold the garment so that wrinkles will be reduced to a minimum. Bath towels should always be folded lengthwise and guided through the wringer. Add a nonprecipitating water sof-

FIG. 8.6. It is a simple matter to transfer laundry from washer to dryer when the dryer door can be opened to a "chute" position.—Norge.

tener to the first rinse water, whether it is in a separate tub or in the rinse cycle of the automatic washer. Such a practice removes any remaining suds carried over from the wash period and prevents yellowing of the fabric in the dryer or under the heat of the iron. Add a fabric softener to the last rinse.

Certain synthetic man-made fibers — Orlon, Dynel, Dacron, etc. — should be washed in warm water, handled as little as possible, and either drip dried or spun at a low speed and for a very short time in the dryer. A number of equipment manufacturers provide a special cycle for the gentle treatment of such fabrics. Some investigators recommend that clothing made of these fibers be rinsed in cold water and spun in the dryer without heat to prevent or at least minimize wrinkling. One manufacturer supplies a separate compartment for delicate fabrics through which warm but not hot air circulates, and there is no agitation. Another places a shelf in the dryer on which clothing may be laid. The drum does not rotate (Figs. 8.7a and b). Acetates are damaged, even melted, by high heat. Sheer materials usually should be washed by hand, as should most knitted woolen garments, gently squeezing the suds through them, rinsing, and then removing excess water with a bath towel. These articles should be dried flat, and shaped as they dry.

One manufacturer has added a cycle marked "Handwash" to the washer controls (Fig. 8.8). It is as gentle and safe as hand washing and more thorough, because independent of individual techniques. Tests on every known fabric usually labeled "hand washable" have demonstrated the truth of this statement to the satisfaction of leading fiber and fabric manufacturers.

This washer actually supplies an infinite choice of speeds, any speed from fast action to very gentle, all made possible by 11 solid-state components, an application of space-age technology to home use.

FIG. 8.7a. The Stop-N'-Dry rack in the clothesline position for drying nylon hose without agitation.—Norge.

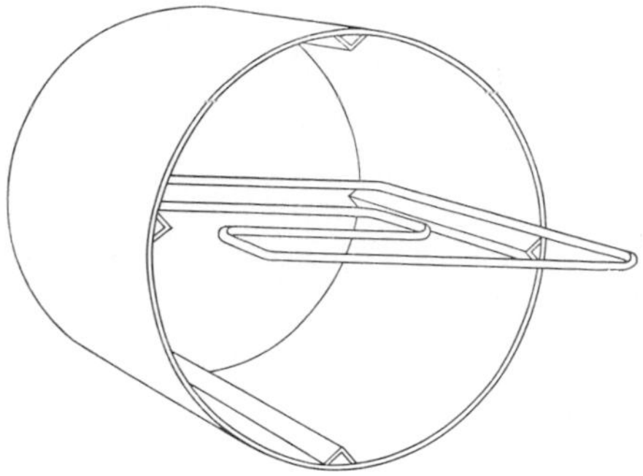

FIG. 8.7b. Stationary drying rack fits inside dryer in either of two horizontal positions to permit drying of clothes without agitation.—Norge.

Other washers and dryers have special cycles to care for Wash and Wear and Permanent Press garments, the latter probably one of the most revolutionary developments in the fabric picture. In the washer cycles the garments are cooled before any spinning takes place, preventing formation of creases and wrinkles. The dryer also provides a cool-down, fluffing period at the end of the drying cycles so that the garments are cooled and their wrinkle resistance restored while still tumbling. Pleats and creases in permanent press materials stay sharp, seams are flat, and the whole garment maintains the pressed shape. (Fig. 8.9).

Research has demonstrated that durable-crease and permanent-press garments have introduced special problems into the laundry process. Durable-crease cotton trousers tend to show abrasive action at the creases when washed in the washer. It is

FIG. 8.8. Infinite variable agitation and spin speeds easily dialed by these two controls. Safe for all machine washables plus anything you now wash by hand.—Hotpoint.

FIG. 8.9. Washer and dryer feature special automatic durable-press settings that eliminate ironing. End-of-cycle signal on dryer reminds homemaker to remove items promptly when dryer stops. This dryer has 2-speed tumbling control for light as well as normal loads.—Frigidaire.

recommended that you turn the trousers inside out before washing. It was also noted that wash-wear cottons show much greater abrasion losses during dry tumbling than in spinning when wet. As soon as such clothing is dry, therefore, it should be removed promptly from the dryer to avoid excessive abrasion. Always place the garments on hangers at once.

To avoid the matting of fibers, blankets should not be agitated. Soaking in warm suds usually is sufficient. They may be put through a loosened wringer or spun briefly and if buffered with bath towels that have been previously warmed, may be partially dried in a dryer. Brushing when slightly damp restores the nap. A new process, treating wool blankets with Dylonize, allows them to be machine washed in hot water with usual detergents and dried without special care. The blanket shows no pilling, matting, or felting.

Electric sheets and blankets should be washed — never dry-cleaned — since cleaner solutions will gradually destroy the insulation on the wires. Do not agitate, twist or wring, or dry in a dryer — the wires may be injured — allow them to drip dry over two parallel lines, shifting now and then so the wires will not be bent at a right angle. If possible, lay flat on bed and gently restore to original shape.

A new blanket has no wires but is heated by warm water circulated by a small pump through a network of flexible plastic tubing. The pump is a part of a control unit which also contains a water reservoir and a sealed heating element of 250 watts. One may sit or sleep on this blanket without damage to the tubing or danger from shock hazard. It may be machine washed in luke-warm water, but cannot be dried in the dryer or dry cleaned.

CARE OF WASHER

At the end of the wash period the washer should be cleaned. The automatic washer is more or less self-cleaning, but the agitator should be removed and the lint screen wiped.

Wash water is removed from most wringer and spinner washers by an electrically operated pump. The tub and wringer rolls should then be rinsed, the agitator removed and dried, the tension on the wringer rolls released, the wringer, tub, and agitator shaft wiped, and the agitator laid back into the tub on its side rather than replaced on the shaft. Any discoloration from iron or hard water may be removed with Calgon or vinegar solution. The cover of the washer is replaced loosely to allow air to circulate and prevent a musty odor. The baked-on enamel exterior of the tub may be rubbed with a wax manufactured for this purpose. And finally, the hose should be lowered into a pail to allow any remaining water to drain out; otherwise gradual deterioration of the rubber will occur.

DRYERS

CONSTRUCTION

A dryer, whether a separate appliance or in combination with the washer, is similar to the tumbler washer in appearance and to a certain extent in construction. The revolving drum has a series of baffles to aid in tumbling the clothes. These baffles, placed at intervals around the inside of the drum, may be straight, flat projections, or wedge-shaped fins (Fig. 8.10). In addition to the revolving drum of porcelain-enameled steel or corrosion-resistant metal, there is a source of heat, either an electric element or a gas flame, which warms the air before it is forced through the clothes. Drying is brought about by a combination of radiation and convection currents. Electrically heated dryers are commonly used on a 240-volt circuit. Dials are set for length of drying time and for low, medium, or high heat, if choice is available. If no choice of heat is given, medium heat is usually supplied and the air circulation speeded up to hasten the drying process. In one dryer a continuous blanket of hot air flows through the entire drum (Fig. 8.11).

DRYING PROCEDURES

In general, items that can be washed together can be dried together. If drying is to be done in a dryer, sort washing loads according to fabric, weight, and bulk. Heavy, bulky articles should be dried in small loads, so that they may have room to tumble freely and dry thoroughly. When the dryer is overloaded,

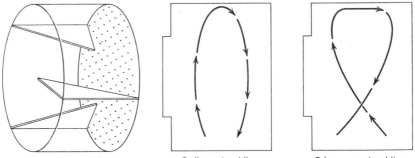

Ordinary tumbling   Criss-cross tumbling

FIG. 8.10. Staggered baffles on dryer drum tumble clothes in criss-cross pattern, speed the drying process and reduce tangling.—Philco.

FIG. 8.11. (1) Centrally located heating unit heats air and not drum; (2) air is pulled through tumbling clothes and exhausted through streamlined channels for quiet, efficient operation; (3) thermostat; (4) centered belt drive; (5) "Teflon" bearings at both ends of drum; (6) belt, motor, and gas controls for easy service access. This combination provides high air volume at temperatures not exceeding 130 F. —Blackstone.

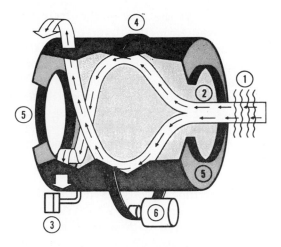

items require a much longer drying time and show a greater tendency to wrinkle. The greater the surface of fabric that can be exposed to the moving air, the more rapid the drying process.

At present the type of fabric may be indicated — cotton, wool, blends, knits — and a special control permits selection of the degree of dryness preferred. Automatic modulated heat drying produces heat to match the amount of moisture, i.e., more moisture, more heat, less moisture, less heat; in other words, as clothes lose moisture, the drying temperature is reduced. Also now available is an electronic control that constantly measures the moisture in clothes and automatically shuts off the dryer when the desired degree of dryness is reached. With this control, the homemaker can damp-dry for ironing or dry clothes completely for immediate use or for storage.

With the increased use of clothing from man-made fibers, some dryers provide a cycle without heat to fluff the garments and remove any wrinkles. Special provision for a cold air cycle is not always necessary; some dryers will operate whether the heat is on or not. There is a dryer which provides an automatic heat dissipator for wrinkle-free drying, but research at Du Pont's indicates that wrinkles in Dacron, Orlon, and nylon fabrics are most easily removed if dried at temperatures between 140 and 160 F. Wash-and-wear garments are dried at similar temperatures, followed by a five to ten minute cooling cycle without heat. In the latest method, known as push-button programming, it is possible to push that button and have the correct temperature and length of drying time selected automatically without further attention. At the end of the drying period the clothing should be removed from the dryer immediately and placed on hangers.

Portable dryers are also available. Compact in size, they operate somewhat on the principle of the hair dryer by blowing warm air into a drying chamber. They come in several styles, one small enough to be packed into a suitcase, another in its own case, contains a 54-inch-long vinyl bag that unfolds into a dress-length chamber sealed by a zipper closing. Clothes are placed on hangers in the chamber, into which hot air is blown from the unit located above the bag. Weights of the dryers vary from $3\frac{1}{2}$ to about 14 pounds.

Agitation is considered undesirable for wool blankets, although they and other wool articles may be dried partly in the dryer if buffered with warm terry-cloth towels. One dryer has a stationary open shelf of metal rods on which a blanket may be placed while low heat is circulated around it (Fig. 8.7b). Many blankets are now of man-made fibers which have less tendency to mat than wool, and, as noted, it is possible to treat the wool to prevent matting.

Clothes dry-cleaned at home should never be put into the dryer to have the odor removed. There is less temptation to clean garments and fabrics at home since coin-operated dry-cleaning machines have been made available in many cities and towns. In the present centers the time for one load is usually between 40 and 50 minutes, but a new service using a dry-cleaning fluid recently developed by Du Pont, in machines especially designed to handle it, will reduce the time per load approximately to 15 minutes. This new fluid, called Valclene, is nonflammable, can be used with elastics, plastic buttons and ornaments, leather and suede, leaves almost no odor, reduces linting to a minimum, and obviates the possibility of harmful effects from any residual solvent in clothing after drying.

Lint Removal

Moisture and lint, varying in amount with the type of fabric, are removed during the drying process. The moisture-laden air passes through a screen of metal mesh or a nylon sleeve which catches the lint, and is then vented directly into the atmosphere of the room, or it may be exhausted through a chimney connection to the outside (A in Fig. 8.12). To operate satisfactorily, the discharge end of the chimney should be at least 12 inches above the ground. Some such arrangement is desirable since excess moisture

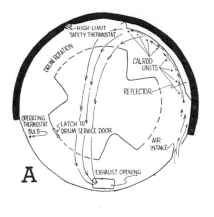

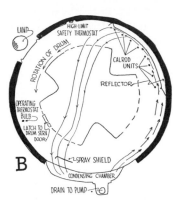

FIG. 8.12. Two methods of removing moisture from clothes in the dryer. (A) Blower Dryer System; (B) Condenser Dryer System.—Hotpoint.

is very enervating to the homemaker and tends to cause paint to scale from walls, and pipes to corrode. A few models are designed to use a spray of water to condense the moisture and carry it and the lint into the drain (B in Fig. 8.12).

The lint trap, originally placed beneath the top surface with an opening onto the top, is now frequently on the door or on the front below the drum, two locations easily accessible for cleaning (Fig. 8.13). The lint trap should be emptied regularly, since any

FIG. 8.13. An extra large lint screen visible as a reminder to clean. Screen can be replaced in any position—lifts straight up and drops back in.—Speed Queen.

accumulation tends to impede the free circulation of heated air and hence reduces efficiency. Other areas under and within the dryer should be brushed free from lint and dust or cleaned with the crevice tool of the vacuum cleaner when the dryer is not in operation. One dryer is provided with an automatic lint wiper to keep the air ducts clean.

The use of a dryer is recommended also for removing from wool clothing the odors of cigarette and cigar smoke, of perspiration or of fried foods. The Hamilton Home Service Department suggests that three or four slightly dampened terry-cloth towels put in with the clothing will absorb the off odors. The towels then can be laundered. Garments stored over winter or wrinkled from wearing also may be tumbled in the dryer to remove the wrinkles. Temperature should be low for this process.

Factors Affecting Length of Drying Period

The length of time required for fabrics to dry depends upon a number of factors:

The amount of water left in the material. When a dryer is used after washing has been done in a nonautomatic wringer washer, the drying period will be longer because the wringer removes less water than the spinning operation.

Size of load. A medium-sized or small load dries much more rapidly than a large one. It is better to dry an extra load than one too large for efficient drying.

Type of fabric. Loosely woven and bulky articles hold more moisture than those firmly woven and light in weight.

A clean lint screen. The speed of drying depends on the rapid removal of moist air, so a screen clogged with lint slows air circulation.

Overdrying tends to leave fabrics wrinkled and harsh in texture and should be avoided. Some dryers have a sprinkler attach-

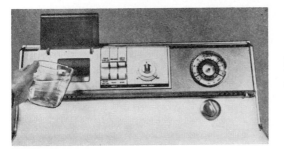

FIG. 8.14. Sprinkler built into dryer automatically dampens clothes for ironing.—Frigidaire.

ment which will dampen a load that has become too dry for ironing (Fig. 8.14). Others notify the homemaker with a musical signal five minutes before shut-off, or with a bell sound when the dryer stops.

IRONING EQUIPMENT

Irons of some kind are used almost universally to restore household linens and personal clothing to their original appearance.

HAND IRONS

Dry irons or combination dry and steam irons usually are 3 to 4 pounds in weight, and occasionally as light as 2½ pounds. The soleplate is smooth and corrosion resistant, occasionally coated with "Teflon" (Fig. 8.15), with a sloping edge tapered to a point to iron around buttons and into gathers. The handle, of non-heat-conducting material, should be comfortable to grasp. A thumb rest is frequently provided. A dial, usually marked with the names of the different fabrics, may be set for any desired heat. Dry irons feature a wide range of temperature; the area for the most efficient use of steam in the combination iron is fairly narrow, usually around the wool setting, although some combinations provide moisture from below wool to as high as linen.

Combination steam and dry irons are easily changed from one type to the other. Combination irons are the flash boiler

FIG. 8.15. A combination dry, steam, spray iron with "Teflon"-coated soleplate that tends to prevent starch and lint from sticking and may be wiped off easily, does not corrode or become rough if accidentally scratched. Button indentation on side of soleplate. By tilting iron, water level is visible, showing when to refill.—General Electric.

type, in which the water reaches the hot soleplate a drop at a time and is instantly converted into steam. The steam condenses as it comes into contact with the cool cloth and the heat from the iron completes the process of removing the wrinkles. Steam irons are very satisfactory for the slight touching-up, which is all that is needed by many of the man-made fibers, for pressing woolens, steaming velvets, and for adding the needed moisture to a dried area of any article. Several new combination irons that also may be used for sprinkling clothes have buttons which, when pressed, eject a fine spray of water from the front of the handle. Water for this spray comes from the same reservoir as for the steam. It may be activated by a pushbutton type of pump that also can be used during dry ironing, or a control may utilize steam pressure to propel the water through the nozzle only when the indicating device is set for steam. The spray will continue as long as the control is depressed.

Even though some manufacturers assure you that tap water may be used in their steam irons, it is usually preferable to use distilled or demineralized water. Distilled water is available in most drug stores and is recommended because other water generally will cause a certain amount of corrosion to build up inside the iron and, if the water is really hard, may stop the steam vents. Overflow or spillage should be avoided to prevent current leakage, the iron should not be used near grounded objects such as the sink. Between uses, the iron usually is turned up on a heel to rest. The iron should be emptied when hot, so the residual heat will dry out the cavity.

Fabrics may be ironed damp or dry. Even, but light, dampening will speed the ironing. Warm water penetrates faster than cold and storing in a plastic bag will prevent the clothes from drying. Natural fibers should be ironed completely dry, but synthetics may be left slightly damp. Iron dark materials on the wrong side to eliminate a shiny surface.

IRONING BOARDS

The ironing board should be adjustable in height so the homemaker may sit or stand (Fig. 8.16). If she sits, she probably will prefer a board with legs so shaped and attached that they do not interfere with her knee room. Newer boards are made of wire mesh or perforated stainless metal which allows the moisture given off from the clothing to escape. Boards are padded for resiliency under the pressure of the iron, and are covered with un-

FIG. 8.16. This ironing board supplies 3 different surfaces: side flips up for wider ironing surface, end flips up
to add length in square instead of tapered form. A posture
chair adds to the comfort of the homemaker.—Proctor-Silex.

bleached muslin, Fiberglas, asbestos, or other materials developed to withstand scorching. A special attachment for the end
of the board may be used to hold the iron cord from contact with
the articles being ironed and prevent wrinkling (Fig. 8.17). A
posture chair, shaped to the contours of the body, reduces fatigue,
conserves energy, and increases enjoyment of the task.

IRONERS

Ironers never have attained the widespread use that other
laundry appliances have, but since some homemakers do use
ironers, brief reference to them is included. They have a number
of good qualities to recommend them. For example, the pressure between the roll and the shoe—the piece of cast iron or

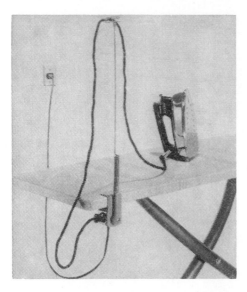

FIG. 8.17. A method of preventing the iron cord from
wrinkling clothes as they are
ironed.—Proctor-Silex.

aluminum that contains the heating element — is much greater
than can be obtained with a hand iron and eliminates the need for
the homemaker to exert that pressure. Because of the increased
pressure, less dampening is needed and the material is more easily
ironed dry, which is essential if it is to remain in the finished form
into which it has been pressed. This also reduces subsequent
wrinkling.

Construction

The surface area of the shoe, located above or below the roll,
is several times that of the soleplate of the hand iron. The roll
is attached to the gear case, either at one end — leaving the
other end open for ease in ironing skirts, dresses, and other
pieces of double clothing—or in the middle, so that both ends
are open. It is padded and covered with firmly woven muslin
and has specially constructed points or edges on the shoe to aid in
ironing ruffles and gathers. The rotation of the roll carries the
material through at a steady pace, relieving the homemaker of
much handling. The fact that one may sit when ironing has less
appeal than formerly since ironing boards have been made adjustable to a low position for use with a chair.

The ironer should have individual switches for control of the
motor and heat, and a heat dial marked in types of fabric as well
as degrees of temperature is preferable. The rotation of the roll

may be operated by knee, foot, or hand, with a separate control for stopping the rotation, if necessary, to dry an especially damp area. A manually operated safety release is provided, in case of power failure when the shoe and roll are in contact.

Care of Ironer

Occasionally rub the shoe with a piece of waxed paper; remove any smears of starch or other corrosion with a dampened cloth or very fine steel wool. If the ironer has a hinged top, allow it to remain open until the shoe has cooled and the roll dried. The motor usually is permanently oiled. Padding on the roll should be removed when it is no longer resilient, then fluffed and reversed in position. The muslin cover should be washed as needed.

Procedures With Ironing Board or Ironer

Clothing should be folded in such a way that the part unfolded first is the part to be ironed first. Arrange the ironing center to save motion and energy. Unironed articles in a shallow basket on wheels regulated to a height that will eliminate stooping should be placed on one side of the homemaker. On the other side have a flat surface or rack to hold the ironed items, and coat hangers for shirts, blouses, and dresses.

EXPERIMENTS AND PROJECTS

1. To compare soaps and synthetic detergents:
   Purchase small boxes of a variety of soaps and detergents. Assign project of classifying them into mild and built groups. Let students observe and report how much information is available from package.
2. To test surface tension of water:
   Fill each of two custard cups half-full of distilled water. To one cup add 3 drops of liquid tincture of green soap (may be purchased at drug store). Using separate medicine droppers* place a drop of the clear water on a 1-inch square of wool flannel and a drop of the soapy water on a second square of the wool material. Float squares of the flannel on the water in each custard cup. Explain difference in action.
3. To compare characteristics of hard and soft water:
   Place 1 cup distilled water in clean bottle or fruit jar, 1 cup of hard water in second clean container; to each add 20 drops of green soap solution. Shake. Note appearance of contents and

---

* The medicine dropper used with the clear water must be spotlessly clean. It is well to buy a new dropper and keep it for this experiment so that it will never be put into a soap solution.

difference in sound when solutions are shaken. To a third bottle containing 1 cup hard water add 1 teaspoon nonprecipitating water softener such as Calgon, then 20 drops of the soap solution. Shake and compare results with those in bottle of hard water.

4. To determine types of rinse water to use with various soaps and synthetic detergents:

   Use six glass mixing bowls of 2- to 3-quart capacity, three water glasses, and three finger towels of terry cloth. Into each bowl pour 1 quart of hard water. Add soap, detergent, and Calgon, as indicated in Figure 8.18. Dissolve by beating with hand beater, rinsing beater carefully between use in each bowl.

   a. Wash one of the glasses in bowl 1, one in bowl 3, and one in bowl 5, and rinse them in bowls 2, 4, and 6 respectively. Drain on a towel—do not dry. After three minutes compare the three glasses in appearance. Apply the results to the method of allowing dishes to stand in wire dish drainer until dry.

   b. Wash one finger towel in bowl 1, rinse in bowl 2, noting increased curd in bowl 2. Then rinse towel, without rewashing in bowl 4. What indication is there that all soapsuds and curds were not removed in rinse in bowl 2?

   c. Empty and replace water in bowls 2 and 4, adding Calgon again to bowl 4. Wash second finger towel in bowl 3, rinse in bowl 2, noting appearance of water, then in bowl 4, noting increased removal of soapsuds. Suggest desirable method for washing and rinsing clothes to prevent "tattle-tale gray."

   d. Wash third finger towel in bowl 5, rinse in bowl 6, then in bowl 4. Note additional removal of detergent in softened water.

5. Visit dealers and department stores to inspect various laundry appliances on the market. Evaluate new features and discuss differences in construction.

6. To compare water action of washers:

   Try to arrange with dealers a demonstration of different makes of laundry appliances. If possible, use piece of colored cloth to follow water movement. Draw diagrams.

7. To determine effect of load on water action in nonautomatic washer:

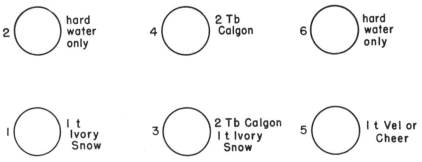

FIG. 8.18. Arrangement of mixing bowls for experiment 4, showing the comparative effect of various combinations of hard water and detergents.

Weigh 5-pound load of mixed materials—household linens and personal clothing. Fill washer to water line, add the 5-pound load and note action, putting hand into tub to various depths. Add 2 more pounds and note action. Again add 2 more pounds and note action. Formulate rule for loading washer.

8. To demonstrate value of careful wringing:
   Put two wet terry-cloth bath towels through wringer, one just any way, the other folded lengthwise in the middle and guided through as evenly as possible. Shake each towel vigorously. Compare wrinkling.

9. To prepare washer for storing until next time of use:
   Empty tub of nonautomatic washer, remove agitator, inspect drain for lint, wipe agitator, tub, and shaft and replace agitator on side in tub, free from shaft, release and wipe wringer rolls, replace washer lid loosely so that air may circulate and prevent the developing of musty odors, lower drain hose into pan so any water left in hose may run out, to prevent rotting of rubber.

10. To compare illustrative material and specification sheets furnished by manufacturer on washers, dryers, and ironers:
    Using materials available, make tables, comparing:
    a. for washers—type of controls, amount of water used, recommended load, number and types of rinses, method of extracting water.
    b. for dryers—controls, method of heating, RPM (revolutions per minute), type of lint exhaust, size of load.
    Use appliances in laboratory to supplement data.

11. To compare a dry iron with a steam iron:
    Use a dry iron with a pressing cloth, then a steam iron for ironing a pleated wool skirt, rayon slip, and Dacron blouse. Compare ease of use and effectiveness of each.

QUESTIONS

1. What is surface tension? How is it decreased? Why should it be decreased?
2. Give the comparative characteristics of soaps and synthetic detergents.
3. What determines the length of the wash period and the temperature of the water? What may cause soil to redeposit on the clothes?
4. Why are bleaches not as widely used as formerly?
5. How do some manufacturers provide for the washing of fabrics of man-made fibers, wash-and-wear garments, etc.?
6. When would you use a drip-dry method for clothing?
7. Why must electric sheets and blankets be washed instead of dry-cleaned?
8. How do you dispose of the lint removed from clothing in the dryer? Which method requires your attention? Why?
9. What type of steam iron is most desirable? Is the steam iron equally efficient for all kinds of fibers?
10. What specific laundry equipment would you advise in the following case: Family of four, father, mother, two small children; basement damp, no stationary tubs; kitchen large with sink and running water; mother does all own work, is not strong; the father does not earn a large salary, so family has a limited amount of money. Give reasons for answer.

Chapter Nine

EQUIPMENT FOR

CLEANING THE HOUSE

So VERSATILE AND EASILY USED are the preparations and equipment for housecleaning that it is no longer necessary to subject the family to the strenuous upheavals of seasonal cleaning. The preferred plan is to clean thoroughly one room at a time, each in turn, until the major cleaning is completed. Often it is almost impossible to obtain outside help for the weekly cleaning, but the homemaker has at hand her modern mechanical servants that relieve her of much of the onetime drudgery. If she is fortunate enough to have an air-conditioned home, filters remove dust and greasy products from the air and make cleaning easier and less often necessary.

There are two general classifications of dirt, dry and moist, which tend to build up and penetrate into surface materials. In many instances a prompt clean-up is recommended to prevent dirt from sinking in, making removal more complicated.

DRY-DIRT REMOVAL

There also are two kinds of dry dirt: (1) surface litter—threads, hairs, scraps of paper, lint "kitties," tracked in dirt (sometimes mud) and common wind-borne dust, and (2) deeply embedded dirt—sand, dust, and grit that sink into the pile of upholstery and carpets, giving a dingy appearance to the material and, even worse, cutting the fibers with the friction caused by weight and movement of bodies and furniture (Fig. 9.1). It is this deeply embedded dirt—not the use of the cleaner, as has been assumed—that causes wear on carpets. Frequent cleaning is recommended, therefore, before the dirt has a chance to work down into the pile.

Vacuum Cleaners

One of the most widely used laborsaving appliances is the electric vacuum cleaner with its various attachments that reduce

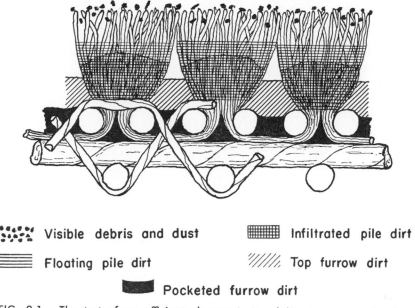

Visible debris and dust	Infiltrated pile dirt
Floating pile dirt	Top furrow dirt
Pocketed furrow dirt	

FIG. 9.1. The test of an efficient cleaner is its ability to remove the four layers of dirt not visible on the surface of upholstery or carpet pile.—Hoover (modified).

to a minimum many cleaning tasks that formerly were exhausting to the homemaker. Vacuum cleaners are of two general types: those with a rotating cylinder—equipped with rows of brushes and in at least one cleaner, beater bars—within the nozzle, and those without such parts, known as straight suction cleaners (Fig. 9.2). Under these types, cleaners may be classified into (1) the full-size upright, (2) tank or canister, (3) hand or portable, (4) light-weight upright, of which the electric sweeper is an example.

Types of Cleaners

Rotating-cylinder Cleaners. Models with the rotating cylinder have a square or rectangular body containing the nozzle, fan and fan chamber, motor, and the opening into the bag which holds the picked-up dirt. This framework is moved across the surface to be cleaned by means of an upright handle, to which the upper end of the bag is attached. Several cleaners are now constructed with the bag enclosed within the cleaner housing (Fig. 9.3). The handle also provides a place for the switch that operates the cleaner and for the supports around which the cord

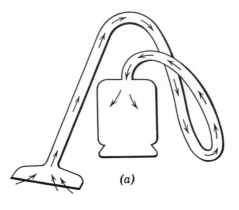

(a)

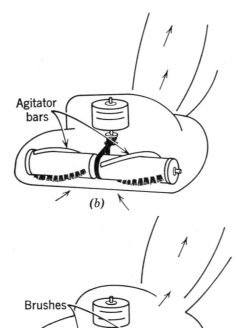

Agitator bars

(b)

Brushes

(c)

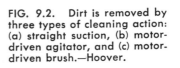

FIG. 9.2. Dirt is removed by three types of cleaning action: (a) straight suction, (b) motor-driven agitator, and (c) motor-driven brush.—Hoover.

is wound for storage. Some upright cleaners have two speeds available, the slower for easier operation on small rugs.

Straight Suction Cleaners. The models without the rotating cylinder within the nozzle—the straight suction cleaners—are rectangular or round in shape and are also called tank and canister cleaners (Fig. 9.4). They have an opening in the top or side to which a flexible tube is attached. For cleaning high and low areas, one or two metal extension tubes are connected to the end of the flexible tubing and then the various brushes that have been developed for the several cleaning jobs are fastened on. Tank and canister cleaners may have wheels or may be pulled across the floor on glides or polished bases.

Occasionally the canister cleaner is provided with a swivel top to which the flexible tube is attached. Such an arrangement allows

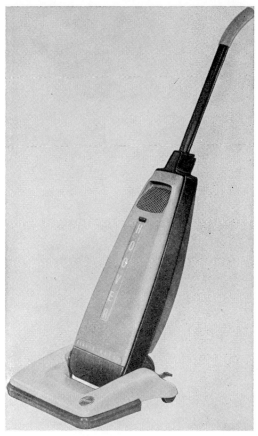

FIG. 9.3. Upright cleaner with vibrator bars. Above-floor cleaning tools may be attached. A large throw-away bag is completely enclosed inside body of cleaner and a "Time To Empty" signal tells when bag is full.—Hoover.

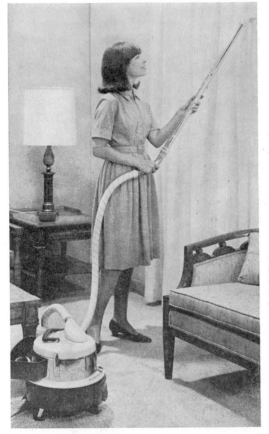

FIG. 9.4. Swivel connection for hose so room may be cleaned in all directions without moving the cleaner. Automatic cord reel and storage container for tools.—General Electric.

the operator to place the cleaner in the center of a room and reach all the areas of the room without having to move the cleaner as she progresses.

Different degrees of suction for different types of cleaning are sometimes provided by an adjustable opening on the metal extension tube, sometimes by a dial on the body of the cleaner.

Some straight suction cleaners may have a brush to provide some pile agitation. The brush may be stationary, floating, or adjustable, or even detachable. Occasionally a toothed comb of metal or plastic is supplied to assist in removing surface litter. The brush and comb usually are mounted outside the nozzle.

Since in these cleaners cleaning action depends principally upon suction, fairly high suction is provided by a $\frac{1}{2}$ to $1\frac{1}{3}$ horsepower motor (p. 277). The light-weight upright electric sweeper is also a straight suction cleaner. With a wattage about half that of the conventional upright—it may use a motor as small as ⅙ horsepower, though it is often larger—it is somewhat similar to a carpet sweeper in function, and serves well for quick cleaning jobs. Few, if any, attachments are supplied. A number of manufacturers now include this type of cleaner among their models.

When the straight suction cleaner is used on carpeting it should be operated for a longer period than the upright cleaner, perhaps twice as long, depending upon the depth of the pile.

A number of manufacturers of canister type cleaners now provide the carpet cleaning attachment with a rotating brush within the nozzle (Fig. 9.5).

Another new cleaner is an upright (Fig. 9.6a) that converts to a canister (Fig. 9.6b). In addition to the main motor (880 watts) which controls the suction that lifts the dirt into the bag, whether in upright or canister positions, an auxiliary motor operates the carpet agitator bar. It has a full-bag indicator and a lightweight handle. The handle comes off to convert the upright cleaner to a canister, and a switch changes the motor over for canister cleaning.

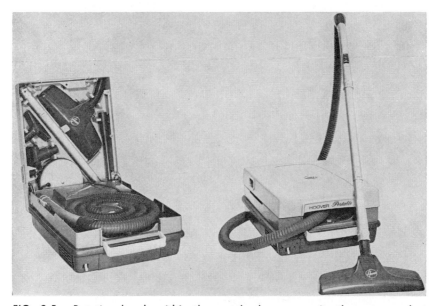

FIG. 9.5. Rotating brush within the nozzle, large capacity throw-away dust bag, 1⅛ horsepower motor, automatic cord reel that pulls out exact amount wanted then locks in place. All attachments fit inside cleaner.—Hoover.

FIG. 9.6a. Upright cleaner that converts to canister. Carpet agitator bar has a combination of nylon brushes and 8 flexible vinyl fingers that tap rug 24,000 times a minute. This is operated by its own motor which is turned off when used as canister.—Westinghouse.

FIG. 9.6b. Same cleaner converted to canister, handle removed and hose attached to front. Dust bag inside housing in front of motor where air is filtered 3 times before returning to room.—Westinghouse.

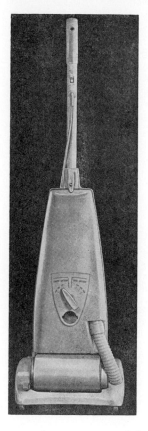

FIG. 9.7a. Upright cleaner with power dials for both carpet and tool sections.—Hoover.

FIG. 9.7b. Detail of dial control.

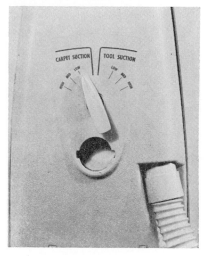

A recent upright cleaner equipped with beater bars has a 1⅛ horsepower motor, supplying 30 per cent more effective cleaning of rugs and carpets and 2½ times more suction for attachment use. Power dials for both carpet and tool sections allow the operator to choose high, medium, or low suction settings for any cleaning operation (Figs. 9.7a and b). A "Time-to-Empty" signal informs the homemaker when she should check the fulness of the bag because the suction has been reduced.

Another new vacuum cleaner requires no cord (Fig. 9.8) as it is powered internally with 8 "D"-sized nickel-cadmium batteries that are automatically recharged when the unit is returned to its battery-charger stand. These batteries have a normal running time of approximately 20 minutes per charge. Designed for ease in getting under furniture and into corners, this vacuum allows easy cleaning without the limitations imposed by a cord.

Undoubtedly best of all is the "Hole-in-the-wall" central

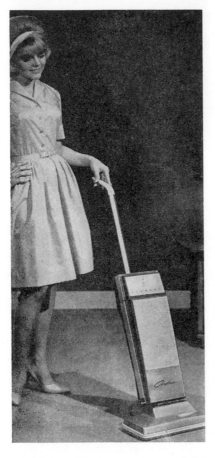

FIG. 9.8. Battery-powered upright cleaner eliminates inconvenience of cord restrictions.—Sears Roebuck.

vacuum cleaner system which eliminates much expenditure of energy because only the hose and nozzle are moved from room to room. Flexible tubing, 25 feet in length, is used to connect the nozzle to conveniently located wall outlets through which the dirt and dust are drawn by a power unit into a collection cylinder installed in the basement, garage, or other suitable remote location. A complete set of attachments is included with the system (Figs. 9.9a and b).

Another model filters collected dust and dirt through water, which is automatically flushed down a drain. This model can be used for picking up water and for all regular dry vacuum cleaning. Central systems have four basic advantages over conventional portable cleaners: maximum cleaning power from unit at all

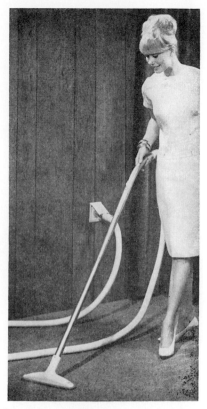

FIG. 9.9a. A built-in cleaning system features quiet operation, constant maximum suction power, ease of handling, and no recirculation of dust as the light weight hose is plugged into wall outlets connected to central unit. —Sears Roebuck.

times, no recirculation of dust, quiet operation, and no machine to push back and forth and pull around.

Parts of the Vacuum Cleaner

Fan. The suction that causes the dirt to pass from a surface to the receptacle on the cleaner is brought about by the rotation of a fan or fans mounted on the motor shaft. These fans force air to the periphery of the enclosed fan chamber, leaving an area of low pressure in the center of the chamber. The difference in pressure within this space and in the air outside the nozzle makes the air flow through the pile of the carpet, picking up the dirt as it does so, then through the nozzle and on into the bag (Fig. 9.10). As was previously noted, straight suction cleaners depend entirely upon suction to bring about the cleaning action, consequently the suction is greater in this type of cleaner than in the upright cleaner with rotating cylinder.

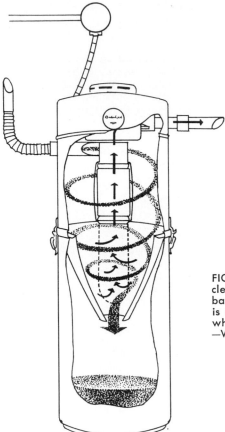

FIG. 9.9b. Power unit for built-in cleaning system may be placed in basement, closet, or utility room. Dirt is drawn through wall outlets into unit where it is exhausted into the outdoors. —Whirlpool.

Brushes. To aid the action in upright cleaners, rows of brushes, varying in stiffness in the different models, are set into the cylinder and cause a certain amount of vibration of the carpet or rug. This vibration tends to bring the embedded dirt to the surface of the rug and the brushes help to sweep it into the air stream (Fig. 9.2). One model has curved steel bars on the cylinder in addition to the brushes. Brushes may wear down and lose their effectiveness but the steel bars never deteriorate. When brushes no longer extend a short distance (1/16 to 1/8 inch) beyond the nozzle lips, they should be replaced. A means of adjusting the brushes to one or more lower positions in the nozzle usually is provided.

Nozzle. The body of the upright vacuum cleaner is supported

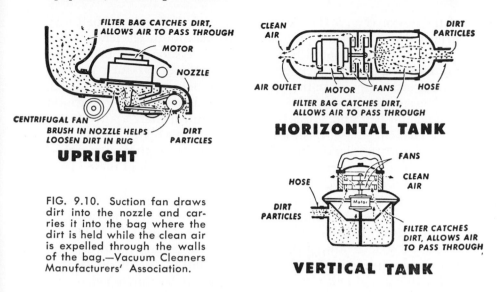

FIG. 9.10. Suction fan draws dirt into the nozzle and carries it into the bag where the dirt is held while the clean air is expelled through the walls of the bag.—Vacuum Cleaners Manufacturers' Association.

on wheels that hold the nozzle the correct distance above the floor covering so that the suction can lift the carpet or rug off the floor and against the nozzle lips to allow it to be vibrated during the cleaning process. For efficient dirt removal, the nozzle lips must make a perfect seal with the carpet. The adjustment to the depth of carpet pile may be automatic or by means of a lever. The contact that the tank and canister nozzles make with the carpet usually depends on the operator, who will find that she must exert a certain amount of pressure to maintain the seal. If she fails to do this, the nozzle will tend to tip to one side, allowing air to flow over the surface of the pile instead of through the carpet; consequently dirt is not removed. Wheels have been placed at either end of the nozzle in some models, increasing ease of manipulation.

In general, the homemaker will find the motor-driven brush or motor-driven-agitator cleaner more satisfactory for floors covered with wall-to-wall carpets or large rugs. On the other hand, areas above the floor are more easily cleaned with a tank or canister model, even though similar attachments are provided for upright cleaners. In the upright cleaners an adapter is used to cut off the flow of air through the nozzle and permit the connecting of hose and tools. The combination is, however, more awkward to move around than are the straight suction models.

Care of Cleaner. The rotation of the cylinder within the nozzle is made possible by a rubber belt connecting it with the shaft of the motor (Fig. 9.11). After a long period of use, the belt may stretch and slip on the pulleys so that maximum efficiency is not obtained; it then should be replaced. Care should be taken during cleaning not to pick up sharp metal objects such as pins, thumb tacks, etc., since they may cut the belt, nick the fan blades, or damage the dirt bag. Hairs and threads sometimes get wound around the belt and brush roll, cutting down their ability to operate efficiently; and dust, often mixed with volatile grease, gets packed into the sleeves in which the cylinder shaft rotates. Now and again the cleaner case should be turned over and these places inspected and cleaned when necessary.

For effective cleaning, the bristles of the rotating brush must touch the carpet at all times; otherwise the sweeping and vibrating action is lost. Bristles wear down with use. Figure 9.12 shows a method for determining the bristle length. When the brush roll has been adjusted to the lowest position and the bristles no longer touch the straightedge, new brushes should be purchased.

The cord, about 20 feet in length, is rubber covered so that it will slide over the floor with a minimum of friction. For flexibility it is made of many fine wires; to prevent their breaking, wind the cord loosely around the supports provided.

The dirt container may be of cloth or paper. In either case it has been especially manufactured for its purpose. It must allow all of the air that passes into the nozzle to pass through the fabric into the atmosphere of the room again; but at the same time, it must retain the dirt that has been picked up. The bag is made rather sizable to provide sufficient filtering area, *not just to*

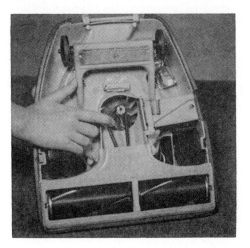

FIG. 9.11. Nozzle of motor-driven agitator cleaner, showing connection of belt to pulley.—Hoover.

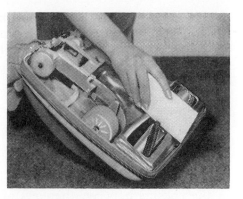

FIG. 9.12. To determine correct bristle length, place a straightedge across the nozzle opening. If the bristles touch the straightedge, they will also touch the carpet.—Hoover.

hold a large amount of dirt. Many homemakers allow the cleaner bag to become too full, not realizing that back pressure is built up when the air cannot pass easily through the bag, thus greatly reducing the efficiency of the cleaner. The bag should be emptied after each thorough cleaning of the house, or at least by the time the bag is half full. Once a month or so the bag should be turned inside out and brushed to rid the meshes of the cloth of dust or, even better, cleaned with one of the attachments of the straight suction cleaner when such is available. Manufacturers have provided dirt receptacles of paper to free the homemaker from the disagreeable job of getting rid of the collected dirt. The paper bag may be thrown away and replaced with a new one. Unfortunately, since these bags cost money, the homemaker tends to use them longer than she should, thereby reducing the effectiveness of her house cleaning operations.

Most present-day electric cleaners are more or less self-lubricating, but it is well to have them checked at periodic intervals by a service man representing the manufacturer.

Other Uses for Vacuum Cleaners

We tend to think of vacuum cleaners mainly in relation to carpeting and upholstery, but they will conserve both time and energy in many other cleaning operations.

The floor brush is used on bare floors, or on linoleum or tile types of covering, and also for dusting painted and papered walls; the soft-bristled brush cleans moldings and baseboards, books, lamp shades, and carved furniture; the upholstery brush may be used on chair and sofa coverings, draperies, and mattresses; and the crevice tool on narrow, hard-to-reach areas, also corners of dresser drawers and even suit pockets and trouser cuffs.

In some cleaners the hose may be attached to the air exit and this forced air is especially helpful in blowing dirt and dust out of the floors and corners of automobiles. Moth-crystal vapors may be blown into the fibers of woolens being prepared for storage in bags or closets.

Carpet Sweepers

Although the electric vacuum cleaner is the most commonly used appliance for keeping the house clean and in order, the carpet sweeper is also used. It will remove surface litter and the light dust in the top of the pile, but not the deeply embedded dirt in the pockets between the rows of tufts. The dust pan should be emptied frequently, probably after each use, and the brush axle kept free from threads, string, and hair which tend to hinder the movement of the roll and hence the cleaning ability of the sweeper.

MOIST-DIRT REMOVAL

Moist dirt encompasses steam, smoke, body oils or perspiration, and cooking grease that permeate deeply into fabrics, forming dust-absorbing films on them and on every hard surface in the home — windows, walls, woodwork, furniture tops, and bare floors.

Much work may perhaps be eliminated, or at least reduced in amount, by the wise selection of new fabrics and finishes that resist absorption of dirt. New finishes on fabrics—silicones, plastics, and glazes, surface-coat the material and make it more soil-resistant. Certain synthetic fibers, because of their molecular construction, resist soil and moisture absorption. Glass fabrics used for draperies, bedspreads, and decorator pillows often may be shaken free of dust; improved new varieties may be machine washed. Tables with plastic tops indistinguishable from wood may be wiped clean with a damp cloth and then waxed to restore the shine.

Cleaning Processes

Frequent cleaning of all surfaces postpones the need for the more intensive cleaning associated with moist dirts. Much of this type of cleaning prolongs the life of the fabric, surface, or furnishings and should be worked into the cleaning schedule, a little each week.

Draperies must be washed periodically or sent to the cleaners. Here again, laundering curtains for just one room a week is not too arduous a task and many new fabrics can be drip-dried and require no ironing.

Color-fast upholstery materials may be shampooed. Wet the fabric lightly but completely with clear water, go over it with a soft brush dipped into a mild detergent solution, then a cloth wrung from clear water, and allow the piece of furniture to dry thoroughly in a warm, breezy place.

Rugs also may be shampooed. Place layers of newspapers or building paper below the carpet. Brush over a section of the rug with foam obtained by whipping a solution of a mild detergent or one of the special rug cleaners on the market, then wipe with a cloth wrung fairly dry from clear water. Continue cleaning one section at a time, overlapping slightly to prevent area edges from showing. Shampooing restores the original color and makes upholstery and rugs look new again.

Rug shampooing appliances are available to buy or rent, and some vacuum cleaners include attachments for this process. Always vacuum the carpet or rug first, then follow the manufacturers' directions. After shampooing, the rugs should be allowed to dry thoroughly and then be vacuumed again to remove any detergent residue.

Wall paper may be cleaned occasionally with a special gum-like preparation. It is a somewhat messy job, lessened to a degree by spreading newspapers at the base of the wall, but it does leave the wall paper as fresh as new. Spots that this cleaner fails to remove usually may be absorbed when Blotex or a similar product is applied. Manufacturers' directions, printed on the package, should be followed explicitly in using all cleaning preparations.

Household ammonia in water or any of the various advertised powdered preparations are used for washing painted kitchen and bathroom walls—any painted wall in fact. Here again it is well to test several products to find the one best suited to your needs. Some preparations do not require a following rinse, thus saving that added effort. Plastic sponges are excellent for the application of all liquid cleaners.

Paper dust cloths are recommended as they eliminate washing. If you do not like the paper duster, you can obtain a non-oily liquid to spray on a cloth; this will hold the dust instead of scattering it. Avoid oil-type dust cloths and mops because they

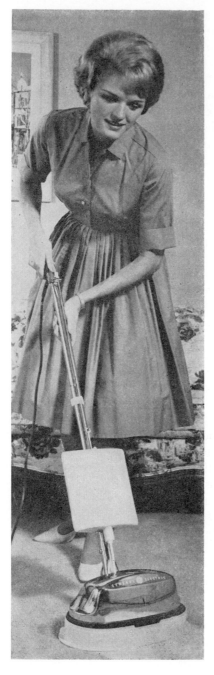

FIG. 9.13. Rugs may be shampooed at home with this appliance.
—General Electric.

tend to leave a film on furniture and floors to which dust and dirt cling, causing a dull appearance and, in themselves, become a type of moist dirt difficult to remove.

Windows and glass-protected surfaces may be cleaned with a special type of wax or with commercial liquid preparations. A homemade solution of two tablespoons vinegar added to a gallon of water is easy to use and leaves glass sparkling. A squeegee may be used for removing water from large areas of glass, reducing the number of drying cloths needed. A family planning to build will do well to investigate types of windows available and select those that provide unobstructed, easily cleaned surfaces instead of the small panes and numerous painted crossbars so frequently found in colonial-type houses.

Waxes are as valuable for preserving surfaces as they are for cleaning and polishing furniture, painted woodwork, and kitchen appliances. Read labels of wax products carefully and apply as directed. You may do a little research yourself to find the one that gives you the most satisfactory results.

Equipment

An appliance designed for shampooing rugs makes this task a pleasant rather than a dreaded one (Fig. 9.13). A dispenser tank holds the cleaning solution; this should be a high-sudsing detergent which is whipped into foam. The dry foam is then dispersed over the pile and down between the fibers without soaking the carpet fabric, a condition always to be avoided. The drying period is minimal, but the carpet should be vacuumed again to remove any detergent residue.

The electric floor machine is very useful in the satisfactory maintenance of floors of wood, linoleum, and certain plastic and tile materials. It is used most frequently for polishing after the application of wax, but may be used for scrubbing and refinishing (Figs. 9.14 and 9.15). It is operated like the upright vacuum cleaner by a handle which carries the switch and connection for the cord. The machine may have one or two brushes. One type of brush, cylindrical in shape, rotates on a horizontal shaft; another is mounted vertically and revolves around a central pivot. If the wax is allowed to dry for from 30 minutes to an hour after it is applied, the brush will buff it to a hard, lustrous finish. Brushes should be cleaned after each use. Detergents usually will remove any residue of wax in the brushes; if not, use turpentine.

FIG. 9.14. Floor washer-dryer operates from blower outlet of canister cleaner. Dispenses mix of water and detergent by finger-tip action. Dries by vacuuming up dirty
water and then blowing warm air over floor.—General
Electric.

After buffing a solid wax, a film of fine powdery wax may remain
on the floor. It should be removed with the floor brush attachment of a vacuum cleaner or a dry mop, since dust tends to cling
to the wax and give the floor a spotty appearance.

A separate floor-washer appliance is also available. It is
supplied with a two compartment tank. One compartment holds
the water and detergent which is released onto the floor area.
As the appliance is moved back and forth, the nozzle bristles scrub
the floor. Pressing a lever causes suction to draw the dirty water
into the second compartment, leaving the floor comparatively
dry. Some cleaners have an additional flow of air that speeds the
drying process.

A variety of brushes is available for such tasks as cleaning upholstery, Venetian blinds, and radiators, and for scrubbing floors
and toilet bowls (Fig. 9.16). Brushes are made of many kinds of

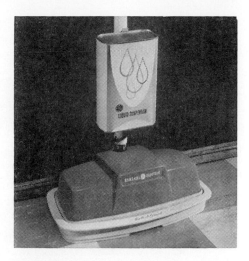

FIG. 9.15. Electric floor polisher equipped with liquid
wax dispenser.—General Electric.

fibers: horse and goat hair, nylon and plastic, pig bristles, Tam-
pico, palmetto, palmyra. The bristles are twisted into wire or
stapled and cemented into wood or plastic. Brushes made of hair
are soft, those made of bristles, stiff. When wire is used, it should
be the galvanized, rustless type.

Brushes should be washed in warm suds, rinsed in clear water,
shaken to remove as much of the moisture as possible, and hung
to dry.

Many jobs may be done more easily and with less expenditure
of energy by the attachments of an electric cleaner, and they
should be used whenever possible.

STORAGE OF CLEANING EQUIPMENT

Vacuum cleaners and their tools, brooms and brushes, dusting mitts and cloths, waxes (both solid and liquid), and various cleaning solutions and powders should be stored in an easily
accessible, centrally located closet (Fig. 9.17). A basket or box
with a handle, or a tray is useful in carrying small cleaning
supplies. When such a carrier is mounted on wheels it will reduce
stooping, and save steps and energy. Doors of the sink cabinet may
be equipped with shelves for storage of cleaning supplies used in
that area. Shelves should be rounded and edged with an inch-high
strip of metal or molding to keep items from falling off as the
doors swing outward. This arrangement eliminates stooping to
reach inaccessible corners and groping in semidarkness for needed
articles.

FIG. 9.16.   Types of brushes used for various cleaning jobs
in the home. From top to bottom:
1. Radiators, around mechanical parts of refrigerators,
   other motor-driven equipment, and inside pianos.
2. Books, lamp shades, around upholstery buttons, or
   other areas where stiff bristles aid dirt removal.
3. Venetian blinds, walls, corners, or moldings.
4. Most of the tasks above, plus toilet bowls.

EXPERIMENTS AND PROJECTS

1. To compare cleaners:
   a. Suggest students bring cleaners from home, if possible, to ob-
      tain a variety. Make outline comparing: parts of cleaner, con-
      dition of nozzle, belt, fan, and dirt container; number of clean-
      ing jobs for which cleaner may be used; ease of operation;
      ease of emptying dirt container; ease of moving from one area
      to another; and method of storing.
   b. Sprinkle corn meal on rug and use cleaners to compare amount
      of vibration produced by each.
   c. Note effort required to hold nozzle of straight suction cleaner
      in contact with rug. Adequate cleaning depends upon main-
      taining a seal between the nozzle lips and the rug. Any tipping
      of nozzle tends to break this seal.
2. To measure amount of dirt removed by 3 types of cleaners:
   Use three identical rugs, 27 to 30 inches by 3 feet in size. Clean
   them thoroughly. Weigh each rug. (If rugs are rolled and tied
   around with string they can be placed on scales.) Rub baking soda
   into area 1-foot square on each rug, measuring number of table-
   spoonfuls used, until last tablespoonful just disappears into pile.
   Roll carefully and weigh rugs again. Using a motor-driven brush
   cleaner on one rug, a motor-driven agitator cleaner on the second

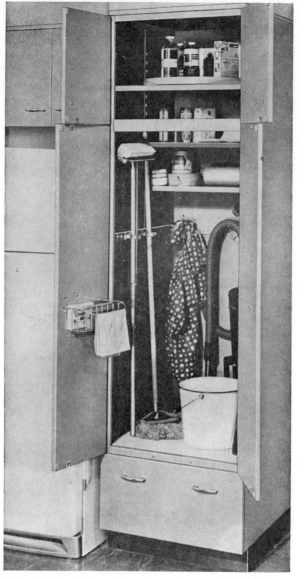

FIG. 9.17. This storage closet has a shelf at the top for a portable tray of supplies, and a deep drawer at the bottom for storage of additional supplies. —St. Charles Kitchens.

rug, and a straight suction cleaner (tank or canister type) on the third rug, clean each for three minutes. Roll and weigh rugs again. Calculate per cent of soda removed by each cleaner and compare:

wt. rug + soda — wt. rug originally = wt. soda in rug
wt. rug + soda — wt. of cleaned rug = soda removed

$$\frac{\text{wt. soda removed}}{\text{wt. soda in rug}} = \text{per cent soda removed}$$

Inspect rugs, bending each to look into rows of pile. Compare appearance of cleanliness.
3. To compare cleaner attachments:
Use attachments from various cleaners to clean upholstery, draperies, Venetian blinds, radiator, carved furniture, bare floors, baseboards, and children's stuffed animal toys. Compare results.

QUESTIONS

1. What causes wear on rugs?
2. Suction in the vacuum cleaner is produced by (1) bag, (2) nozzle, (3) fan? Give reasons for answer.
3. What dirt is hardest for the cleaner to remove? How do the two types of cleaners try to remove the dirt?
4. Why is there a large dirt container on the cleaner?
5. How often should the dirt container be emptied?
6. Why should you not pick up sharp metal objects with your cleaner?
7. When a usually effective motor-driven brush vacuum cleaner is not picking up lint and dirt as it should, what three possible causes would you investigate to try to locate the trouble?
8. What will be the deciding factor in your choice between an upright and a canister cleaner?
9. What part will you as a homemaker play in the efficient operation of your cleaner; in other words, what attention will you give the various areas of your cleaner?
10. What brushes will you need in caring for your home in addition to those supplied with your cleaner?

Chapter Ten

SAVING MOTION

AND ENERGY

IN PREVIOUS CHAPTERS brief reference has been made to ways of reducing the motions needed to perform certain tasks, with a resulting decrease in the waste of energy. The need to expend energy wisely is now recognized as equal in importance to the need to spend money wisely.

When you become homemakers you will be interested in the civic affairs of your communities — in the need for obtaining well-trained teachers and adequate classrooms for the schools, in desirable recreational facilities for teen-agers, for honest, economical city government. You will work through PTA, League of Women Voters, Womens' Clubs, and other organizations to attain these objectives. There are only twenty-four hours in a day, and a large slice of these hours must be spent in necessary rest. To squeeze, from the hours that remain, enough time to participate in activities and pleasures outside the home, a maximum amount of work must be done in the shortest time possible with a minimum of effort. This is another way of saying that motion and energy must be conserved.

THE KITCHEN—HEART OF THE HOME

The most efficiently arranged kitchen is one so planned that the everyday tasks may be accomplished without lost motion. Does that mean a small kitchen? That is what was once thought, a goal to which kitchen specialists had been working, but lately ideas have been changing. A judge in Washington is quoted as saying that there would be fewer divorces if there were larger kitchens. Why? The old, large kitchens had room for the whole family and family life centered in it. Not only was it the scene of extensive food preparation upon which the health and happiness of the family depended, but also much of the social life of the family was carried on in this room. The children helped, or at least watched Mother make cookies and fry doughnuts, and enjoyed samples while they were still warm. Themes were written and arithmetic problems worked on the corner of the kitchen table where it was easy to ask Mother for help. During the colder months the warm kitchen was the first place sought when the children came in with nipped fingers from skating or sliding. And Mother was always there. And if she weren't the first question asked was, "Where is Mother?" The family shared ideas and thoughts and plans, and grew and developed together.

But think of the miles the homemaker walked in those old kitchens! A study made some years ago of families living on Iowa farms showed that the average size of 247 kitchens was 171 square feet, with total distance connecting work centers averaging 37 feet. (Today a distance of 22 feet is considered maximum, and 15 or 16 even more desirable.) And Mary Heiner of Cornell University has pointed out that "efficiency ceases when fatigue begins" so, as the ability to work decreases, it naturally follows that there is a decrease in the pleasure taken in work and a decrease in enjoyment in doing other things after the work is over.

ANALYZING WORK PROCESSES

Motion and energy studies usually are considered in the field of home management, but insofar as household equipment is involved — and it frequently is — such studies may be included in a discussion of the use and care of appliances.

Time and motion saving has long been an objective of industry, but only a few methods adapted to large-scale operations would be practical in the home. Homemaking is an individualistic occupation. Household tasks are varied, interruptions are frequent, each homemaker tends to develop her own work pattern, depending upon the size of the house and family and the kind of equipment she has.

Types of Fatigue

Industry has learned that working conditions have an important effect on fatigue, and that rest periods increase the amount of work that can be done in a day. Tests have shown that men in the army march better and hold up longer if they throw down their packs and rest ten minutes out of each hour. Irma Gross, head of Home Management, Michigan State University, defines two kinds of fatigue — physiological and psychological.

Physiological Fatigue. Physiological fatigue brings about bodily changes that can be measured. Energy is obtained when body glucose oxidizes to form carbon dioxide and water. Complete oxidation takes place only if the supply of oxygen is sufficient; if not sufficient, the oxidation of the glucose stops at the lactic acid stage and this results in fatigue. Both muscles and nerves are affected with decrease in the ability to do work — a good argument, certainly, for working in an adequate supply of fresh air. The body can entirely eliminate physiological fatigue only in sleep, but short rest periods help tremendously. Try lying flat for ten minutes with your feet up on a stool; you will be surprised how your pep returns.

Psychological Fatigue. Psychological fatigue also reduces your output. It results from having to do one thing when you want to do something else. It can be produced by the many frustrations that may occur when a young mother has several small children who cause interruptions, keep her at home away from the companionship of friends her own age, or the chance for outdoor exercise. It is not a sign of lack of mental ability. In fact the more highly intelligent the person, the more frustrated and bored she may feel. It may be brought about by worry or inexperience in doing the job. It increases one's sensitivity to objectionable features, such as heat and noise. It shows itself in restlessness, discontent, even in frequent yawning. It can be relieved by the husband and father sharing the home responsibilities and affording the wife more opportunities for developing outside interests. Anger, tenseness, a feeling of being neglected use up a lot of energy. Happiness, on the other hand, is its best stimulant.

IMPROVING WORKING CONDITIONS

Work processes may be studied so that they may be improved. First decide if the job is necessary. R. M. Barnes[1], recognized authority on time and motion techniques, estimates that from 25 to 50 per cent of the work done in the home is unnecessary. If the task cannot be eliminated, then see whether the method of doing it can be improved to reduce motion and energy requirements. Various methods of studying work procedure have been

---

[1] Barnes, R. M. *Motion and Time Study,* 5th ed., John Wiley & Sons, Inc., N.Y., 1963.

developed commercially. Perhaps the simplest for home use is the flow chart.

Flow Chart

On a piece of cross-sectioned paper, make a drawing of the kitchen to scale putting in the equipment, work surfaces, and storage areas as they are. Take any menu for a meal or even a single food in the menu. Draw lines from place to place to indicate the path followed in preparation of the food or meal. Then measure the distances traveled and draw them in on the floor plan. If a friend or member of the family can watch, he can count the steps taken. Study the plan carefully to see where changes may be made to eliminate steps or movements. Make the changes, repeat the operation, and note how steps have been saved and yardage reduced. Possibly rearrangement of equipment and storage areas may reduce distances traveled to less than half.

Improving Area Arrangements

Much effort has been given to adapting appliances and working areas to the task, not enough, perhaps, of adapting the appliance to the worker. It once was considered desirable to have a streamlined kitchen, all work surfaces the same height. But when the bottom of the sink is the correct height, the drainboards or counters on either side are too high for mixing operations, and if the counters are the correct height, the bottom of the sink is too low. Surfaces of more than one height are, therefore, necessary — one for the sink, one for the mix center, and a third where cookies and piecrust may be rolled. The length of the homemaker's arm has an influence on the height chosen.

Storage To Save Energy. Less energy is used when utensils and supplies are stored between waist and shoulder height; reaching to 56 inches above the floor requires twice as much energy as reaching to 46 inches, and reaching up to 72 inches or down to 22 inches, about four times the energy. Of course not all of the family supplies and utensils can be stored within the magic circle of least energy expenditure, so it should be reserved for heavy articles and utensils most frequently used.

Store everything near the place of first use; for example, saucepans near the sink, frypans at the range, paring knives and spoons at the sink, mix center, and range. When duplicate equipment is provided in more than one area, mark it in such a way that each will be returned to its proper location.

As far as possible, unstack and unnest utensils of different sizes and store them separately, so that any one may be picked up without moving the others. Half-width shelves in cabinets, utensil files in drawers or between cupboard shelves, and sliding trays in deep drawers and low cupboards all help to reduce congestion and confusion.

Partitions in drawers will help in keeping each utensil in its own section. If the section is to hold knives, spatulas, a ladle, etc., place a slotted board in the section. Knives stored in this way are safer to pick up, and they stay sharper. Much energy and time are saved by having sharp knives — more pressure must be exerted on a dull knife and it is more apt to slip and cut the hand.

Use of Tray or Cart. When the storage space is limited so that supplies and utensils cannot always be stored at the place of first use, the necessary articles may be collected on a cart or a tray and brought to the work area. They should be arranged within a circle of easy reach, all plainly visible, so that no motion will be wasted in their use. As far as possible use both hands for a task and work with a circular motion, not with abrupt, jerky movements that cause more rapid fatigue.

Trays will save many steps. When setting the table, such items as bread from the box or drawer; milk, butter, and jam from the refrigerator; salt, pepper, and sugar from a cabinet; and salad from the mix center may all be collected on the tray and carried in one trip to the table. To do this comfortably with the least effort indicates the need for work counters beside the refrigerator, sink, and range where the tray may be placed for loading. Removing all items from the refrigerator at one time not only saves motion but also saves money. Experiments in the household equipment laboratories at the Iowa State University have indicated that frequent opening of the refrigerator door adds to the operating time of the motor, and increases the formation of frost.

IMPROVING WORK PROCESSES
Proper Use of Muscles

Less energy will be required if you stand while performing tasks of only a few moments duration, but you should sit to perform a long task if possible. Be sure the shoulders are level or slightly dropped to make use of large muscles rather than small, and that the feet are resting comfortably on the floor. Relax and sing or hum a catchy tune or recall a favorite story. When necessary to move heavy equipment, use the leg muscles to push, pull, and lift, for they are the strongest. Bend the knees to a crouching position to reach a kettle on the lower shelf of a base cabinet; this saves a strain on back muscles that would be caused by stooping. Use long-handled tools to avoid unnecessary bending over.

Dishwashing

Even when a dishwasher is not a part of the kitchen equipment, it is much more sanitary not to dry the dishes (except, perhaps, silver and any utensil that will rust or spot). After rinsing and placing in a rack, cover the dishes with a clean towel and let them stay until needed for the next meal. When the family is small and the dish supply adequate, it is a good plan to wash dishes only once a day. They are easy to hide in a dishwasher but, when that is not available, they may be stacked and covered. This is a saving on water and detergent, as well as on energy, and also reduces the volume of detergent in the sewage system that pollutes water supplies.

Floor Care

And the same advice may be given for washing the kitchen floor. Manufacturers of linoleum claim that more linoleum is washed out than worn out. Wash the floor carefully, using as dry a mop as is feasible, and apply two or three coats of liquid wax, allowing a half-hour to an hour for drying time between coats. Go over the floor with a dry mop daily, and perhaps once a week with a mop wrung nearly dry from cold water; if a floor polisher is available, run it around occasionally. Unless there are small children, pets, and muddy weather, a thorough washing should not be needed again for nearly a month.

Dusting

How about dusting! Practice what someone has called "intelligent neglect." Put away articles that need a good deal of care, especially during the warm months, when windows are open and more dust blows in. If the home is a sufficient distance from the street, draperies may be taken down in summer — more air can get in and the drapery material will wear longer.

Use a dusting mitt on each hand and use both hands simultaneously. Learn to use the tools that come with the electric vacuum cleaner. Many of them can be used when the homemaker is sitting down, especially if she has a posture chair on casters that runs around from place to place with a minimum of effort.

Collect cigarette ash and stubs, waste paper, candy wrappers, etc. in a paper bag; it is light in weight and easily carried from room to room and finally to the trash barrel or incinerator. Use a basket, tray, or cart to carry dusting cloths, brushes, polishes, and similar articles together from one work center to another.

Laundering

Wet laundry often weighs twice as much as the same articles do after drying — so a dryer eliminates much heavy lifting. When it is necessary to transport wet laundry, be sure to use a basket elevated on wheels to reduce the amount of lifting, carrying, and stooping.

Clothes washed in a wringer-type machine to be dried on the line will be more easily ironed or stored if they are folded in halves or quarters and put through the wringer "straight with the goods," and hung with the same care, avoiding sags between clothespins.

Sheets, knit underwear, terry-cloth towels and certain other items may be folded from the line and placed at once into storage. Contour sheets that fit tightly over the mattress really never need ironing. If, however, the homemaker prefers to smooth them with an iron, any article folded from the line has fewer wrinkles and is more easily ironed than if dumped hit or miss into the clothes basket.

Many of the man-made "miracle" fibers used today require very little ironing and often none at all. These should be hung on hangers or suspended with pins so the garments will dry in their natural shape; collars, cuffs, plackets, and pleats should be smoothed or stretched to assure smooth drying.

Ironing

It is not necessary to have an ironer in order to sit down to iron. Present-day ironing boards (see Fig. 8.16) are readily adjustable to a variety of heights and one may sit or stand with ease. Here is another use for the posture chair with its padded seat and shaped back that fits one's curves and angles. The cord-minder attached to the end of the board keeps the iron cord away from the clothing during the ironing process and prevents wrinkling the freshly ironed fabric. The lightweight iron (see Fig. 8.15) reduces energy requirements to a minimum.

USING ENERGY WISELY

With the aid of a good assortment of laborsaving appliances now available, and improved working conditions and practices, the homemaker will find she has renewed interest in living a fuller life. She should study and evaluate her abilities and her resources to find ways to enrich her life.

Lillian Gilbreth and associates[2] point out that you have three kinds of resources at your disposal — money, time, and energy. You know your own money limitations, you can schedule your twenty-four hours to suit your needs, but energy is not as easily measured or budgeted. Energy must be used, the authors point out, or it tends to accumulate as fat, and fat is hard to get rid of. Just as money savings are intended to be wisely used, so should savings in time and energy be wisely used — more time with husband and children, more participation in civic affairs, more time to read and develop interests, more visits, personally or by letter, with friends or other persons to make their lives and yours more interesting. Some homemakers may find ways to add to the family income.

As your own life becomes more satisfying, so will that of your family, and the opportunity to grow "and develop together" will not have depreciated because the pace and demands of Mother's life have changed.

EXPERIMENTS AND PROJECTS

1. To find arrangements and processes that waste motion and energy:
    a. Draw to scale on chalkboard any poorly arranged kitchen, where distances connecting work centers are long, there is cross traffic, not enough counter space, and limited storage space.
    b. Draw this plan to scale on laboratory floor, using one foot per foot if possible.
    c. Students suggest a menu for a meal to be prepared in the kitchen. Write it on the board. Decide where supplies and utensils would be kept in this kitchen, assuming that it is a typical one. Decide on order of preparation of meal.
    d. While one student goes through motions of preparing meal in order agreed upon, let one other student measure with a yard stick the distances covered, and a third count the steps taken.

---

[2] Lillian M. Gilbreth, Ortha Mae Thomas, and Eleanor Clymer, *Management in the Home*, Dodd, Mead & Co., N. Y., 1959.

Three other students may relieve the first three at any point in the operation, if desired.

2. To correct arrangements and processes so motion and energy may be saved:

   a. Remodel kitchen to conform to optimum arrangement, letting students suggest changes. Draw remodeled plan on board and on floor.

   b. Prepare same meal in remodeled kitchen, again measuring distances and counting steps.

   c. Compare results.

   d. List basic rules for arranging kitchen to save motion and energy.

QUESTIONS

1. Why are studies of saving motion and time difficult to carry on in the home?
2. Give four ways in which energy may be saved in the kitchen.
3. How may a cart or tray aid in saving steps?
4. What muscles should be used in performing various tasks? Illustrate with examples.
5. Suggest an efficient method for dusting.
6. How can you make a flow chart? Of what value is it?
7. Distinguish between physiological and psychological fatigue.
8. What can you do to reduce each kind of fatigue?
9. How can you expend the energy that you save to obtain personal satisfaction?
10. Have you been able to use any of the ideas that you have learned in this chapter to help others to save time and energy? In what way?

Chapter Eleven

LIGHTING THE HOME

Sight is undoubtedly the most precious of the five senses, the one any person would be least willing to part with. It becomes doubly important when we realize that three-fourths of all we do depends upon sight, that at least 25 per cent of our energy is used in seeing. Yet it alone of the senses needs outside help to function satisfactorily. Adequate light is necessary for adequate sight.

NEED FOR ADEQUATE LIGHT

In evaluating the lighting conditions in your own home, first concern is given to family members who may have problems with eyes or vision. Defective eyes require two to three times as much light as normal eyes. Older people require more light than younger people, for pupil size decreases with age and eye tissues grow more opaque. Light eyes need a higher level[1] of illumination for a given task than dark eyes; fair eyes are much more sensitive to glare, and careful consideration must be given to minimizing this factor.

Faulty sight may be aided by increasing the intake of Vitamin A, which is found abundantly in green and yellow vegetables and dairy foods. The story is often told of young men hoping to join the air corps who strengthen their vision by drinking as much as a quart of carrot juice each day. This method has proven successful, especially when vision has been weakened by illness.

Good vision is an asset that should be preserved at any cost. Like so many blessings of good health, little appreciation or attention is given good vision until some danger signal is apparent. The ability to see with certainty and ease is increasingly important because the growing number of complicated occupations, the stepped-up speed of daily lives, hazardous driving conditions, increased activities and entertainment after daylight hours all

---

[1] The terms "level of light" and "level of illumination" are derived from the figurative definition of "level" as: intensity, standard, degree, quality, etc.

subject the eyes to longer periods of concentrated usage. Eyes become defective through use as well as misuse; when work requires much visual effort or is continued over a long period, pupils gradually dilate and may not return entirely to normal during the hours of sleep or a weekend of relaxation.

Too little light or light wrongly directed will cause a person to hold his book too close to his eyes; doing this day after day easily results in nearsightedness. Parents should carefully watch children for indications of eyestrain. Strain from trying to adapt the eyes to unfavorable lighting conditions may not show in eye trouble, but in indigestion, sleepiness, headaches, irritability, and even in apparent laziness.

One should be able to read comfortably with a page held 12 to 15 inches away from the eyes; when this is not possible, either the sight or the light needs attention or correction.

Factors Affecting Level of Light

Dirt. Except in very gloomy weather most daytime tasks are carried on with light from outside. The window area of a room should be about one-fourth of the floor area but, even then, enough light may not be able to get in unless the windows are kept clean. Ordinary dirt on the outside may cut down 15 to 20 per cent of the entering light, and in very smoky localities the percentage is higher. On the inside, steam from cooking, along with dust, gradually forms a film over the glass, making a room look dull and uninviting instead of bright and sparkling as it should.

Shades and Draperies. Shades and draperies also influence the amount of daylight available in a room. Light coming through the lower half of the window is reflected mainly from trees, shrubbery, or near-by buildings. These frequently absorb more light than they reflect. The difference is noticeable when the ground is covered with snow, for all rooms seem lighter because snow reflects so much more light than the bare ground. Light through the upper half of the window is reflected from the sky. For that reason keep shades near the tops of the windows in the daytime or, better still, use no shades at all, only draperies that can be pulled across the windows at night, and to one side during the hours of daylight.

Screens. Screens also cut out light; rooms are noticeably brighter when screens are taken off in the fall. Copper and bronze screening is preferable to iron since iron screening must be painted to prevent rusting; when this painting is repeated year after year, the transmission of light is still further reduced. Recent use of glass bricks in wall construction has helped to improve daytime lighting of the home (Fig. 11.1).

During evenings and on dark mornings artificial light is used. Electric lights are available in most areas but do not necessarily mean a well-lighted house and that is, after all, the main objective.

Adequate Wiring

The foundation of satisfactory lighting is adequate wiring. Information on different types of circuits used in the home is given in the section on electricity (p. 275). Light outlets are installed in the general-purpose circuit and conform to regulations set up by the National Electric Code (p. 269). Other safety measures recommended, but not specified by the Code, include a sufficient number of convenience outlets to allow floor and table lamps to be used anywhere in a room without extension cords running across doorways or under rugs or in any area of the room

FIG. 11.1.   Glass bricks provide privacy and at the same time flood the room with light.
—Owens-Illinois Glass.

FIG. 11.2. Plug-in strips (note arrows) greatly increase the number of wall outlets. They are especially adaptable for old or poorly wired homes, but care must be taken to have circuit capacity increased to carry the additional loads.—Wiremold Co.

where they may be stepped on (Fig. 11.2). Usually double outlets are positioned about ten feet apart around the room, but not in the middle of a long wall where a large piece of furniture would be placed. Since most lamp cords are about six feet in length, the lamp may be located in any desired position. Switches should be so placed that it is possible to light a room when it is entered and to leave it in darkness without the attendant danger of knocking against furniture or falling over it as one feels his way in the darkness.

LIGHTING THE ROOMS
Living Room

It is a good rule to have a central fixture in every room, controlled by a switch at the door. In the living room this central light frequently is omitted. Table and floor lamps, valance and cornice installations, and sometimes wall bracket fixtures take its place (Fig. 11.3), but one of these should be plugged into an outlet that is connected to the switch so that the room may be at least partially lighted from the doorway. The chief objection to the wall bracket is that it so often is a bare, unshaded bulb in the line of vision, a condition that always causes glare. Any kind of glare is detrimental to the eyes and should be avoided (Fig. 11.4). All lamps should be shaded, with the possible exception of a light in a closet that is used for a short period of time and is usually placed higher than the line of vision.

Dining Room and Kitchen

The dining table is the focus of interest in the dining room and should be well illuminated (Figs. 11.3 and 11.5). Wall outlets near the chair of the hostess provide connections for toaster, coffee maker, or other electric appliances used at the table. In the kitchen a central fixture close to the ceiling spreads light uniformly throughout the room and eliminates sharp shadows. This room is the homemaker's workshop and she will find additional convenience and comfort if there also are lights above the sink and the most frequently used work surfaces (Fig. 11.6a and b).

FIG. 11.3. Cornice lighting for well-diffused general lighting in this living-dining room. A spotlight in the ceiling highlights the dining room table.—Westinghouse.

FIG. 11.4. These floor and table lamps provide general illumination in the room as well as a high level of light for reading, studying, or sewing in local areas. Note the absence of glare.—General Electric.

Bedroom and Bath

In the bathrooms and at the dressing table in the bedroom it is desirable to have all parts of the face illuminated equally for ease in shaving and applying make-up.

Most modern bathrooms have a large mirror over the entire length of the dressing-table type of counter surface, which encloses one or two wash bowls. A long fixture over the mirror, lighted by fluorescent tubes or a series of incandescent bulbs, gives a high level of illumination (Fig. 11.7). Sometimes the whole ceiling is made of luminous panels.

Some people like to read in bed, and it is a double pleasure if the book or magazine is adequately lighted. A lightolier fixture that may be pulled down to the desired height or a pin-up lamp will solve this problem, one with a diffusing bowl and broad, white-lined shade. The lamp should be placed high enough

FIG. 11.5. Traditional multiple-light fixture, controlled by a dimmer, with low-brightness plastic shades. An adjustable eyeball unit is over the serving counter.—General Electric.

above the head of the bed to throw a circle of light, not just on the printed page, but on enough of the surroundings to eliminate any spotty contrast between the light and dark areas of the room. The bottom edge of the shade should be 30 inches above the top of the mattress. A wall bracket is also recommended. It probably provides more even lighting across the bed and thus allows greater freedom in position.

FIG. 11.6a. Fluorescent lamps are mounted in 6 joist spaces and concealed by decorative plastic panels. Fluorescent lamps installed under the upper cabinets provide local lighting on the counters; a deep baffled unit with a 150-watt bulb floodlights the sink.—General Electric.

Stairs

All stairways and entrances both within and without the house require careful lighting to prevent accidents (Figs. 11.8 and 11.9). Fixtures should be placed so that the stairs are always well lighted and without shadows cast ahead of the person walking over them. This is only possible if lights are placed both at the top and bottom of the stairs.

Colors of walls, ceilings, floor coverings, and furniture will partly absorb, partly reflect the light. The reflectance factor, obtained by dividing the amount of light reflected from the article by the amount of light incident upon it, indicates how much light is available for use. Possible levels of reflectance in the home are: ceilings, 60 to 90 per cent; walls, 35 to 60 per cent; floors, 15 to

FIG. 11.6b. Well-lighted pass-through snack bar interconnects kitchen and family room. Installation over the cabinet of a continuous run of 40-watt Warm White Deluxe Fluorescents, concealed by a slanted wood shielding element, ties this wall into the over-all design of the room, highlights beam construction, and shows off beauty of natural wood cabinets. Additional fluorescent lamps, concealed on underside of cabinets, light the serving surface. Adjustable eyeball fixture lights picture on the entrance wall.—General Electric.

35 per cent. Harmonious effects are best obtained when reflectances in major areas do not vary greatly, and preferred levels are usually 25 to 35 per cent for floors, 40 to 50 per cent for walls, and 70 to 80 per cent for ceilings.

SELECTION OF LIGHT FIXTURES
Portable Lamps

The present tendency in home lighting is to combine traditional with the contemporary or modern. Floor and table lamps, the first source of interior lighting, are traditional, however modern their design. These portable lamps have the advantage of easy transportation from one location to another and flexibility in arrangement, as well as adding important decoration to a room. For most satisfactory use the lamps should incorporate certain fundamental characteristics which may be summarized as follows:

1. Lower edge of shade of table lamp about on a level with eyes of person using it; floor lamps may be somewhat higher if placed at rear of chair.

2. Diameters of bottoms of shades of both types of lamps between 16 and 18 inches.

3. Depth of shade sufficient to prevent anyone from seeing bulb from top. Sometimes shades are supplied with diffusing or perforated disks to shield the bulb or bulbs.

4. Closed shade not recommended; upward light helps in general illumination, and open shade dissipates heat from the bulb, heat that may damage certain kinds of shade material.

5. Diffusing bowl surrounding bulb increases size of light source, reduces reflected glare, gives soft shadows.

6. Bottom of shade on a level or slightly below top of lamp socket, allows from 60 to 70 per cent of light to come down, a proportion considered desirable.

7. Shade with white or pale inner surface for good diffusion of light.

8. Shade dense enough to prevent seeing bright spot where bulb is located.

Pole lamps are popular. They stand between floor and ceiling

FIG. 11.7. Luminous plastic ceiling louvers, four feet square, provides a high level of illumination for shaving or applying makeup. Decorative carriage lanterns contain low-wattage bulbs and may also be used as night lights.—General Electric.

FIG. 11.8. Stairs should be well lighted to prevent accidents.—General
Electric.

and have three to five light sources along the pole. They make
attractive room dividers or give character to an otherwise dark
corner, but are not suitable for work or study lamps, and sometimes cause glare.

Opaque shades are desirable when room walls are dark, and
light-colored opaque shades are recommended for desk study
lamps.

A special lamp on the market is the high-intensity lamp (Fig.
11.10). At first used primarily by dentists, watchmakers, jewelers,
and professional people in occupations requiring a bright light in
a relatively small area, it is now being used in desk lamps, and a

FIG. 11.9. When light over the door leaves steps in shadow, additional light is needed to furnish safe illumination.—Lighting Fixtures by Moe Light.

table lamp also has appeared on the market. The light is used on the regular 120-volt household circuit, but the lamp itself contains a built-in transformer that cuts the voltage to 6 or 12 volts. The bulb is an automotive type, about the size of a Ping-pong ball, and gives more foot-candles of light than the usual small incandescent bulb, from 50 to 115 foot-candles. Whereas the 60-watt standard bulb furnishes approximately 1,000 hours of light, these miniature bulbs average only 300 to 600 hours. Like all concentrated light sources the lamp should be used where general lighting supplies at least a fifth as much light, if glare is to be avoided. The bulbs become very hot and can cause burns or a fire if they come into contact with flammable material. This lamp should be supplied with its own fuse or circuit breaker and should carry the UL seal.

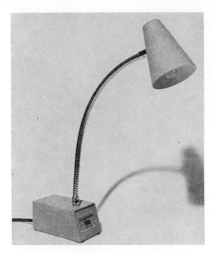

FIG. 11.10. The high-intensity lamp provides a bright light focused on a relatively small area.—Tensor.

Diffusing Bowls

Two types of diffusing bowls are available one of real bowl shape, corrugated or plain, known as the blown-glass bowl (A in Fig. 11.11), the other, the CLM (Certified Lamp Makers) diffusing bowl of quite a different shape (B in Fig. 11.11). The latter is more satisfactory, for it directs 60 per cent of the light down and 40 per cent up, whereas the blown-glass type directs about 60 per cent up and only 40 per cent down. The White Indirect-Lite (C in Fig. 11.11), may be used without a diffusing bowl, but requires a harp or adapter to support the shade (Fig. 11.12). The White Indirect-Lite has a heavy white coating on the sides to diffuse the downward light, but a less heavy coating on the flat top to permit more light to go upward.

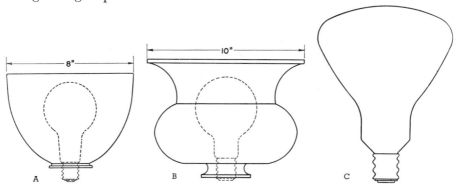

FIG. 11.11.   Three methods of diffusing light: (A) Blown-glass bowl; (B) CLM bowl; and (C) R-40, "White indirect" lamp bulb.

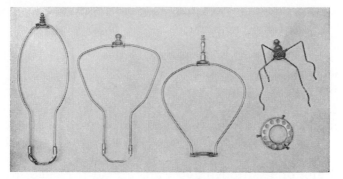

FIG. 11.12. Various types of harps and adapters make possible the use of larger lamp bulbs. The two adapters (right) are used with a diffusing bowl or the R-40 bulb in improving inadequate lighting.

Ceiling Fixtures

Nothing adds more sparkle and freshness to the appearance of a room than clean fixtures. Ceiling fixtures frequently have inverted bowls that need to be taken down and washed, or at least wiped out, but it is a temptation to leave them because they often are out of easy reach. The ceiling also should be washed or whitened at definite intervals. Very dark walls and ceilings absorb more light than they reflect and should be avoided.

Care of Light Fixtures

Artificial lights as well as windows must be kept spotlessly clean. Bulbs cannot be put into water but they may be wiped off with a damp cloth. At the high temperature at which the filament lamp is used, the filament slowly disintegrates, throwing off a fine black powder that deposits on the inside of the glass. Lamps commonly are used until they "burn out," but they should be discarded whenever the black deposit is sufficient to darken the bulb noticeably, since the dark film absorbs the rays of light and greatly reduces the lamp's efficiency. Or the old lamp may be used in a closet where the level of illumination is not so important. The price you pay for an incandescent bulb is only about 10 per cent of the total cost of the light, the other 90 per cent is the cost of the electric current.

The diffusing bowl of glass or plastic material used on many floor and table lamps should be washed regularly every week or two, and several times during the summer the lamp should be tipped upside down to shake out tiny insects that venture too near the alluring light, are killed, and drop into the bowl. Shades should be dusted or, better, cleaned with the attachment of the electric cleaner.

TYPES OF LAMPS (Bulbs)
Filament

The white, inside-frosted lamp bulb—lamp is the correct term, rather than bulb—is the most widely used of the filament lamps. It can be obtained in sizes from 25 watts to 200 watts. Today bulbs are smaller than formerly, while producing more light. Bulbs of 40 through 100 watts are all the same size. The frosted and the clear glass lamps often are installed inside of diffusing bowls. Lamps should never be used unshaded in the line of vision because the bright spot of the filament is visible through the glass. Another white lamp, often called the white bowl lamp, has an inside coating of white silica that diffuses the light sufficiently well so that it may be used without a shade if necessary. It conceals blackening and may be used in any fixture, but is especially adapted for use in closets.

Three-way bulbs have two filaments; each filament may be used separately to give two levels of lighting, then the two together for the highest level of light. They vary from 30–70–100 watts to 100–200–300 watts. Cluster-Lites, the newest 3-way bulb, is a 25–35–60-watt size, and is recommended for dining or bedroom fixtures with three or more 3-way sockets.

Colored Lamps

Colored lamps are available, but in general should be used only for decoration, and rather conservatively even then. The one exception, perhaps, is the tinted lamp for use in living and bedroom fixtures to bring out certain colors in the furnishings and produce a feeling of warmth or coolness as desired. Colored bulbs are not as efficient as white, giving 10 to 25 per cent less light, so a bulb of at least the next higher wattage than if it were white should be used. The blue "daylight" lamp is useful for matching colors, but has only about half the foot-candle output of the white inside-frost lamp of equal wattage.

Silver bowl lamps direct all the light upward and are consequently used for indirect fixtures. The GA lamp, a combination of frosted and clear glass, also sends much of the light toward the ceiling, but does diffuse some downward through the rather heavy, ivory or dawn-pink coating with which it is frosted. It is used to advantage in the ring-type, multiple-bulb ceiling fixture.

Also available for the exposed-light fixture are the new decorative lamp bulbs, known as the Flair line. They follow the present-day trend of matching bulb to fixture. Three types are offered for sale: a slim, fine-pointed bulb in clear glass and also with an outside coating of matte white that does not chip, is washable, and will remain white; then a Colonial Amber for installation in Spanish-Mexican fixtures (Fig. 11.13) and finally the "Auradescent" in three different wattages, with all the glints and tints of colors fused into a rainbow hue (Fig. 11.14).

Orange-brown, flame-colored lamps are low in blue wave lengths and are irritating to the nervous system.

Shapes

All the lamps discussed so far are the filament type. They come in several different shapes, designated by letters: G, globular; F, flame-shaped; PS, pear-shaped; A, inside-frost, etc. Shape

FIG. 11.13. One popular fixture for today's contemporary home is the "Spanish influence" or "Mediterranean" style. The wrought iron has a simple elegance enhanced by use of Flair bulbs with pearl-white finish which makes fixtures attractive even in daytime when not in use. Lighted, lamps have overall white glow.—General Electric.

FIG. 11.14.   Another Flair line bulb is the Auradescent that catches all the colors of the rainbow, full
hues from base to tip.—General Electric.

(a), shown on the left in Figure 11.15, is most commonly used.
The new Eye-Saving bulb, shown beside shape (a) is considered
the best bulb for seeing so far developed, and it is especially recommended for reading and any task requiring close attention.
The inside (a of Fig. 11.16) has a silica coating put on by a new
process that coats the inside surface with millions of glare-deflect-
ing silica particles which produce a soft glareless light from the
entire surface. This bulb may be obtained in the single-watt rating and also in a 3-way, 50–100–150 watts.

Wattage

High-wattage lamps give more foot-candles in proportion to
rating than low-wattage lamps. For example, five or six 25-watt
lamps are needed to obtain as much light as that furnished by one
100-watt lamp—certainly poor economy. Three-way lamps are very
satisfactory since the one bulb may be used to give a low light
when no exacting task is performed and, at the flick of a switch
may be changed to a high level of illumination. The 50–200–250-
watt lamp is especially versatile. The 50-watt position is recommended for TV viewing and the 200- or 250-watt for studying
and sewing. In general, the lower edge of the shade on a table
lamp should be even with the eyes of the person using the lamp.
The bottom of the lamp socket, however, should be approximately
1½ inches below the bottom of the shade to bring the lamp
bulb into the most desirable position for spreading the light
over a wide area.

FIG. 11.15. A conventionally-shaped inside-frost lamp bulb (left) compared with shape introduced in 1958.—Westinghouse.

Fluorescent

In contrast to the filament lamp in which the electric current flows through a wire, is the fluorescent tube in which electricity is conducted from one end of the tube to the other by means of mercury vapor (Fig. 11.17). Small, coiled wires, called electrodes, one at each end of the tube, are coated with a material that starts the activity in the tube. When a fluorescent lamp is switched on, the end coils heat and throw off particles known as electrons that activate the mercury vapor with which the tube is filled. The mercury produces ultraviolet radiations. The ultraviolet wave length is changed to the wave length of daylight by the fluorescent powder with which the tube is lined. There are seven different whites in fluorescent tubes from which to choose, but two are recommended as most desirable for home use: the Deluxe warm white, which is somewhat warm in color, and is reported to be flattering to the complexion and to the usual home decorations and the Deluxe cool white that creates a cool atmosphere and tends to make all colors appear accurate and true. It should be used when cool colors predominate in furnishings and decorations.

Fluorescent tubes may be the preheat type which requires a

FIG. 11.16. Inside of Eye-Saving light bulb (left) and inside frost bulb (right). The inside of the two bulbs is alike with the exception of the position of the filament.—Westinghouse.

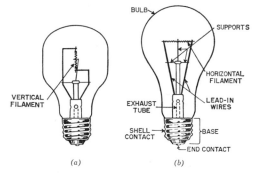

VERTICAL FILAMENT

BULB

SUPPORTS

HORIZONTAL FILAMENT

EXHAUST TUBE

LEAD-IN WIRES

SHELL CONTACT

BASE

END CONTACT

(a) *(b)*

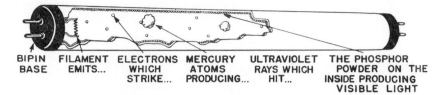

| BIPIN BASE | FILAMENT EMITS... | ELECTRONS WHICH STRIKE... | MERCURY ATOMS PRODUCING... | ULTRAVIOLET RAYS WHICH HIT... | THE PHOSPHOR POWDER ON THE INSIDE PRODUCING VISIBLE LIGHT |

FIG. 11.17. Detail showing how the fluorescent tube operates.—Westinghouse.

starter to allow the electricity to flow through the end coils and heat them before the current will be conducted through the mercury vapor creating a delay of several seconds after the switch is thrown before the tube lights. Once the coils are hot, the starter is thrown out of the circuit. A second type is the Rapid-Start tube which requires no starter. A new universal tube, known as the Preheat-Rapid-Start, may be installed in either preheat or rapid-start fixtures, but will have a time delay in fixtures with starters.

Because there is no wire, as in a filament lamp, to keep the current controlled as it flows through the tube, a "ballast" is needed. A ballast is a current-limiting device without which there would be such a surge of current that the lamp would burn out almost instantly. Ballast consumes electricity and this should be reckoned into the cost of operation, about $4\frac{1}{2}$ watts for a 15-watt tube and 25 watts for the 100-watt tube. Starters may need to be replaced occasionally, but the ballast should last as long as the tube. Because of these additional parts, fluorescent lamps cost more than filament lamps to install and are more expensive to replace. They do, however, give three to four times as much light per watt and will last seven to ten times longer.

A new light source is the Panel fluorescent light, approximately 12 inches square and $1\frac{1}{2}$ inches thick. It can be surface mounted, recessed, or hung from the ceiling.

Voltage Required

A fluorescent lamp operates most successfully at the rated voltage; to use it on a higher or lower voltage will shorten the life of the tube. If a family lives at the end of a line — the last house on a rural line or at the far edge of town where voltage tends to drop — fluorescent lamps probably are not a good choice. They operate best when the temperature is about 80 F., one reason why they are especially recommended for the kitchen, although they will not start as easily when the humidity is too high.

New tubes frequently are coated with silicone to take care of the effect of humidity.

To allow more flexibility in the use of light, dimming equipment has been developed for installation in the home. Long available for dimming incandescent lamps in theaters and other public buildings, it is now possible to dim the 30-watt Rapid-Start and 40-watt Preheat-Rapid-Start fluorescent tubes. In such installations a dimming-type ballast must be used and a separate switch must be placed before the dimmer to cut off current from the ballast.

Cool Light

Fluorescent lamps give a cool light, one reason for their popularity. They may be used for cove and cornice lighting, in valance lighting above windows, along the edges of bookcases, or in the fireplace mantel. There is less glare from fluorescents, the shadows are softer; it is desirable, however, to use louvers or a diffusing glass below ceiling fixtures. Fluorescent lamps increase in intensity any colors containing tints or shades of blue and green, while reds and yellows tend to be dulled or grayed. Upholstery, drapery fabrics, wall colors, and even dress materials and make-up should be selected under the type of lighting with which they will be used most frequently. There is a lamp which combines fluorescent and filament lighting, giving the advantage of both kinds of light. A similar effect is obtained by using separate fluorescent and filament sources of light in any room. When combined lighting is not available in the store, the purchaser should test the fabric with the kind of lighting under which the fabric will be used.

Care of Fluorescents

If the fluorescent tube blinks on and off, it generally means that the lamp is no longer good. The coating on the coiled wires at the ends of the tube gradually evaporates, causing the tube to cease to light. The evaporation is hastened by turning the lamp on and off too frequently. It is desirable to let the tube remain lighted for several hours at a time; so if one leaves the room for fifteen or twenty minutes or even for a half hour or more, do not turn the fluorescent tube off. For this reason a tubular filament lamp instead of fluorescent lamp is recommended for the bathroom installation, for filament lamps are not so easily damaged by frequent turning off and on. Tubular filament lamps are called "lumiline" lamps and in outward appearance look very much like a fluorescent tube, but a filament runs through the tube from one end to the other.

Other Lamps

Electroluminescence is a potential light source for tomorrow. It does not use the filament bulb or fluorescent tube, but produces light from electroluminescent panels no thicker than window glass. At present it is less efficient than other light sources. One application of electroluminescence has been a night light for bedroom or bath, which continues to glow year in, year out, without need for replacement. Such lights may be used also in vestibules, halls, closets, stair risers, nurseries, and basement areas, and in weather-proof units for walks, outside steps, driveways, house entrances, patios, and pool areas. These units are almost fail-proof, and use so little current that they can remain on continuously.

Ultraviolet lamps, infrared lamps, and spot lamps and flood lamps are available for certain specific purposes, as their names imply. Special lighting arrangements add immeasurable beauty to pictures in the home, a pool, a bird bath, or a bit of statuary in the garden. Strings of Christmas tree lights may be used for obtaining subtle party settings throughout the year, and many unusual effects may be created by using special lights to accent holiday decorations (Fig. 11.18).

A fairly recent trend is the use of gaslight at the end of the driveway and in the garden, patio, and around swimming pools. The soft glow is very pleasing, a nostalgic reminder of earlier days. It has the advantage of offering less attraction to insects and bugs. Equipped with a pilot light and a photosensitive control that dims the light at dawn and turns it up at dusk, the typical cost of operation per month is about $1.00.

Reminiscent of the days of old-time lamplighters, "One man swears that when his driveway light goes on in the evening now, he sometimes hears a ladder scrape against the post and footsteps go shuffling off down the street."[2]

The present interest in more adequately wired and lighted houses certainly is a move in the right direction, and should be

---

[2] Changing Times Family Success Book. 1962 edition, p. 95.

FIG. 11.18. The Christmas spray is lighted by a spotlight screwed into the porch ceiling socket and by a floodlight on the porch floor. Dual lighting accents the shadows, increasing both beauty and interest.—Westinghouse.

enthusiastically supported by all who desire more efficient and attractive homes.

CONTROLLING GLARE

There may be enough light in a room but it may be wrongly directed and cause glare. Glare results when a bright, unshaded light is directly in the line of vision. Light should be on the work, not in the eyes. Glare is caused also by light reflected into the eyes from a shiny table top (Fig. 11.19) or highly glossed magazine page, and from too great contrast between light from a local lamp and the general lighting in the rest of the room. Any person reading or working under a bright light with the rest of the room almost dark, tends to look up frequently, causing the pupil of the eye to adjust each time. Consequently the eye muscles will be overworked, and soon the individual feels tired and decides he had better do something else. The whole trouble is caused by lack of enough general lighting. General lighting in a room should be at least one-fifth of the local light from a floor or table lamp. Many of the modern semi-indirect lamps help to supply general light as well as light at the place where one is sitting. Several such lights in a room may make a ceiling fixture unnecessary, but light should always pull all corners of the room together to form a unit.

Glare by contrast occurs, too, when the study book or paper is placed on a dark table top or blotter (Fig. 11.20a). For some reason dark green blotters have come to be regarded as a sign of academic standing. Discard them, and use one of peach color, or light blue, green, or gray and notice the improvement in the effect. Raising the lights above eye level and facing the desk to-

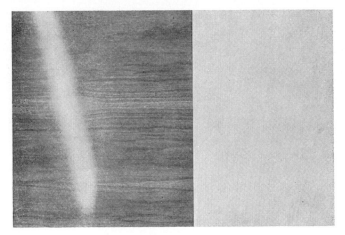

FIG. 11.19. Reflected glare of luminaire (left) on a polished dark desk top disappears (right) when the desk is covered with a piece of light, unpolished linoleum. Actually, it doesn't disappear but is so diffused as to be imperceptible.—Better Light Better Sight Bureau.

FIG. 11.20a. A poor lamp placed on the wrong side of a study table, which has too dark a top, causes contrast glare; the book lying flat on the surface forces the student to bend over; the figured wall paper distracts the attention to the wall itself and to its reflection on the polished table top.—Westinghouse.

FIG. 11.20b. Two pin-up lamps give a high level of well-diffused light, eliminating dark shadows; light-colored blotter reduces contrast; the book holder makes reading easier and ensures correct posture; and the plain wall draws no attention to itself or its reflection.—Westinghouse.

ward a plain wall eliminate other faulty features (Fig. 11.20b). Placing a bright light against a dark wall also causes too great a contrast. A window in a dark-papered wall is equally undesirable, especially on a sunshiny day.

New study lamps, carrying the approval tag of the Better Light Better Sight Bureau are now available (Fig. 11.21). Representatives from this bureau and from the Illuminating Engineering Society worked on a research study to obtain information on desirable study lamps. As a result new lighting performance requirements for a table study lamp were issued. Industry has introduced a number of new lamp designs capable of achieving these recommendations, lamps that are said to represent the greatest technical advance in portable lamps in 25 years. These lamps have semi-opaque white shades, topped with perforated or lou-

FIG. 11.21.   Approved study lamp and shade, one of 9 different models, made by 7 manufacturers. All lamps have these characteristics in common: wide light distribution over the critical working area, soft shadows without direct or reflected glare, upward and outward light, and a range of footcandles within acceptable limits. The tag indicates that the lamp on which it hangs, when equipped with the proper bulb and positioned correctly on the study area, meets specifications of the Better Light Better Sight Bureau. —BLBS Bureau.

vered metal discs, and conform to recommended dimensions: lower diameter of shade 16 inches, upper diameter, 10 inches, depth of shade 16 inches, distance from table to bottom of shade approximately 15 inches. A 200-watt lamp bulb is used, either inside a prismatic refractor bowl or above an aluminum cone, which supplies a minimum of 70 foot-candles of glare-free light over the entire work area, even on the farthest corner of the work surface opposite the working hand — known as the "coffin corner" because of its frequently dimly lighted condition. The maximum light on any part of the area should not exceed the minimum amount by a ratio of more than 3 to 1. The previous standard for light on the work plane was an average of 40 foot-candles.

Further recommendations for study situations indicate that in general you should avoid squatty low lamps or narrow tall ones that give only a small spread of light; lamps such as gooseneck, bullet, and pole lamps that provide no upward light; lamps showing poor diffusion of light. Instead, study lamps should supply a high level of light, distributed uniformly over the entire work area, some light thrown upward on walls and ceiling, no direct view of lamp bulb, no spot of light from bulb seen through shade, no shadows on the work. The desk should have a non-glossy, light-colored surface, the wall behind the desk should be light colored and plain in texture, and there should be good general lighting in the room. Pull-down lamps may be used, if they are adjusted so that the bottom of the shade is at eye level.

Factory owners and superintendents supply a high level of illumination because they know that with more light a person can see easily and quickly, do the job faster, and use much less energy. The home is a workshop, too, for the mother, for school children with homework to do, for the preschool child playing with his toys, for the father at night mending a piece of furniture or reading the newspaper. The quality of paper and size of type used for telephone directories and newspapers make it necessary to have three times the amount of light to read with the same ease as one reads a well-printed book or magazine. This is caused by lack of contrast between the print and background paper. Mother needs more illumination to sew on dark or light cloth with the same colored thread than when thread is a contrasting color. H. R. Blackwell, Director of the Institute for Research, Ohio State University, has noted that a 7 per cent improvement in contrast is equivalent to 100 per cent increase in level of illumination.

MEASURING ILLUMINATION WITH A SIGHT METER

The family may be interested in determining the level of illumination in the different rooms. A sight meter has been developed for this purpose (Fig. 11.22). It is constructed with a film, equivalent to the sensitivity of the human eye, on which the light rays fall, and a scale that reads in foot-candles — the unit in which the illumination on any surface is recorded. The meter is usually available at the local electric utility company and may be borrowed for taking readings in the home. Less than 10 foot-candles of illumination is not considered adequate for any energy-demanding task. From 10 to 20 foot-candles is usually sufficient for reading well-printed pages, from 20 to 50 will be needed for newspapers and fairly exacting work, from 50 to 75 for most sewing jobs, and over 75 for prolonged and severe tasks. Remember, however, that the general lighting in the room must be at least a fifth as much and recent research has indicated that a third as much general lighting is even more desirable.

IMPROVING POOR FIXTURES

People frequently are unable to purchase complete new lighting fixtures for a home already supplied, inadequate though they may be. However, the old installations often may be improved with a minimum of expense. A bare lamp at the end of a drop cord may be raised to the ceiling and surrounded with a glass diffusing bowl or a parchment shade. Direct lights may be changed to semi-indirect by reversing the position of the lamp and enclosing it in a diffusing bowl, then using a white-lined shade (Fig. 11.23). All unshaded lamps should be shaded. Strip wiring, which supplies convenience outlets spaced at various short distances, may be installed above the work surfaces in the kitchen and above base boards in other rooms (see Fig. 11.2). This makes possible the adaptation of fixtures that might be wrong in one

FIG. 11.22. Footcandle meter for determining the level of illumination at the place where light is used.—General Electric.

FIG. 11.23. The goosenecked lamp which tends to provide too many footcandles of direct illumination on the work surface may be remodeled into a satisfactory desk lamp.

location, but adequate when placed in an area where conditions can be corrected to fit the fixture.

Thought and ingenuity combined will help the homemaker improve the lighting in any home — no matter how impossible the task may seem in the beginning.

EXPERIMENTS AND PROJECTS

A light meter, also called a sight meter, should be obtained from the local power company. This will record the foot-candles of light at the spot being tested.

1. To compare the amount of light given by various lamps:
   a. Connect to a wall outlet a cord with a socket on the end and suspend it two or three feet above a work surface. Place light meter directly below socket. Screw into the socket, one at a time, the following lamp bulbs of identical make and 100-watt rating: inside frosted A; white ceramic inside; blue daylight; clear glass; yellow insect; inside frosted A, blackened on inside from use; inside frosted A, artificially soiled on outside, representative of an accumulation of dust over a period of time. Also use a single inside-frost, 25-watt lamp. Read foot-candles of light given by each lamp. Note the cost of obtaining with 25-watt lamps the equivalent light output of one 100-watt lamp; also cost of obtaining equivalent light from blue daylight lamps.

2. To improve poor lighting conditions:
   a. Arrange study table as follows: dark top surface; dark green blotter; low lamp, goosenecked type, if possible, placed at left side of blotter; magazine or textbook on blotter for studying. Read light meter when placed at each corner of book and in center. Note glare by contrast between blotter and book and between bright area of table and rest of room. Can 1/5 of light on table be obtained in other areas of room?

b. Replace dark green blotter with light blotter or entirely cover table with light blotters. Use peach, light blue, light gray, or light green. Take readings. Compare glare by contrast with (a).

c. Make goosenecked lamp into improved study lamp: Remove opaque shade, straighten neck, add adapter with diffusing bowl and 100-watt light bulb, or use wide harp with R-40 lamp, add white-lined shade. Place lamp 12 inches back from front edge of table and 15 inches to left of center of book. (See recipe on page 10 of *See Your Home in a New Light*.[3]) If necessary raise lamp on block of wood or books so that bottom edge of shade is 15 inches above table surface. Repeat readings on table and in other parts of room. Note increased amount of general light in room by reflection from ceiling above lamp. To obtain maximum amount of reflected light, what should be color of ceiling?

d. Arrange a desk set-up using two pin-up lamps as in Figure 11.20b. Take readings.

3. To compare dispersion of light:

a. Use desk lamp with blown-glass diffusing bowl, 100-watt lamp, white-lined shade, on light blotter. Take readings on light meter at base of lamp and at 5, 10, 15, and 20 inches from base of lamp.

b. Replace blown-glass diffusing bowl with CLM diffusing bowl and repeat (a). Compare readings. Within what area is adequate light for studying obtained?

c. Repeat (b) using white-lined shade of wider bottom diameter, red translucent shade, and white translucent shade. Which shade causes most glare? Which least glare?

4. To compare filament and fluorescent lamps for their effects on colors:

a. Use duplicate sheets of colored construction paper—red, orange, green, violet, blue, blue-green, blue-violet, and yellow-green. Place identical sheets under light from filament lamp and light from fluorescent lamp. How would you apply this information in the home?

5. To compare the reflectance of light from various colors:

a. Hold or thumbtack white blotter against well-lighted wall. Hold light meter with sensitive cell toward blotter, 2 inches to 6 inches away from blotter, at point where reading is constant. Record reading. Replace white blotter with blotters of various colors and repeat readings.

b. Draw conclusions as to desirable colors for walls of rooms in the home. Note blotters have mat surfaces that diffuse the light.

---

[3] See *Your Home in a New Light*, 2nd ed. Obtainable from General Electric Co., Lamp Division, Nela Park, Cleveland, 12, Ohio.

QUESTIONS

1. How can you measure the illumination on a surface? It is measured in what unit?
2. What causes glare? Have you had trouble with any of the three kinds of glare in your home? How have you taken care of the problem?
3. What types of surfaces give the most comfortable reflection of light?
4. What should be the relation between the amount of light on the book that you are reading and in the rest of the room? Do you have that much light in the room where you study?
5. What lamps are recommended because of the tests that they have had to meet?
6. What determines how many switches you need in a room?
7. Mary bought a new study desk. To protect the top from scratches she placed a glass cover over it. Does Mary need advice? What will you tell her?
8. If there is no central fixture in a room, how can you provide general lighting?
9. How can you obtain a high level of light in your living room during the daytime?
10. From the following, select the best combination of three for your study situation. Give reasons for choice.
    (1) white blotter
    (2) pale peach colored blotter
    (3) red blotter
    (4) transparent shade
    (5) opaque shade
    (6) translucent shade
    (7) 100-watt, inside-frost lamp bulb
    (8) 100-watt, inside-frost lamp bulb with diffusing bowl
    (9) 100-watt, blue daylight lamp bulb

Chapter Twelve

THE HOME WATER SYSTEM

WATER IS ESSENTIAL FOR LIFE. Though the ages the need of an adequate and reliable supply has determined the places where man has lived. After people settled in congested areas, consideration also had to be given to sanitary means for the disposal of waste. City and town governments usually take the responsibility of providing pure water and sewage control for those dwelling within their limits, but rural dwellers must procure for themselves a source of water and guard against contamination of the supply.

The convenience of a sufficient quantity of hot and cold water available at the opening of a faucet, of a well-appointed bathroom, and of modern automatic laundry equipment, all necessary for cleanliness and health, is more or less taken for granted. Plumbing has become a professional job requiring scientific knowledge and training, and skilled persons should be employed to assure the home a satisfactory installation.

METHODS OF HEATING WATER

Water may be heated by various methods. The water-back (a reservoir for storing a supply of hot water at the back of the range) in the coal or wood range was first used and still may be used occasionally. When houses began to be heated by furnaces, the water coil was placed in the fire-box of the furnace, and a separate heater used only during the summer. This method is not entirely satisfactory, because of variation in weather conditions. Moreover, heat absorbed by the coil is not employed for general house heating; in fact, tests have shown that as much as 20 per cent of coal burned goes to heat the water and an additional 40 gallons of oil is needed in an oil furnace each month for the same purpose. In severely cold weather the water in the tank tends to reach the boiling temperature, steam is formed, and unless the tank is vented into the drainage system, an explosion may occur.

Automatic Storage Heater

The type most frequently used in the present-day home is the automatic storage heater, although other types are available, such as nonautomatic and instantaneous heaters. The storage tank may be made of copper, stainless steel, Monel metal, galvanized iron, or glass-lined steel, usually is insulated with Fiberglas, and heated by gas or electricity. In soft-water areas copper tanks are recommended with connecting pipes of brass. A galvanized tank tends to become corroded and, to hinder this tendency, a rod of magnesium may be suspended within it. The rod may need to be replaced occasionally. Brass pipes should not be used with a galvanized tank, since electrolytic action will develop between the zinc and the brass, gradually causing disintegration of the zinc. Glass-lined tanks are especially desirable for use in hardwater regions.

Within the last few years plastic pipes have been widely used. They are certified by the American Gas Association Testing Laboratories and not only eliminate discoloration and corrosion, and so lengthen the life of the heater, but also decrease its weight.

Water heaters are of two types, slow recovery and fast recovery. Fast-recovery heaters can raise the temperature of the water in the tank 100 degrees in about an hour; slow-recovery heaters require from 3 to 10 hours for the same heating job. Fast-recovery types are recommended since they are able to supply sufficient hot water in the case of any emergency which may occur without warning. The nameplate should give the recovery rate; that is, in the case of the gas heater, specify the number of gallons of water heated through 100 F. in one hour. The nameplate on the electric heater indicates the wattage rating. Since 250 watts per hour are required to increase the temperature of one gallon of water 100 F., dividing the wattage rating by 250 will give the hourly recovery rate.

Gas Heater

When gas is used for the heating fuel, the burner is placed below the water reservoir and the heat rises through a central flue or circulates in a flue around the outside of the reservoir, between it and the insulation. The central flue often is provided with a series of baffles to prevent too rapid loss of heat (Fig. 12.1).

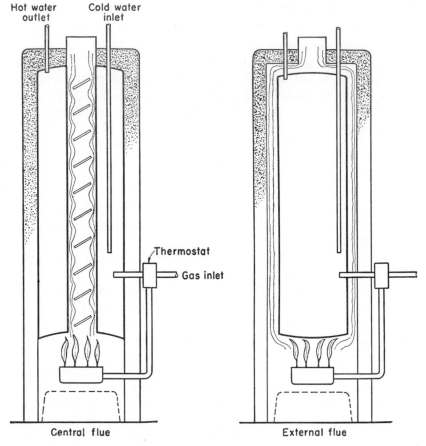

FIG. 12.1. Two gas water heaters showing different types of flues and methods of heating water.

Natural gas heaters use 1,000 to 1,500 cubic feet of gas a month. Connection to a vent usually is mandatory.

Electric Heater

Electric units may be fastened to the outside of the water storage chamber, or may be the immersion type. No vent is required. If two electric units are provided, each will have its own thermostat. In such an installation the lower unit operates for the primary heating of the tank, frequently during the off-load hours of the utility company. The upper unit is used during the daytime for emergency heating (Fig. 12.2).

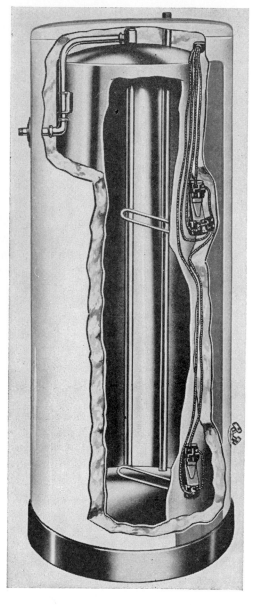

FIG. 12.2. Electric water heater. Two radiant-tube, thermostatically controlled units are placed directly in the water, one at the top and one toward the bottom of the tank. The lower unit usually operates under a time control and is metered separately from the electricity in regular household use. The upper unit is free to operate whenever hot water is needed to meet unusual requirements. Since no vents or flues are required, the heater may be installed in the most convenient and economical location with short connecting pipes to plumbing fixtures to minimize heat loss.—Frigidaire.

Thermostat Controls

The heating process is controlled by a thermostat. In the gas-fired heater the thermostat is commonly of the snap-action type in which the full flame is entirely on or completely off almost instantaneously, with only the pilot burning between times to maintain a fairly constant temperature in the water. Should the gas flame be accidentally extinguished, the flow of gas will shut off within a few seconds, and the sensitive strip of metal beside the pilot valve must be warmed with a lighted match before the valve will again open.

A gas heater that supplies water of two different temperatures is also available, temperatures up to 180 F. for automatic washer and dishwasher and 130 F. for bathroom and other household uses.

Both electric and gas heated tanks should be supplied with a relief valve in case themostats fail to function — a rare occurrence in the automatically controlled tank — and the water is heated to 212 F. and the steam generated builds up excessive pressure. A faucet near the base of the tank permits flushing out the tank to get rid of lime sediment. Such deposits form easily in hard water regions, especially if the temperature of the water is maintained at a rather high level, and they should be washed out frequently; drawing off two quarts of water once a week is recommended. The deposits tend to decrease the efficiency of the heating process to an appreciable extent, resulting in increased fuel consumption, and also shorten the life of the tank.

Water is heated to temperatures between 150 and 160 F. and for most purposes this is hot enough; in fact, since the thermostat control is readily accessible, it may be set for 110 to 120 F. and only turned to the higher setting when laundry is to be done. Such an arrangement is possible if the family is small and the clothes washer is used only once a week, and when no dishwasher is used or, if provided, has its own separate tank that supplies the necessary hot water for the dishwasher alone. Higher temperature must be maintained for large families requiring increased amounts of hot water for more frequent use of the clothes washer and for family baths. The hot water may be diluted with cold for personal use. The lower temperature certainly is preferable when there are small children in the home, eliminating the possibility of serious burns.

Size of Tank

In the past the 30-gallon tank was widely used, but with the increased demand for hot water, probably a 50-gallon tank should be considered a desirable minimum. It is estimated that homes average 10 to 15 gallons of hot water per day per adult. A baby, in its needs, is considered equivalent to two adults. When the majority of the family members are away at business or school for many hours during the day this estimate would be reduced considerably. When the heater is installed as close as possible to the areas where the largest amounts of hot water are used, hot water is more quickly available and less heat is lost as it flows through the pipes. Heat loss is greatly reduced by insulating the pipes, and such a practice is highly recommended. To determine the size of heater suited to a family's need, find the performance rating. This equals the storage capacity of the tank plus the recovery rate.

SOFTENING WATER SUPPLY

The value of soft water has been discussed in the chapter on laundry equipment (p. 149). The hot-water system is more commonly softened than the cold, but both may be. It is desirable, however, to by-pass the softener in providing water for the bathroom closet and for lawn sprinkling. Some people also prefer unsoftened water for drinking.

BATHROOM APPLIANCES

The bathroom with its lavatory and tub for cleansing the human body, and the closet for the sanitary disposal of human excretions is a vital part of the home. These three appliances are now obtainable in a variety of hues to harmonize with any color scheme.

Lavatory

The lavatory—round, oval, or rectangular in shape—has an overhanging lip to prevent splashing, an overflow outlet to the drain, and is supported on legs or fastened to the wall. Some lavatories have a soap receptacle on the edge of the bowl, a shelfback to hold a water glass or other article, and towel bars on either side. Other basins are built into a counter surface (Fig. 12.3) that forms a part of a dressing table, concealing the connecting pipes and furnishing drawers and shelves for the more adequate storage of toilet and make-up items than is provided by the shallow wall cabinet often hung above the lavatory. The faucets, individual or connected through a mixing spout, may be on the back splash or the back ledge of the basin, with the open end of the faucet at least

FIG. 12.3.   The lavatory built into the counter will furnish level space for toilet articles and a storage area below for towels. Lucite handles of acrylic resin resist chipping and are not harmed by water, soaps, or detergents. —Crane.

one inch higher than the water level in the basin. The latter type is preferred because it eliminates any possibility of the spout being submerged in dirty water that would get into the supply system and contaminate it. It is customary to place the hot water faucet on the left. A rubber stopper or pop-up cylinder is used to close the waste pipe, into which the overflow also opens.

Tub

The tub, square or rectangular in shape, of porcelain enameled iron or steel, has a flat bottom and sloping end and, when built in, a wide rim on the room side on which the bather may sit. Steel tubs may be made with ridges along the bottom surface, an aid in preventing slipping. A mixing faucet should be installed above the end of the tub, as in the lavatory. There is a rubber stopper or pop-up waste closure and an overflow opening. The piping often is concealed in the wall, but should be accessible for servicing.

Shower Bath

Because of the saving of time, the shower bath has become popular. It may be a part of the tub installation or may be placed in a separate compartment, finished in tile or marble, or may be of bonderized metal, coated with synthetic enamel (p. 293). When the tile is set in cement mortar, there is occasional trouble with some of the tiles loosening. There may be one spray or a series located around the shower stall. A mixing valve, controlled by a temperature regulator, is recommended, especially if the water heater is maintained at a high temperature. Otherwise, when cold water is diverted to other areas of the house, particularly flushing a closet tank, a sudden surge of very hot water in the shower may cause serious results. The shower compartment may be closed with a curtain or a glass door.

Toilet Closet

The lavatory and bath tub may be made from enameled cast iron and steel or of vitreous china, but the toilet closet is always of china made from fine imported clay which is resistant to the rather strong alkaline agents frequently used in cleaning it. Two types of closets are used in the home, the siphon wash-down and the siphon jet (Figs. 12.4 and 12.5). The wash-down model is somewhat quieter, but the jet eliminates the waste more rapidly and has a more extensive water surface area that maintains a cleaner bowl. The trap is at the front of the wash-down bowl and in the rear of the siphon jet fixture, an easy method of distinguishing between them. In both types when the closet is flushed, water

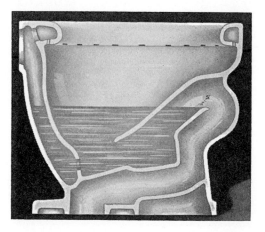

FIG. 12.4. The siphon wash-down closet needs less floor space, making it more adaptable to small rooms.—Crane.

FIG. 12.5. The siphon jet closet provides a broad water surface, but needs more floor space.—Crane.

flows in around the rim to help remove any soil clinging to the sides. The flush tank is usually the low type, built in one unit with the closet bowl (Fig. 12.6). When the handle on the tank is operated, the tank ball is raised from its seat at the bottom of the tank, allowing the water to discharge rapidly into the bowl. The receding water draws the ball back into position, stopping

FIG. 12.6. The flush tank is connected to the closet in such a way that the flush pipe is invisible.—Crane.

the water flow. A float valve controls the refill. The tank apparatus should include an overflow pipe and also an after-fill tube which allows a tiny stream of water to run into the closet bowl to reseal the trap against the entrance of sewer gas.

A new type, the wall-hanging closet, is increasingly popular because of the ease of cleaning around and beneath it (Fig. 12.7). It is particularly adapted to new construction since the space within the partition behind the closet must be at least two inches deeper than for the conventional installation. This greater depth can be provided when a house is being built. The framework that supports the closet, known as the chair, is placed in the wall, and frequently the tank is installed there also out of sight.

SAFETY FEATURES

Trap. Certain other accessories are needed and certain precautions must be taken if sanitary conditions are to be maintained in the home. One of these is the trap. The pipe draining each plumbing fixture should be equipped with a trap. The P-shaped is preferred to the S-shaped one because there is less likelihood of the water siphoning off from the P-shape. A main house trap is installed in the house drain, inside the foundation of the house and prevents the entrance of gases from the public sewer. These gases include methane, carbon monoxide, hydrogen sulfide, and other gases which not only are deleterious to health, but are frequently flammable and may cause disastrous explosions.

Venting System. A venting system also is essential to protect the water seal. A branch of this air pipe line is connected to the sewer side of each trap. Toilet closets discharge into what is

FIG. 12.7. A wall-hung closet with tank concealed in the wall is easy to clean under and requires less space.—Crane.

known as the soil pipe, a pipe about four inches in diameter; other fixtures, such as bath tubs, lavatories, sinks, and laundry tubs, discharge into the smaller waste pipe. Both pipes—usually made of cast iron—empty at the lower end into the house drain which in turn is connected to the city sewer when available, or to a septic tank. At the upper end, the combined soil and waste pipes extend through the roof and become a part of the venting system, to which they are connected above the highest installed fixture (Fig. 12.8). The section of soil pipe vent above the roof should be of

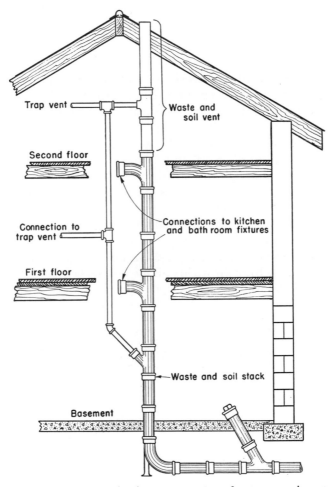

FIG. 12.8.   Main plumbing connections for traps and vents
in the home.

sufficient diameter to prevent any chance of frosting over during the winter months.

When floor drains are provided in the basement, water will tend to evaporate from the traps during periods when not in use. To cut off the entrance of noxious gases, water should be poured into the traps from time to time.

It has been previously suggested that faucets be installed far enough above basins and tubs that dirty water may not pass into them and contaminate the house water supply. Similar trouble occurs from cross connections between fill and drain pipes of the clothes washer and dishwasher. To avoid this difficulty, an air break usually is left in the fill pipe and should be required.

EXPERIMENTS AND PROJECTS

1. Visit plumbing contractor. Arrange for talk and demonstration on bathroom fixtures, water heater, etc.
2. Examine a toilet tank. Note manner of flushing, refilling, and after-fill.
3. Students report on placement of faucets, type of traps, type of water heater, type of toilet bowl and tank used in their homes.

QUESTIONS

1. What is the desirable method of heating water? What size tank is recommended?
2. Why should the water heater have a relief valve?
3. For what temperature is the thermostat of the heater usually set? What influences the choice of temperature?
4. Where are the faucets in lavatory and tub placed? To avoid what?
5. Discuss advantages and disadvantages of tub versus shower.
6. What are the essentials of a satisfactory toilet closet? What type do you have?
7. Why are traps a necessary part of all plumbing systems? Which type of trap is recommended? Why?
8. Why is venting essential? Explain how it works.
9. What is an air break? Where is it frequently used? Do you use an air break anywhere in your home?

Chapter Thirteen

HEATING AND AIR-CONDITIONING

THE HOME

ALTHOUGH RESPONSIBILITY for heating the home usually is left to the man of the family, certain information should be shared by the homemaker, especially when the man's business necessitates frequent and somewhat lengthy absences from home. Fortunately house heating is increasingly automatic and demands a minimum of attention. When selecting a heating system for a new home, both husband and wife need to study all available equipment.

HEATING SYSTEMS

Three systems are commonly available, hot water, steam, and warm air; and there are two types of warm air furnace, the gravity type, and the forced air, in which an electrically operated fan forces the air into the pipes. Willis H. Carrier of Carrier Corporation points out that, to be satisfactory, the system chosen must utilize the fuel efficiently at the lowest cost, must be quiet, safe, require a negligible amount of servicing, be clean, and, since it is occasionally installed in the basement recreation room, it should be compact in size and attractive in appearance.

CONDITIONS AFFECTING SELECTION OF SYSTEM

Before deciding upon any system, certain preliminary investigations must be made. The size of plant needed depends of course upon the amount of heat it must supply, a requirement influenced by conditions within the home, by external weather conditions that usually prevail, and also by the construction of the house itself. The comfort of the occupants of a room is contingent upon the temperature of the air, its humidity, and its amount of movement. The effect of these three factors in causing a sensation of cold or warmth is known as the "effective" temperature. When the air movement is from 15 to 25 feet per minute, then a feeling of warmth depends on the interrelation of temperature and relative humidity. A temperature of 75 F. and a relative humidity of 30 per cent usually is preferred. When the relative humidity is increased much above 30 per cent, undesirable condensation often develops. On the other hand, if the air is too dry, the skin may become rough from too great evaporation of moisture from the tissues, and mucous membranes of throat and nose may be irritated.

Weather

Variable outside weather conditions occur in all localities. Minimum temperatures and maximum wind velocities may be disregarded since they are infrequent and of short duration. Fifteen miles per hour is accepted as average wind velocity in most areas, and the lowest temperature is considered as being 15 F. above the previous 10-year average minimum in a given location, taken from reports by the United States Weather Bureau.

Construction of House

The effect of the construction of the house on ease of maintaining rooms at a comfortable temperature depends upon a number of factors—age of the structure, window area, cracks around doors and windows, presence or absence of storm windows and weather stripping, amount of insulation, etc.

Fundamental principles upon which home heating is based are the same as those used in the operation of a refrigerator. Heat always flows from a warmer to a cooler area. Insulation hinders the transmission of heat, and consequently heat loss may be greatly reduced by insulating partitions next to unheated spaces, such as ceilings below a cold attic or roof and floors above crawl spaces; then temperatures throughout the rooms will be more uniform (Figs. 13.1a and b). When side walls of a house are completely insulated a moisture barrier should be placed in the wall on the side next to the room to prevent condensation of moisture that may damage the plaster and wallpaper and lessen the effectiveness of the insulation. Storm windows may reduce as much as 50 per cent the infiltration of cold air caused by a strong, blustery wind, saving at least 20 per cent on fuel consumption. Weather stripping is even more effective than storm sash, but it is expensive to weather strip old windows that do not fit too well.

FIG. 13.1a. Insulation lowers the cost of both heating and cooling the home. Here the Fiberglas is enclosed in an envelope of aluminum foil which forms a moisture barrier. —Owens-Corning Fiberglas.

CENTRAL HEATING SYSTEMS

Warm-Air Furnaces

Gravity Type. The gravity type of warm-air furnace, widely used for many years, has now been largely replaced in new homes by the forced-air system. In the gravity system, air circulating through the casing that surrounds the fuel box is warmed and rises into sheet-metal pipes—leaders by name—opening from the casing, and then in turn into vertical ducts in the walls which end in registers set into floors or walls in the different rooms. For greatest efficiency the furnace should be located in a position as central as possible in the basement so the leaders may all be of approximately equal length. Recirculating ducts return the cooled

FIG. 13.1b. Insulation below the open attic helps to keep rooms cooler in summer and warmer in winter.—Owens-Corning Fiberglas.

air to the furnace. The difference in pressure of the warm and cold air makes the action possible.

Forced-air Furnace. The forced-air furnace is much more effective than the gravity type in heating a room uniformly and, since it at the same time filters and humidifies the air and can be automatically controlled, this type of heating is known as "winter air-conditioning." This system can be combined easily with summer air-conditioning and is so flexible, convenient, and economical that it has largely replaced the hot water and steam systems. The fan should operate at fairly low speed and with a minimum of noise. Since the fan forces the warm air through them, less attention need be given the grade at which the ducts are set and the length of the pipes, but short, straight pipes conduct heat with the least waste. There is a loss in pressure when the direction of air flow changes because of an elbow. A 90-degree elbow offers as much resistance as a 10-foot straight pipe. Ducts running through cold areas should be insulated sufficiently to prevent excessive loss of heat.

For greatest comfort, to avoid what has been called the "cold 70," (those chilly moments just before the thermostat activates the furnace burner) Continuous Air Circulation, called CAC, is recommended. This is made possible by adjusting the thermostat to a small difference between the cut-in and cut-out settings, not more than about 15 F., so the blower will run most of the time in fairly mild weather and almost all the time when the temperature is at freezing or below. This method of regulation prevents long pipes from becoming filled with cold air which is blown into the rooms when the fan starts. The registers, covered with louvered diffuser plates, usually are placed in the floors of the rooms close to the outside walls, frequently below windows, so the heated air will rise and cover the cold walls and glass surfaces with a blanket of warmth. In either type of warm-air system the circulating air passes through filters (Fig. 13.2), usually of spun glass, which must be kept clean if the system is to operate efficiently. Filters prevent dust from settling on furniture, carpets, and draperies and increase the ease of keeping the house in good condition. Dirty filters reduce the circulation of air, and consequently heat output, as much as 25 per cent. Several other types of filters are available (Fig. 13.3). One of these is a plastic filter that sets up an electrostatic charge which catches the dirt. When its meshes become clogged, the filter can be removed and easily washed in cool water to which a detergent has been added.

To increase the humidity, a valve device connected to the water system may allow water to drip onto a porous brick in a trough placed inside the shell of the furnace above the warm air chamber. Moisture is supplied to the circulating air in amounts proportional to the chamber temperature.

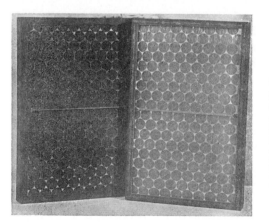

FIG. 13.2. The Fiberglas Dust Stop air filters are treated with a special dust-catching adhesive and protected with thin sheet-metal grills, stapled to fiberboard frame. When dust is removed from the air, the home is a cleaner, healthier place in which to live. —Owens-Corning Fiberglas.

DRY TYPE FILTER

Dust can be trapped in the tiny spaces (smaller than dust particle) between the fibers of a "dry" filter.

ELECTROSTATIC TYPE

An electrostatic precipitator electrically "charges" dust particles which are then pulled from the air by an opposite charge.

IMPINGEMENT TYPE

In this type filter, dust strikes and sticks to adhesive coated fibers as the air flows around and between them.

COLLECTOR-ARRESTOR

The dust collector or arrestor whirls air so that the heavier dust particles are thrown out to settle on a dust collector.

FIG. 13.3. Four types of air filters. Three interrelated factors determine how good a filter is—life, efficiency, and resistance to air flow.—Owens-Corning Fiberglas.

Hot-water and Steam Systems

In steam or hot-water systems a boiler takes the place of the furnace and the heat is passed on to the rooms by radiators or convectors. In the past the chief advantage of hot water and steam has been the evenness of heating; now that forced warm air can be carried to all the corners of a room it has quite largely replaced the boiler in present-day construction, except for panel heating. Boilers should be provided with a safety valve to allow excess steam to escape and prevent the building up of high pressures that could cause an explosion.

Panel Heating

Panel heating has become popular within the last few years, especially for ranch-type houses. Hot air may be used, but pipes through which hot water circulates are more commonly installed. They may be placed in concrete floors, in metal baseboards, or be imbedded in the ceiling. This type of heating produces a uniform temperature similar to that obtained with forced air. Radiant heat from panels may fail to reach the person, however, if chairs, tables or other objects are in the path of the rays. Cold walls, too, may increase the discomfort of people in the room, for the rule holds in this situation also, that heat always flows from a warmer to a cooler area, and heat will flow out of the body toward cooler areas of the room.

OTHER TYPES OF HEATING

Space Heaters

In the southern states space heaters and floor furnaces are widely used. Because of the availability of natural gas, it is usually the fuel. The panels are of glass, ceramic material, or metal and each room has its own thermostat.

Radiant wall or ceiling heaters, electrically operated (Figs. 13.4 and 13.5), are adaptable to many needs, and may be added to small areas where more heat is needed than in the remainder of the home controlled by a thermostat on the central heating system.

Heat Pumps

The heat pump (Fig. 13.6) is an adaptation of the well-known refrigeration cycle (p. 44), in which the heat that is removed from the refrigerant in the condenser is utilized to heat the house. Air, or more commonly water, from a source normally warmer than the existing atmosphere is pumped through a jacket surrounding the evaporator. This heat is absorbed by the refrigerant in changing from a liquid to a vapor. As noted, the heat will be removed in the condenser and it is then distributed through the house heating system. Deep wells or underground streams are the most satisfactory source of heat, but underground air may be used. A constant temperature source is essential.

Solar Heat

In the strictest sense of the word, solar heating is obtained by allowing the sun's rays to fall on a dark surface, preferably black,

FIG. 13.4. The combination light and heater, or the heater alone, may be built into the ceiling. They are especially adapted for bathrooms, eliminating the danger of shocks and burns. A recirculating fan prevents overheating and wasted heat. Notice (bottom right) the central plate is hinged for ease in replacing lamp bulb.
—Nu-Tone, Inc.

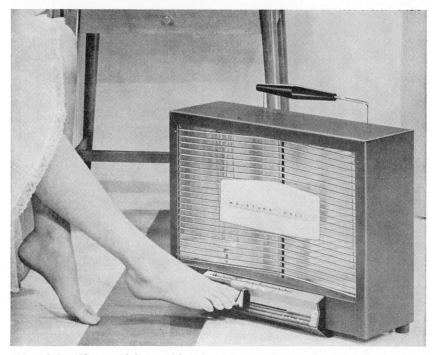

FIG. 13.5. This model portable electric room heater has a tip-toe control and humidifier. Fully automatic, the heater has its own thermostat to keep room temperatures at the selected level. Heat is fan-forced into the room. The humidifier is a moisture cell which keeps the air from becoming parched and dry.—Westinghouse.

beneath which pipes are installed. Water, circulated through the pipes, is warmed by the absorbed heat and is then distributed to the various areas of the house, often through pipes embedded in floors or ceilings.

In the broadest terms solar heating may include heat obtained through a wide expanse of floor-to-ceiling windows on the south exposure of a house. Infrared wave lengths beyond the visible spectrum produce heat and, unlike ultraviolet rays, are transmitted through window glass. The heat is absorbed by rugs and furniture and the people in the room. This method of house heating is most effective in southern states where sunny days are common, but even in northern states such windows may increase the warmth in rooms during winter months.

FUELS

Coal. Central heating systems may be operated by coal, gas, or oil. When coal is used, a stoker makes the equipment auto-

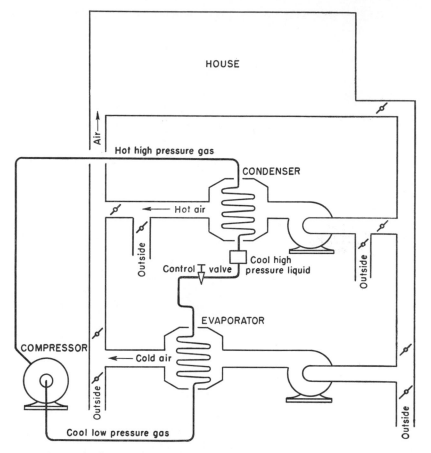

FIG. 13.6. The heat pump is an application of the compression refrigeration system in which heat is absorbed by the evaporator and given off in the condenser. The air heated by the condenser, or cooled by the evaporator, may be obtained through ducts from outside the house or recirculated from inside the house. A system of dampers directs the air in the desired path.

matic, controlled as it is by a thermostat. The underfeed type of stoker is commonly installed in the home, and when it is fed directly from the bin, work and dirt are largely eliminated. It is an advantage to have the ash also removed automatically.

Gas and Oil. Although gas and oil are both used for furnace fuels, the present availability of natural gas in most areas of the United States makes it now the leading fuel in residential heating. The fuel line is opened by thermostat control, and in forced-air furnaces the fan is activated by the degree of heat attained and operates only after the burning fuel has raised the temperature of the circulating air the predetermined amount. These fuels eliminate ash, and gas requires no storage tank unless LP (liquid petroleum) gas is used.

Electricity. Heating the home by means of electricity is still in the early stages of development but is growing, and its increased adoption may be expected in the years ahead. It gives the advantage of individual room temperature control. Several different types of electric heating equipment are available; the most widely used at present being the resistance wall heater, the radiant panel, and the heat pump (Fig. 13.5). Radiant heaters are rated at 3,000 watts on a 240-volt system and 500 watts on 120 volts. Resistance heaters used in the home vary from 1,000 to 4,000 watts capacity.

Fuel Controls

Automatic controls that regulate the dampers in response to the setting of a thermostat help to maintain a uniform heat and consequently aid in the efficient use of any fuel. Safety controls should be installed to prevent excessive feeding of any fuel, for an overheated furnace may result in setting the house on fire. Gas and oil burners must have safety devices that shut off the fuel immediately when the pilot flame is extinguished.

Chimney Vents

All fuel-burning house heaters require a chimney to carry away smoke and the final gaseous products of combustion. Chimneys, with their dampers, are also a part of the fuel control system. Regulations of the National Board of Fire Underwriters require that a chimney have only two openings, one into the furnace or boiler, the other into the outside air. Unless the walls are at least 8 inches thick with inner bricks of refractory clay, chimneys must be lined with a smooth, 3/4-inch-thick layer of fire clay that extends 4 inches below the opening into the furnace and 4 inches above the chimney proper, where it is capped with concrete or a similar material. The regulations further state that chimneys shall extend 2 feet higher than any ridge pole nearer than 30 feet, and 3 feet higher than a flat roof.

The rapid increase in use of gas for home heating has demonstrated the need for improved gas venting codes which will insure safe, trouble-free operation of the furnace, water heater, or other appliance. Only a double-wall gas vent (chimney) meets the safety requirements of the Underwriters Laboratories, Inc. A vertical vent from furnace to outside opening is desirable; if a lateral is necessary, a maximum vertical rise above the appliance should be allowed before the lateral begins. Vents must maintain specified clearance away from combustible materials and have fire stops where they pass through floors and ceilings. The vent extends 18 inches to about 5 feet above the roof, depending on the pitch of the roof and local building regulations; a vent extending more than 5 feet above the roof must be braced. The vent is covered with a cap to prevent clogging. The gas vent installation must provide a positive flow that will exhaust all combustion gases.

CARE OF HEATING SYSTEMS

Coal-fueled furnaces and boilers need a certain amount of care at the end of the heating season, otherwise they tend to deteriorate during the summer months. Excessive ashes are removed daily during the winter to prevent damage to the grate. When ashes are moistened at the time of the night firing they may be removed early the next morning without causing dust. After the fire is out in the spring, the boiler should be drained and the ash pit, grate, and the inside surfaces and flues should be thoroughly cleaned. They may then be sprayed with lubricating oil and the doors oiled or greased.

In the fall the hot-water system is flushed to remove any sediment that may have deposited in the radiators, and then refilled. A definite procedure must be followed. The expansion tank valve is opened to allow the flow of water and then the boiler valve to the water supply line. Now, starting on the first floor, the air vents of all radiators are opened in turn until each one is filled with water. The water is allowed to continue to flow until the gauge on the expansion tank registers about one-third capacity. After the boiler has been operated for several days, the radiator vents should again be opened to expel any air that the water may have contained.

Chimneys will also need to be cleaned occasionally to remove deposits of soot.

Special mention has been made of the need for operating the forced-air system, at a fairly even rate, and this is a recommendation for all types of furnaces. The practice of greatly reducing the heat during the night in a coal-fired furnace or boiler and then forcing the fire in the morning may cause an excessive over-load on the system and shorten its life. This procedure is also a doubtful economy; when such large amounts of fuel are burned rapidly, much heat may be carried up the chimney. Usually it is preferable to open the drafts in the morning and let the fire burn for some time before adding new fuel which tends to cool the hot coals and so slow the heating process. A sudden surge of gas or oil will send heat up the flue in a similarly wasteful manner.

In the gas-fired furnace it is advisable to leave the gas pilot on during the summer months. It consumes a negligible amount of gas and reduces to a minimum the corrosion of furnace parts. Leaving the pilot on also decreases humidity in the basement to some extent, since it produces a slight draft up the chimney which carries away some of the damp air. It makes possible the easy use of the furnace on a sudden cold, rainy day which frequently occurs during an otherwise warm, sunny summer period.

Before the normal heating season begins in the fall the fur-nace and ducts of warm-air systems should be cleaned either with the use of the household vacuum cleaner or by a service man, con-trols should be tested, and the filters cleaned or replaced. If filters are removed for cleaning, care must be taken to replace them with the same side up as before removal. If sides are reversed, any residual dust left in the filter—and it is very difficult to get it all out—will be blown into the rooms during the next operation of the blower. The motor and fan should be oiled.

AIR-CONDITIONING

Air is essential for life. While man averages about three pounds of food and four pounds of water each day, he breathes in during the same time, thirty-four pounds of air. Most people spend the larger percentage of the time within the walls of some building, so indoor air has a greater influence on their health than outdoor air.

In the chapter on saving motion and energy it was noted how essential fresh air is in the prevention of unnecessary fatigue. During the warm summer months fresh air may be obtained by opening doors and windows, but modern air-conditioning units (Fig. 13.7) supply the needed fresh air free from dust, undesirable odors, and excessive heat and moisture.

SELECTING AN AIR CONDITIONER

In selecting a conditioner the daily range of temperatures during at least 5 to 10 per cent of the season should be taken into consideration. Dry areas of the southwestern United States have a fairly large difference between maximum and minimum, the moister coastal areas have a comparatively low range, and in the central plains the change is medium. Humid air always feels warmer than dry air.

Sources of Heat

Heat that must be removed by the air conditioner comes from both the outside and inside the house. Heat from the out-

FIG. 13.7. A remote-control room air conditioner. The push of a button or twist of a knob directs air up, down, right or left, controls temperature, exhausts stale air. Thermostat is located in control panel instead of air conditioner for ease of control, especially useful for invalids.—Whirlpool.

side comes from sun shining on roof, walls, and especially on windows; on the inside, from refrigerator, range, and other cooking appliances, from laundry equipment, and from radiation from the human body. The amount of heat given off by a single person averages about 300 Btu per hour. To prevent or get rid of some of this heat various methods may be used. Heat in the kitchen may be vented to the outside by means of a fan. Heat penetration from outside may be lessened by insulation, by installing a vapor barrier in the walls, by ventilating the attic, by leaving storm windows on the year around, and shading windows and walls by planting of trees or using awnings. When the awning has a side flap, an opening should be left between the top of the awning and the house wall to prevent a pocket of warm air. High windows on south walls receive less direct sunlight than low ones. A light-colored roof and walls will absorb a minimum of heat.

The total heat load can be figured approximately, and from it the size of air conditioner determined. Manufacturers' catalogues frequently contain tables of valuable information which the householder may consult and so not need to be entirely dependent on the dealer's opinions.

OPERATING THE AIR CONDITIONER

The air conditioner, both the central system and the single-room type, is similar in construction to the refrigerator unit. It uses a refrigerant, usually Freon-12, which changes from a gas to a liquid in the condenser and from a liquid to a gas in the evaporator, the part that absorbs the heat. The condenser may be cooled by air or water. When water is used, the amount for a central air-conditioning system may be as great as 1200 gallons a day, even more in extremely hot weather. Before installation the prospective buyer should check city ordinances that may restrict such large water consumption, for the city water system may be unable to furnish this much water and the sewage system unable to carry it away. At present many manufacturers have designed their conditioners to be cooled by air, and this method has proved to be entirely satisfactory in most climates.

It is customary to maintain an inside temperature of approximately 80 F., which may be as much as 10 to 25 degrees cooler than out-of-doors. It is well, however, to avoid too great a difference between inside and outside temperatures and not expect to install equipment to take care of the highest temperatures of the season, since extreme heat is usually of short duration. Such equipment is generally oversized and will tend to cycle (turn off and on) frequently; most satisfactory results are obtained if the conditioner operates continuously. Equipment slightly undersized rather than oversized maintains more desirable conditions of comfort and has lower initial and operating cost.

Central System

When a central system is used, the registers through which the cold air enters the room should be baffled in such a way that they can be adjusted to diffuse the cooled air upward at an angle of at least 60 degrees, so that the air will not strike against the furniture or occupants of the room, but will blanket the walls, from which it will be evenly distributed throughout the room. If the ducts pass through warm areas, they should be insulated.

Room Conditioners

Single-room air conditioners are commonly installed in windows (Fig. 13.7). They are rated from 800 to 1400 watts for use on a 120-volt circuit and from 1600 to 4800 watts on the 240-volt circuit. Most conditioners now carry the NEMA seal, indicating that the Btu per hour cooling capacity, watts, and ampere ratings given on the nameplate are certified accurate by the National Electric Manufacturers Association.

Before installing a conditioner, wiring should be checked to ascertain its ability to carry the load. Homes older than ten years frequently do not have adequate wiring, and the air conditioner may easily cause an overload and become a fire hazard.

Noise has been greatly reduced in the newer model air conditioners. The discharge and blower fans move more air at a slower fan speed, reducing fan and motor noises and vibration. Large grill openings let the air flow freely, diminishing the sound of rushing air. When the motor, compressor, and fan are mounted on rubber, vibration noises are less noticeable.

Special Features

New features that may be added to older air-conditioning systems appear frequently on the markets. Among the more desirable ones are filters. Many models are supplied with a washable filter with a permanent germicide, or one which may be treated against germ build-up. Others discharge the moisture to the outside without dripping.

Other Methods of Increasing Home Comfort

In the portable *air cooler* an electrically operated blower draws air through a fiber filter which is kept moist from water in an enclosed reservoir. This process cools the air, just as most summer showers do. In muggy weather the circulation of the water may be cut off, but the moving air helps to evaporate perspiration and makes a person feel more comfortable (Fig. 13.8).

The *air purifier* removes 90 per cent or more of common airborne particles—dust, smoke, smog—and also odors. Forty-four cubic feet are drawn every minute through the unit which is made up of several layers: a washable foam filter, a glass fiber filter, and a bed of activated charcoal. Finally the air is exposed to the rays of an 18-inch ultraviolet lamp (Fig. 13.8).

In areas of high humidity a *dehumidifier* may aid greatly in increasing comfortable conditions within the home. In construction it resembles the room air conditioner. A fan draws the moist air over cool evaporator coils, on which any excess moisture condenses. It then drains into a pan below the coils. If the dehumidifier is placed in the basement, it may be connected to the drain. The motor is usually $\frac{1}{5}$ horsepower.

In using the dehumidifier, doors and windows are kept closed. The filter must be cleaned to allow the air to circulate freely, the water must be emptied regularly, and the motor oiled according to directions (Fig. 13.8).

EXPERIMENTS AND PROJECTS

1. Visit a furnace factory. If not available, visit local furnace dealer for discussion and demonstration.
2. Students inspect home heating system and report. Note any care needed.
3. Obtain samples of new and used furnace filters from forced-air furnace. Note value of filters.
4. Arrange for demonstration and inspection of air conditioners.
5. Students report measures taken in their homes to reduce summer heat when air conditioning is not used.
6. Obtain from local or state weather bureau a report of maximum and minimum temperatures, for at least the last three years. Apply information to show need for using means to combat summer heat and to increase ease of heating home in winter by use of insulation, etc.

FIG. 13.8. Three appliances that help supply comfortable living conditions: Portable air cooler (top); Air purifier (above); Dehumidifier (left).—General Electric.

QUESTIONS

1. Which system of house heating is now most frequently used? Why has it been adopted? Do you have this or some other type? Is it easy to heat your home?
2. What determines the size of heating plant that must be installed?
3. How does the construction of the house affect the ease of maintaining the desired temperature? Is there anything that you can do to improve the ease of heating your home?
4. What fuels may be used? Discuss their relative desirability.
5. Interest is increasing in the use of heat pumps. Do they have limitations or are they practical? Do you know of any home that is so heated?
6. What care do heating systems require? Can you help give your system this attention?
7. To what other system may the air conditioner be compared? Explain the similarity.
8. What factors determine the satisfactory operation of an air conditioner?
9. How may you help the air conditioner to function without unnecessary demand upon it.
10. The air conditioner frequently becomes a noise nuisance. How may this difficulty be minimized?

Chapter Fourteen

ESSENTIAL FACTS ABOUT

ELECTRICITY, GAS, AND THERMOSTATS

M ANY PRESENT-DAY household appliances are operated by electricity or by gas, and frequently they are automatic, controlled by thermostats. It has seemed desirable, therefore, to summarize some basic facts on electricity, gas, and thermostats for ready reference in case of need.

ELECTRICITY

Have you ever stopped to think how many tasks in the home electricity can perform for you? It toasts your bread and perks your coffee for breakfast, and may cook your bacon and eggs in the electric frypan and your pancakes on an electric griddle. It will grind your garbage and wash your dishes; refrigerate and freeze your food; mix and bake a cake; roast your meat; wash, dry, and iron your linens and clothes; vacuum your floor coverings, furniture, and draperies; wash, wax, and polish your floors; sew for you; keep your house warm in winter and cool in summer. Electricity is indeed an indispensable servant and friendly helper.

ELECTRIC CURRENT

Electricity is a fundamental part of all materials. Materials are made up of atoms and these atoms, in turn, consist of a nucleus of positive electric charges, surrounded by negatively charged electrons. Under certain conditions the electrons can be made to move along from atom to atom. When this occurs and the electrons are in motion, an electric current is said to flow. Man has succeeded in capturing that force, sending it along wires for hundreds of miles from its source, into communities, factories, and homes, where it performs an inestimable number of tasks for him. The unit of electric current is the ampere.

Voltage

To set electrons in motion, an electric pressure or force must be applied. This is obtained from a generator and the force is known as *voltage*. The generator consists of field magnets and an armature. The armature rotates, cutting the lines of force that pass from the north pole of one magnet to the south pole of the other. The rotating part is turned by a turbine which is operated by steam—or by water if a stream is available in which a large volume of water flows from a higher to a lower level as it does in a waterfall or dam. In other words, *a generator is a device for transforming mechanical energy into electrical energy.*

Conductors and Insulators

Although materials vary greatly in their ability to conduct or oppose an electric current, for practical purposes they may be placed in one of two groups: *conductors* that offer slight resistance to the passage of an electric current, enough to control the amount going through, and *insulators* that present high resistance to current flow, enough to prohibit its passage. Most metals, especially copper and aluminum and their alloys, are good conductors. The family water supply, which contains dissolved minerals, is also a good conductor. Glass, ceramic materials, rubber, cotton, and silk are insulators. In a conductor the electrons surrounding the nucleus are loosely bound in the atom and pass easily from one atom to another; in insulators the electrons are tightly bound and resist displacement. Insulators help to keep the electric current in its proper path.

Types of Electric Current

There are two types of current, *alternating* and *direct*, designated a.c. and d.c.

The rotating part (the armature) of the generator cuts a varying number of the lines of force between the magnets, depending upon its position at any one instant; the number cut increases from zero to a maximum, then decreases back to zero, after which the direction reverses and the number cut again increases to a maximum and again drops back to zero. The result is alternating current, a.c. In Figure 14.1, the distance from A to B is

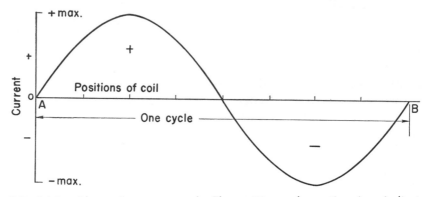

FIG. 14.1. Alternating current cycle. The positive and negative signs indicate that the direction of current flow changes every half-cycle.

known as a cycle, and the number of cycles per second is the frequency of the current. The common current frequency in the United States is 60 cycles per second.

For certain operations, e.g., plating of metals and charging of batteries, it is obvious that alternating current would not be satisfactory, since what is done in one half-cycle is undone in the next half-cycle. In this case the solid contact rings used in the a.c. generator are replaced with split rings known as a *commutator*. When the direction of the rotation of the armature changes, the contacts with the ring halves also change so that the current always flows in the same direction. This is known as direct current, d.c.

Transformers

Alternating current is widely used because it can be transmitted over much greater distances than can direct current. For such transmission, a step-up *transformer* is used. This step-up greatly increases the amount of original voltage, ten, one hundred, perhaps even one thousand times and for any given power the amount of current is correspondingly reduced so that it may be carried on comparatively small wires.

The current flows across country over a high-voltage line (commonly called "hi-line") to the edge of a town or a city or, in rural areas, to the driveway into a farm where in a step-down transformer, the process is reversed, the voltage is reduced and the current increased to normal rating (Fig. 14.2). From a pole near your home, wires are run to the side of the house, or are

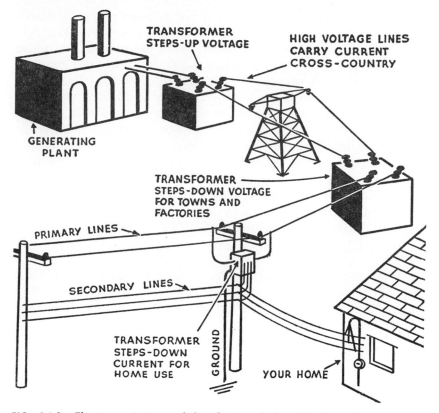

FIG. 14.2. The transmission and distribution of electricity from the generating plant to the home.—Westinghouse.

brought there underground in a cable. They then are brought through the wall, and inside the house through the main switch, the main fuse, the meter (if it is not on the outside of the house) to the fuse panel, and out on circuits to wall outlets in each room. A toaster can be plugged into the outlet near your breakfast table, and the electricity is ready to go to work for you.

Rules for Wiring Inside the House

The *National Electric Code* now comes into the picture. It is a set of minimum regulations drawn up by the Electrical Committee of the National Fire Protection Association and adopted by fire insurance companies. Its rules for home wiring must be followed to reduce possibility of fire from faulty installations, and to prevent any question of collecting insurance, should a fire be caused by a short circuit or other electrical defect.

A 3-wire, 220–240-volt system is now commonly installed in the home. The three insulated wires from the pole to the house, known as the service drop, should have a minimum capacity of 100 amperes. A capacity of 150 or even 200 amperes is often recommended to take care of the increasing number of appliances used today. These three wires, to conform to the Code, must be at least 18 feet above driveways and 10 feet above sidewalks. The wires are fastened to the house by insulating knobs and brought down the side of the house, usually in a conduit pipe—a pipe very similar to a water pipe in appearance, but with a smooth inside finish to prevent damage to the wires. The meter is frequently installed on the outside of the house to be readily accessible for the meterman to read (Fig. 14.3).

Meters

The meter usually has a series of dials, three or four in number, that record the *kilowatt-hours* (kw-hr) of electricity used in a given period of time. The kilowatt-hour is a unit of energy,

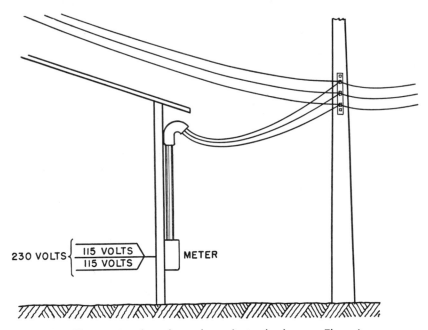

FIG. 14.3. The service drop from the pole to the house. The wires are enclosed in a conduit pipe for safety where they follow down the side of the house.—Westinghouse (modified).

determined by multiplying the power of an appliance in kilowatts by the length of time it is operated in hours. The meter dials are interconnectd by a system of cogwheels and consequently each dial is numbered in the opposite direction from the dial preceding or following it (Fig. 14.4). To understand the position of the meter hands, it may be well to start with the dial at the right. The hand must rotate all around dial 4 (which reads in tens) while the hand of dial 3 (which reads in hundreds) rotates from zero to one; similarly the hand on 3 rotates around dial 3 while the hand of dial 2 rotates from zero to one. Dials 2 and 1 follow the same pattern. The number that the hand has just passed is read. The dials are read from left to right and the numbers recorded in that order. For example the reading indicated on the dials of this meter is 1593 kilowatt-hours. The hand of dial 4 has rotated a little more than 3/10 of the complete dial. On dial 3 the hand has gone 3/10 of the distance between 9 and 0; on dial 2, 9/10 of the distance between 5 and 6, and on dial 1 almost 6/10 of the distance between 1 and 2.

The hands on the dials are not turned back to zero each month, but the reading of the previous month is subtracted from the current monthly reading. This method tends to eliminate any error in readings.

In rural areas kilowatt-hour meters with a cyclometer dial, similar to the automobile odometer, are often used. This type may be easily read by the customer and mailed to the utility company, eliminating trips by the meterman.

Main Switch to Fuse Panel

The wires are brought from the meter through the walls in an insulating pipe to a main switch that controls all the wiring in the house and may be pulled when any repairs need to be made. The main fuse is next. This protects interior wiring from excess

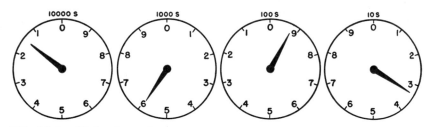

FIG. 14.4. Dials of an electric meter, to be read from left to right, and numerals recorded in that order. This meter reading is 1593 kilowatt-hours.

current entering the house from outside, such as might occur should lighting strike the service wires. If the meter is not on the outside, it is installed next to the main fuse. The final member of this part of the system is the fuse panel with one fuse for each separate 120-volt circuit with which the house is wired and two fuses for each 240-volt circuit.

Fuses

As has been mentioned, fuses (Fig. 14.5) are protective devices. The common type used in the home is the plug fuse that screws into a socket. It contains a strip of low-melting alloy with a narrow link that melts when excess current passes through it, causing too much heat. A glass or mica window over the strip shows when the fuse has "blown."

Motor-driven appliances use high current momentarily when they start, and may cause the standard plug fuse to blow. To obviate this difficulty a fuse known as a Fusetron has been developed which allows this brief overflow of current without the ribbon melting. If the overflow continues, the Fusetron goes out as any ordinary fuse would. Sometimes landlords, especially apartment-house owners, have had difficulty with tenants replacing a fuse with one of a larger size. Such a practice causes a fire hazard. To prevent this practice there is available a special type of fuse, a Fustat, which is used with an adapter of the correct size. The adapter is screwed into the fuse socket first and locks in place, so that it cannot be removed. A fuse-type circuit breaker is also on the market. Known as a Mini-Breaker, it has the desirable characteristics of the standard circuit breaker and needs only to be reset when it interrupts the flow of current. All fuses should carry the inspection label of the Underwriters' Laboratories.

Recent installations may use circuit breakers in place of fuses. A circuit breaker (Fig. 14.6) usually is constructed of two metal strips that expand at different rates when overheated and auto-

FIG. 14.5.   Various types of household fuses.

FIG. 14.6. Circuit breakers such as shown in this cutaway may be used in place of a fuse. The bimetallic strip A makes contact at B to allow the current to flow. Excessive heat from too great a current causes one of the elements of the bimetallic strip to expand more than the other element, and so breaks the contact.

matically open the circuit. The only visible part is a toggle switch that is reset manually, once the cause of the tripping is known and corrected. Because of the ease of manipulation, circuit breakers are recommended for installation when new homes are planned or old homes are remodeled (Fig. 14.7).

Necessary Precautions To Prevent Accidents

Because fuses are safety devices they should be used with the circuits for which they are designed. Using too large a fuse in a circuit or replacing a fuse with a piece of metal such as a penny may easily lead to a disastrous fire. Adding pennies is even more dangerous than using too large a fuse, but both will have the same effect on the wires. Wires expand when carrying an overload of

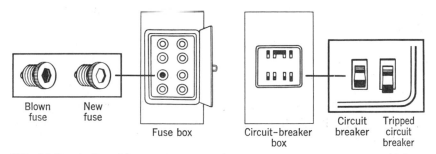

FIG. 14.7. A fuse blows or a circuit breaker trips to protect against over-heated wires.—National Adequate Wiring Bureau.

current because of the excess heat generated. This excess heat may cause the insulation gradually to deteriorate so that it cracks or the expanding wires may rub against rough places in the studding and wear off the insulation. In either case, live wires become exposed and may set fire to nearby flammable material. Such a tragedy occurred in Des Moines when a night fire took the lives of four people in an apartment above a restaurant. Later inspection disclosed pennies that had been placed under three blown fuses in the restaurant fuse-box.

Periodic checking of house wiring is recommended to assure no damage to insulation from rodents or from surface friction caused by uneven "settling" of a house.

Other electrical accidents may be fatal. One of the most common occurs when too great a charge of electricity passes through the body.

One side of the residential distribution system is grounded at the power plant. If a person then comes in contact with a defective electric appliance when he is in contact with the ground, a parallel circuit will pass through his body, with perhaps fatal results. Since water pipes are connected to the ground, it is safer not to use electric appliances near the sink or in the bathroom. To quote a few examples, reported in the newspapers:

1. A teenage girl took her radio to the bathroom that she might listen to a program while she had a bath. When she was in the tub, she evidently decided to rotate the knob to obtain a different station. She was electrocuted.

2. During rainy weather a man crawled under his front porch with a light on an extension cord. He was killed by current leaking from the cord or the socket.

3. A small child climbed up beside the sink near which his mother was operating an electric mixer. While leaning against the sink he touched the shiny metal on the mixer, and death resulted.

4. In a similar accident, another child was killed while leaning against the metal band along the front edge of the work counter when he contacted an electric mixer. This metal strip usually touches the framework of the sink where it joins the counter. In this case an older person might have received only a shock, but children's hands are more moist than an adult's and their bodies are lower in resistance. This accident would not have happened had the band along the front edge of the table been of a nonconducting plastic matrial.

Of course accidents would not occur if there were no defective part that allowed current leakage to the frame of the appliance, but it is too late once the accident happens.

Since no one can tell when defects will occur, each person should train himself to practice three major precautions:

When using laundry equipment in the basement, wear rubbers or stand on a wooden platform.

Disconnect the motor head of the mixer before washing off the rotating beaters under the faucet.

Never turn lights on or off or touch electric equipment when in a bathtub or when hands are wet.

HOUSE CIRCUITS

The different circuits that make up the home wiring system start at the fuse box. The minimum size of wire allowed for a given circuit and the size of fuse that must be used with that wire are specified in the Code. Fuses are rated in amperes.

Three types of circuits are found in most homes: general purpose, appliance, and individual circuits.

General Purpose Circuit

The general purpose circuit uses No. 14 wire, which is fused with a 15-ampere fuse. This type of circuit is in the living room, dining room, halls, and bedrooms. It supplies electric current to ceiling and wall fixtures and to the convenience outlets to which floor and table lamps and small electric appliances are attached. A general purpose circuit also is used for ceiling fixtures in kitchen and utility rooms.

Power plants seek to supply 120 volts to the customer. Any general purpose circuit would, therefore, allow the connection of lights and appliances of a total wattage of not more than 1800 watts (120 volts $\times$ 15 amperes, the rating of the fuse). The Code, however, recommends that not more than about 80 per cent of the full load be used at any one time, or about 1500 watts. This number of watts was adequate in the days when nonautomatic toasters, coffee makers, and irons, rated at 350 to 660 watts, were our only appliances. But with automatic appliances of 1000, 1150, 1200, even up to 1650 watts available in ever increasing numbers, such a small general purpose circuit is totally inadequate, and a No. 12 wire circuit, fused with a 20-ampere fuse, supplying 2400 watts, is recommended.

Appliance Circuit

The appliance circuit uses No. 12 wire, a 20-ampere fuse, and supplies 2400 watts (120 × 20). As the name implies, this circuit is used only for supplying current to convenience outlets. But again a No. 10 wire with a 25-ampere fuse, supplying 3000 watts (120 × 25) is preferable. There should be at least two appliance circuits in the home, one in the kitchen and one in the laundry area. It is suggested that a No. 12, 3-wire, split circuit be installed in the kitchen, then some of the outlets can be on one side of the circuit and some on the other. The two sides together would supply 4800 watts. This method of wiring is called polarization or perimeter wiring and some authorities recommend it for the wall outlets in all the rooms.

Outlets on circuits, both those for fixtures and the convenience outlets for portable lamps and small electric appliances, are wired in parallel.

Individual Circuit

The individual circuit uses No. 6 or 8 wire with a 60- or 50-ampere fuse. The range, electric water heater, and usually the electric clothes dryer are used on 240-volt circuits, and each must have its own individually fused circuit.

It is recommended, and some municipalities require, that the automatic electric washer, the dishwasher, and the freezer also have their own individual circuits, although these appliances are used on the 120-volt circuit. They are all, it is noted, motor-driven appliances and a motor-driven appliance requires several times as much current for the start as is needed for continued operation. If a number of motor-driven appliances should start to operate at the same time, a fuse may be blown; hence the desirability of individual circuits for these appliances.

COST OF OPERATING APPLIANCES

As has been noted, the amount of electricity used is paid for in kilowatt-hours. The meter records only the total amount; it is possible, however, to approximate the cost of using any appliance.

Nameplate

Information with regard to an appliance is given on the nameplate. It records the name and address of the manufacturer (in case repair parts are needed and a service man is not readily available); the range of voltage on which the appliance will operate satisfactorily; type of current, a.c. or d.c.; frequency of current; and usually the power rating in watts. This rating is essential in figuring the cost of an appliance. Occasionally amperes are given instead of watts, but watts may then be obtained by multiplying the amperes by the volts. The nameplate may also give special information such as, "Always connect to a wall outlet," or "Do not immerse unit in water."

Watts and Horsepower

Most appliances are rated in *watts,* although occasionally motor-driven appliances are rated in *horsepower* (hp). One hp is equivalent to 746 watts. The small, fractional-horsepower motors used in the home are not very efficient and often require 50 per cent more watts than the rating would indicate. Consequently it is considered fairly accurate in this case to assume that one hp equals 1000 watts.

The watt (symbol W) is the unit of power. It may be obtained by multiplying the *amperes* (symbol I) by the *voltage* (symbol E).

Figuring Cost of Operating an Appliance

Any homemaker may, if she so wishes, determine quite easily the cost of using any appliance for a certain length of time. The wattage of the appliance must be changed to kilowatts and the time must be expressed in hours. Following is the method for figuring these costs:

The nameplate of the toaster indicates a power rating of 1100 watts, and the toaster is estimated to be used an average of 20 minutes a day during April. What will be the cost of operation at 5 cents per kw-hr?

          1100 watts = 1.1 kilowatts
          20 min. per day for 30 days = 600 min. = 10 hours
          1.1 kw × 10 hr. = 11 kw-hr
          11 × $.05 = $.55, cost of operation.

A ¼-hp washer is used for 2 hours a week. What will be the cost per month at $.04 per kilowatt-hour?

          ¼-hp (assuming 1 hp = 1000 w) = 250 w = .25 kw

2 hr. per week for 4 weeks = 8 hr
.25 kw × 8 hr. = 2 kw-hr
2 × $.04 = $.08, cost of operation.

A roaster oven rated at 120 volts and 11 amperes is used on Monday for 1 hour and 20 minutes, on Tuesday for 2 hours, on Thursday for 1 hour and 40 minutes, and on Saturday for 30 minutes. What is the cost for the week at $3\frac{1}{2}$ cents per kilowatt-hour?

W = EI = 120 volts × 11 amperes = 1320 watts
1320 w = 1.32 kw
1 hr., 20 min. + 2 hr. + 1 hr., 40 min. + 30 min. = 5.5 hr[1]
1.32 kw × 5.5 hr. = 7.26 kw-hr
7.26 × $.035 = $.2541 or $.25, cost of operation.

It will be observed that motor-driven appliances are much less expensive to operate than are heat appliances.

Resistance

In accordance with the rule for resistance, the resistance of the wire or metal ribbon used in electric household appliances varies directly with the length, and inversely with the cross-sectional area of the ribbon or wire.

Resistance also varies with kind of material, but since nickel-chromium ribbon and wire are almost universally used in household appliances, this factor may be disregarded.

Volts, amperes, and resistance have a relationship to each other shown in the equation, $R = \dfrac{E}{I}$. Resistance is measured in *ohms*.

When a manufacturer designs an appliance, he builds into it a length of wire of a given cross area to give a definite resistance so that at the recommended voltage, a certain current will flow and a certain power be obtained. The resistance is a part of the construction of the appliance and does not change appreciably during the life of the equipment.

Example:

What is the resistance of an 1100-watt toaster?

Assume that the toaster was constructed to be used on a 120-volt circuit.

---

[1] It is always easier to solve problems if all common fractions are changed to decimal fractions.

$$W = EI$$

$$1100 = 120 \times I; \text{ then } I = \frac{1100}{120} = 9.2 \text{ amps}$$

$$R = \frac{E}{I} = \frac{120}{9.2} = 13 \text{ ohms}$$

Drop in Voltage

Cords used to connect appliances to outlets also offer resistance to the flow of the current and if the cord is long, the resistance may be sufficient to cause a drop in voltage, resulting in slow heating. It is good practice to connect equipment as near to the place of use as possible. Customers living near the end of a city distribution system or of a rural line frequently have trouble with appliances heating slowly at times of the day when the majority of customers on the line also are using the current. This is a good example of drop in voltage.

Circuits Within the Appliance

The path which electric current follows through the appliance is also a circuit. In a *closed circuit* the path will be complete and the electric current will flow. On the other hand the path may be broken by the throwing of a switch and no current will flow. It is then an *open circuit*. When the metal frame of an electric appliance is connected to the earth, frequently by attaching a wire from the appliance to a sewer pipe — NEVER to a pipe through which water flows to a faucet — the circuit is a *grounded circuit*. It is a safety precaution to ground laundry equipment, especially when used in a basement, as well as the electric range and dishwasher. An *overloaded circuit*, if sufficiently overloaded, may cause a fuse to blow; otherwise it results in an undesirable drop in voltage because of the increase in resistance.

A *short circuit* usually causes a blown fuse. As has been indicated, a definite resistance is built into each appliance. If the insulation on the two wires of the cord attached to the appliance becomes worn so that the bare wires come into contact with each other, the current will not flow through the resistance of the appliance, but will quite literally take the short path through the "cut-off." Then R in the equation, $E = RI$, becomes negligible, I increases tremendously, and the excessive heat melts the link in the fuse. Sparks frequently occur where the wires touch and if the fuse does not blow, a fire may result. Too great a flow of current always results in an increased amount of heat.

Motor

Motors are of two types — *universal,* used on a.c. or d.c., and *induction,* used only on a.c. In each type there is a stationary and rotating part in which magnetic fields are set up. Interaction between these two fields causes motion of the rotor. Washers, dryers, refrigerators, freezers, dishwashers, and air conditioners are operated by induction motors; the electric blender, mixer, and some vacuum cleaners use a universal motor. The motion of the shaft of the rotor may be transmitted to gears that change the direction of the motion and conduct it to where it is to be used. *A motor is a device for changing electrical energy to mechanical energy — just the opposite of the generator.*

GAS

TYPES OF GAS

In America three kinds of gas are available for use in the home: manufactured, natural, and liquid petroleum — the latter commonly called LP gas and known also as tank, cylinder, and bottled gas. Manufactured gas, made by passing steam over heated carbon (coal, coke, or charcoal) was once widely used. It now has been replaced in many areas by natural gas, which is piped long distances from the fields where it is found. LP gas is used where the other two gases are not locally available, especially in rural homes. It is obtained from certain natural sources or from oil refineries, is liquefied and distributed in tank cars and then to individual homes in cylinders.

BTU CONTENT

Gas is used for cooking, for the operation of the gas refrigerator, dryer, and water heater, and for house heating. Its heating value is expressed in Btu (British thermal units) per cubic foot. A Btu is the amount of heat necessary to raise one pound of water one degree Fahrenheit. The Btu content of manufactured gas is commonly 500 to 550, of natural gas 1000 to 1100, and of LP gas 2500 to 3000. The meter, of cast iron or cast aluminum, measures the gas consumption in cubic feet. It is located close to the place where the gas pipe from the street main enters the house. The dials are similar in appearance to those of the kilowatt-hour meter.

Gas flows from a place of higher pressure to one of lower pressure; when, therefore, a valve handle on an appliance is turned to open the valve, pressure is reduced and the greater pressure in the gas main outside the house causes the gas to flow into the house, through the meter, and through the connecting pipes to the appliance. Because of the difference in heating value of the three gases, the orifice in the valve varies in size, being largest for manufactured gas and smallest for LP gas. If a family move from one community to another involves a change in type of gas, an adjustment in the size of orifice must be made to correspond to the new type.

Natural and manufactured gases are lighter than air and tend to diffuse upward; should a leak occur, the gas rises and will be dissipated if it can reach open air. LP gas, on the other hand, is heavier than air and settles to the ground, increasing danger of a fire or an explosion.

PRODUCTS OF COMBUSTION

When a gas flame is correctly adjusted, the products of combustion are water vapor and carbon dioxide, two constituents always found in the atmosphere. The deposits frequently found on a kitchen wall behind a range are not from the combustion of the gas but from the condensation of volatile substances, especially fats, given off in the cooking process. The oven vent was once on the back of the range and these deposits tended to be most noticeable on the wall above the vent. Now that the vent is so placed as to direct the volatile matter away from the wall, it is deposited in a thinner layer over all the kitchen surfaces and attracts less attention — but it is still there unless a fan is installed to remove it.

SAFETY FEATURES

Modern gas appliances are safe. In the refrigerator, water heater, dryer, and furnace, the pilot flame is positioned beside a sensitive metal finger called a *thermopile*. If for any reason the pilot is extinguished, the thermopile cools below its operating temperature, causing the pilot valve to close and shut off the flow of gas to the burner. This occurs within one minute after the flame goes out. The thermopile must be warmed, usually with a match flame, before it will operate to open the pilot valve again. Surface burners on ranges have constantly burning pilots to ignite them instantly, and all gas ranges carrying the Blue Star seal have similar pilots in oven and broiler. Moreover, the valve handles controlling the flow of gas to all range ovens are the lock type, so that gas cannot be turned on accidentally.

THERMOSTATS

Most modern household equipment is thermostatically controlled. A *thermostat* is a device used to maintain a fairly constant temperature and eliminate fire hazard.

TYPES OF THERMOSTATS

Two thermostats commonly used are the hydraulic type and the bimetallic strip; a third type, less commonly used, is the probe tube.

Hydraulic

The temperature of range ovens, refrigerators, and freezers is regulated by the hydraulic thermostat. It has a small tube filled with a liquid that expands as the temperature rises, causing the electric switch to open or close the circuit at a predetermined point, and contracts as the temperature drops, allowing the circuit to close or open again. In at least one case the gas thermostat uses mercury for the regulating material. When the temperature rises in gas appliances, the valve is partially closed to restrict the flow of gas, although a few ranges feature an on-off cycle. The temperature is regulated by the setting of an indicator on a dial.

Bimetallic Strip

The bimetallic-strip thermostat is found in many of the small electric appliances. Similar in action to the circuit breaker (Fig. 14.6), it is made of two metal ribbons, each a different metal, fastened together at either end. As the temperature increases beyond that indicated on the thermostat dial, one of the metal strips expands more than the other, causing a tension that breaks the circuit connection. As the appliance cools, the ribbons assume their original position, the circuit is closed, and current flows through it once more.

Probe Tube

The probe tube is a newer thermostatic control completely removable so small electric appliances are immersable for washing — the frypan, griddle, percolator, etc. A probe tube is filled with silicone fluid, and as the fluid expands during the heating process, it activates a piston that pushes against and opens the electric contacts, allowing them to close again with contraction of the liquid. This type of control is said to provide closer accuracy.

EXPERIMENTS AND PROJECTS

1. Take class to visit local generating plant if arrangements can be made.
2. Trace electricity from the generating plant to its use in operating an electric cleaner on the living room rug. Define terms used.
3. To compare costs of using various electric appliances:
   a. Determine cost of using the following appliances for the month of November at 5 cents per kilowatt-hour:
      Washer, ⅕ hp, 2½ hours a week
      Electric iron, 1100 w, 1¾ hours a week
      Refrigerator, ⅛ hp, operates ¼ of the 24 hours
      Toaster, 1000 w, 15 minutes a day
      Percolator, 800 w, 10 minutes a day
   b. Which appliance is most costly to operate?
4. Determine resistance of percolator in problem 3a.
5. To figure a monthly bill for electricity from meter readings:
   The dials in Figure 14.8 indicate meter readings in May and June.

May

June

FIG. 14.8.   Electric meter readings for May and June.

What would be the June bill, if the rate per kilowatt-hour is 4 cents?
6. For lessons on nameplate and rewiring of plugs and sockets see *Choosing and Using Home Equipment* by Elizabeth Beveridge, 4th ed., pp. 41–49 (Iowa State University Press, 1963).
7. Take class to visit local gas plant if arrangements can be made.
8. Report on natural gas: source of local supply, how stored, cost per cubic foot, variation in Btu content per cubic foot from day to day.
9. To compare various types of thermostats:
   a. Examine thermostat bulbs in ovens and refrigerators in the laboratory, noting location of each, and bimetallic strips in any small appliances that can be taken apart.
   b. Students report on location of thermostat bulbs in home ovens and refrigerators.
   c. Students suggest improvements for type or location of thermostat.

QUESTIONS

Electricity

1. The generator brings about what change in energy?
2. To transmit electricity 20 miles, what must happen to the voltage?
3. What is the purpose of the fuse? What types of fuses are available? What is the advantage of each kind?
4. In what unit are most appliances rated? In what unit do you pay for electricity? What is the difference between them?
5. What three types of circuits are found in most homes? What are the National Electric Code requirements for each? Why is overfusing a circuit dangerous?
6. What causes a short circuit? What usually happens when you have a short circuit?
7. In the cottage in which Nancy and Bob live there is only one electric outlet in their kitchen. To use their toaster on their breakfast table they must attach it to the outlet by a 15-foot extension cord. What is the result? Why?
8. Do household appliances used for heating purposes require more or less power than motor-driven appliances? Can you think of a reason for your answer?
9. A thermostatically controlled electric iron rated at 120 volts and 10 amperes was in operation 50 per cent of the time. How many kilowatt-hours of electricity would it use in two hours?
10. Give the equations that show the relations between amperes, volts, watts, and ohms.

Gas

1. What is the term used to express the heat value of gas?
2. How do the heat values of manufactured, natural, and LP gases differ?
3. At what rate do you pay for gas?

4. If the rate for all three gases is $\frac{1}{4}$ cent per cubic foot, which kind would be most efficient to use? Reason for answer.
5. In buying gas equipment what seal of approval would you look for? What does the seal stand for?
6. A gas refrigerator is rated at 2625 Btu per hour. In one hour it burns 2.5 cubic feet of gas. What kind of gas is used?
7. Mrs. Perry has moved to town from a farm where she used LP gas. In the town she will use natural gas. What adjustments will the service man make in the orifices of the burners on her range?
8. What are the products of combustion of gas?
9. Do they usually cause dirt in the kitchen? If not, what does?
10. What precautions are taken to make the use of gas safe? Is any one gas more dangerous than the others? If so, why?

Thermostats

1. On what principle does any thermostat operate?
2. What two types of thermostats are available? Where is each used?
3. What is the probe tube? How does it compare with the bimetallic strip?
4. What does the use of a thermostat eliminate?
5. Would you consider that a thermostat is a necessary accessory to an appliance, or not? List points to prove your belief.

Chapter Fifteen

MATERIALS USED

IN HOME EQUIPMENT

S ELECTION OF CORRECT COOKING UTENSILS will improve the quality of the food prepared and aid in the economical operation of your range. In the case of surface units some important things to keep in mind are: (a) a pan of good heat conductivity, obtained most easily with aluminum utensils of medium to heavy gauge, (b) straight sides to conserve heat, (c) a flat bottom to "hug" the surface unit for good contact, (d) a tight-fitting lid to hold steam within the pan and so reduce cooking time, and (e) a handle of proper length that does not overbalance the utensil (Fig. 15.1). The utensil should be of the correct size to fit the unit and also the amount of food being prepared. When controlled heat is available, a double broiler will not be necessary for cooking such delicate foods as sauces, custards, puddings, icings, and most cereals. When using "Teflon"-coated utensils, manufacturers' directions should be followed carefully. Overheating the pan by leaving it on a hot unit while empty or allowing it to burn dry can damage not only the utensil, but also may injure the cooktop of the range. Oven utensils should usually be of a material that is a good absorber, since oven heat is transmitted largely by radiation.

Household utensils and appliances are made of a variety of materials, the choice in any given case depending upon the properties of the materials that are best suited for the intended use. Three general classifications of materials are metals, glass, and plastics.

METALS

Certain properties of metals that determine their usability in constructing home equipment are: ability to be welded, ability to conduct heat, and ability to absorb heat.

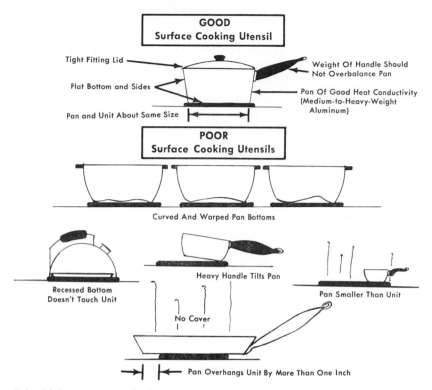

FIG. 15.1. Points to look for in selecting good cooking utensils, and undesirable characteristics which should be avoided.—**Mmm, Meals in Minutes**, H. Ec. Dept., Kelvinator Div., American Motors.

Properties of Metals

Low-carbon steel has largely replaced iron for the framework of ranges, refrigerators, freezers, washers, dryers, and other large appliances because it is lighter in weight and can be welded. Welded unions are especially important in the inner and outer frames of the range and refrigerator to prevent moisture from seeping into the insulation between the two walls. Moisture is a good conductor of heat and would greatly reduce the effectiveness of the insulation.

Utensils, or nonelectric housewares as they are sometimes called, are used for surface and oven cookery. Transfer of heat from surface units and burners is largely by conduction; hence the material used in a surface utensil should be a good conductor. The present emphasis on cooking with a minimum amount of water in order to preserve the mineral and vitamin content of the food emphasizes the need of using a utensil of a good conducting material, since otherwise a larger amount of water is required. If this water is poured into the sink drain at the end of the cooking process, valuable food nutrients are lost.

In the oven, heat is transferred by conduction, convection, and radiation, but once the oven lining is hot, a large percentage is by radiation. Therefore, the material of the oven utensil should be primarily a good absorber.

Surface Utensils

Materials Used

Surface utensils may be of iron, aluminum, stainless steel, porcelain enameledware, and heatproof glass. Aluminum and iron are good conductors, the other three are not, and in their use more liquid should be added to prevent the food from sticking and burning. Certain manufacturers have improved the conductivity of stainless steel by electroplating onto the steel utensil a copper bottom (Revere Ware), or an aluminum bottom (Farberware and Futura Ware as in Figure 15.2) or by using a thin iron core between two steel plates (Flavorseal), or a core of carbon steel between the two layers of stainless steel (Patriot Ware). Another manufacturer uses vanadium steel instead of stainless steel and the core of a special type of iron alloy (Flint Ware), and one company uses a copper core (Copper-Heart).

Iron. No material has all the advantages or disadvantages. Iron utensils are heavy and will rust if not cared for. This corrosion is red iron oxide, but a blue or black iron oxide may be obtained by heating the utensil in oil and this oxide protects the surface. This is known as Russian iron. Cast iron used in frypans and Dutch ovens is somewhat porous and a new utensil should be treated before use by brushing over with unsalted fat and heating for several hours at a low temperature in an oven.

Aluminum. Aluminum is light in weight. Pure aluminum is soft and has a low melting point. Most aluminum for utensils has copper or magnesium added to increase its strength. Aluminum is darkened by alkalies, and utensils of this material should not be washed with strong alkaline soaps or used for the cooking of eggs, but the discoloration is difficult to prevent when the water of the area is naturally hard. Acids, either vinegar-water or acid foods, will remove the discoloration. Aluminum will become

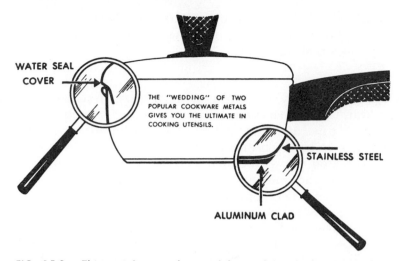

FIG. 15.2. This stainless steel utensil has a bottom plating of aluminum to increase its conductivity.—Futura Ware, West Bend Aluminum.

pitted when a salt solution is allowed to stand too long in contact with it.

Stainless Steel. Stainless steel, a combination of steel with chromium and nickel, has a smooth, impervious surface and gives a lifetime of service. Excessive dry heat may cause oxidation in spots. These spots are dark gray or brown in appearance and are removed with difficulty.

Porcelain Enameledware and Heatproof Glass. Porcelain enameledware and heatproof glass have many characteristics in common: either may chip if roughly handled, and glass may break if subjected to sudden changes of temperature, especially when moisture is present. These two materials and stainless steel are especially desirable for the cooking of white sauces, custards, lemon pie fillings, etc., which may acquire a grayish tinge when cooked in aluminum. Heat should be kept moderately low for thickened foods to eliminate scorching, and stirring should always be done with a wooden spoon.

Pyroceram, a nonporous, glass-ceramic material was first used in guided missile nose-cone fabrication where it had to withstand tremendous temperature changes. It is now made into Corning Ware (Fig. 5.6b) which may be employed for all types of cookery — top of range, broiler, and oven. It is resistant to scratching, crazing, and cracking and is not affected by extreme changes in temperature; i.e., a dish of Corning Ware may be taken from a freezer and placed immediately in a heated oven or even over direct heat on top of the range.

Oven Utensils

Oven utensils may be of tinned steel, glass, iron, porcelain enameledware, or earthenware. Aluminum is used, too, for cookie sheets, muffin pans, and cake and pie pans. Aluminum is not a good absorber, as has been noted; it tends to reflect radiant heat, but for this reason, allows the food to cook more slowly and consequently cakes and muffins may rise to greater volume and cookies and biscuits will brown more evenly. Foods baked in aluminum are less apt to burn when the homemaker is interrupted and leaves food in the oven somewhat longer than was intended. New tin is shiny, but quickly darkens when heated. The temperature should be reduced or the cooking period shortened when dark tin, glass, or enameledware is used.

Methods of Forming Utensils

Utensils may be formed or shaped by one of four different methods; they may be cast, stamped, drawn, or spun.

Cast. Cast utensils are usually of aluminum or iron and are formed by pouring the liquid metal into a mold to harden. They tend to be somewhat more porous than utensils of sheet metal, and because of impurities in the metal itself they frequently are more subject to pitting. The shank to which the handle is fastened is cast in one with the saucepan, and the rim of the pan has a straight edge; a bead is formed on the lid to hold the cover in place. These features distinguish cast construction from most sheet-metal construction.

Stamped and Drawn. Stamped utensils are made in a single operation in a punch-and-die set and are simple in line. When tin is used in the operation excess material is folded over against the sides of the pan (Fig. 15.3a). Utensils of more complicated design are "drawn." This is a series of stamping operations, from two to ten or more in number, during which the utensil is stretched into shape. This method preserves the position of the molecules and eliminates any strain in the metal that might lead to flaws in the surface of the finished product. Sometimes it is necessary to reheat the metal between steps to reshape the crystals (Fig. 15.3b).

Spun. In the spinning operation a metal sheet — or blank as

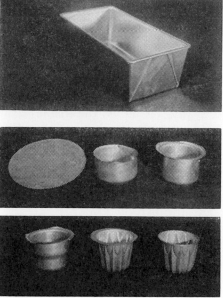

FIG. 15.3a. (Above) stamped utensil; excess tin has been folded over at the end of the pan.

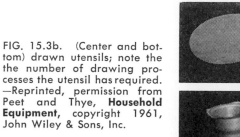

FIG. 15.3b. (Center and bottom) drawn utensils; note the the number of drawing processes the utensil has required. —Reprinted, permission from Peet and Thye, **Household Equipment,** copyright 1961, John Wiley & Sons, Inc.

it is called — is fastened to the end of a moldlike chuck that is rotated at a certain speed, during which the blank is shaped over the form. Less intricate utensils, such as bowls of aluminum and stainless steel, are made by this method. Usually a series of striations is visible on the interior surface of spun utensils and it may be possible to see the tiny hole where the blank was fastened to the chuck. Occasionally utensils are formed by a combination of stamping and cold rolling; the latter operation is related to spinning.

Methods of Assembling

Accessory parts such as spouts and handles may be fastened to the main body of the utensil in a number of different ways, by soldering, brazing, bolting, riveting, or welding. In soldering, tin or lead is used for the flux[1] and the temperature is moderate; in brazing, the materials are red hot, and brass is the common flux; no flux is needed for welding, done with an electric torch at a high temperature.

Bolts or screws are used to attach handles to large appliances and to cooking utensils when there is a possibility that the part may some time need to be replaced, or when the handle will need to be removed before a utensil commonly used for surface cookery is to be placed in the oven. Screws and bolts often provide crevices in which dirt may collect and give a rough surface that is difficult to clean.

When rivets are used, the size should be suited to the space, and they should be flat and smooth for ease in cleaning. When the shank of a handle is riveted to a pot or pan, part of the rivet is always visible on the inside surface. In contrast, welding leaves no mark or, at most, a very tiny dimple (Fig. 15.4).

Handles should be of a material that is impervious to heat; they should be comfortable in the hand and not so long as to overbalance the pans when empty or only partially filled. A hole or ring in the end of the handle allows the homemaker to hang the pan on a hook.

Covers are of the same material as the pan, or occasionally of glass so the cooking process may be more easily watched. They usually are flat or domed and should fit tightly to prevent the escape of steam when a minimum amount of water is used.

Finishes

There are two methods of finishing the surfaces of materials — applied and mechanical — depending upon the corrosive property of the base metal.

Applied Finishes

When the base metal is subject to corrosion, a noncorrosive finish is applied over the base. This finish may be metallic or nonmetallic in nature. The common metal finishes are tin, zinc, copper, nickel, and chromium. Tin and zinc are applied by dipping the base sheet into a bath of the metal or by spraying it on. There are various grades of tin, depending upon the thickness of the coating. Since tin is pliable the base metal sheet is covered with the tin coat before it is formed into utensils.

Galvanized. Zinc-coated sheets are known as galvanized metal and are used for utensils that are simple in construction, such as water pails and movable wash tubs. A zinc coating may be applied to the outside of water pipes installed in damp areas, to prevent corrosion.

Plated. When copper, nickel, or chromium is used for the

---

[1] A flux is any substance applied to surfaces of materials to aid in joining them together.

FIG. 15.4. The use of rivets and welding in fastening handles to utensils. (Above) outside views; only tiny dimples appear where spot welding was done. (Below) inside views; the rivets project as far on the inside of the pan as on the outside, making a cleaning problem. The welding is scarcely visible on the inside, does not interfere with cleaning.—Reprinted, permission from Peet and Thye, **Household Equipment**, copyright 1961, John Wiley & Sons, Inc.

surface finish, the process is known as plating or more correctly as electroplating, since it is carried on in an electric bath. Here the base metal becomes the cathode, and films of the surface metal are deposited on it. Nickel has a slightly yellowish tinge; chromium is silvery in color.

Porcelain and Baked-on Enamels. The common nonmetallic finishes are porcelain enamel and synthetic enamel. The base metal to which the enamel is applied must first be formed into the utensil, since enamel is not pliable. The metal is then cleaned in

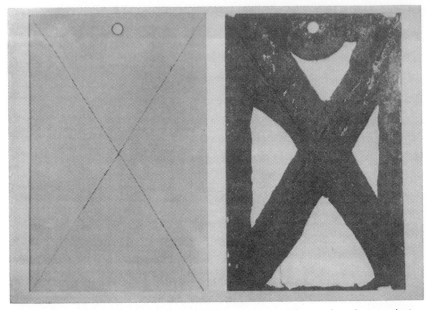

FIG. 15.5. Identical steel panels; (left) treated with a phosphate solution "Bonderite," (right) untreated. Finished in enamel, then scratched and sprayed with a salt solution for same length of time. Finish over "B Monderite" unaffected.—Parker Rust Proof.

an acid bath, a process called "pickling," then washed and dried. To prevent rusting, it is now coated with zinc or "bonderized," the latter a patented process in which the metal is dipped into a solution of nonmetallic phosphate (Fig. 15.5).[2] The first coat of porcelain enamel contains, in addition to the inorganic minerals from which it is made, cobalt and nickel oxides which give it a dark blue color. The enamel is fused on in an electric furnace at approximately 1600 F. and makes a close bond with the metal base. This first coat may be used by itself for the lining of range ovens, because it has almost the same coefficient of expansion as the steel base and, therefore, will not chip or craze. At least two coats of light porcelain enamel must be used to cover up the dark first coat unless the enamel contains titanium. Titanium enamel has a very uniform, pure white color and has largely replaced other porcelain enamels as a finish for utensils because it increases the opacity of the enamel to such an extent that one coat is sufficient. Research seems to indicate that eventually an enamel may be developed that can be used in a single coat without the base

[2] Developed by Parker Rust Proof Co., Detroit.

FIG. 15.6a. "Teflon" is widely used as a nonstick lining for pans.—DuPont.

coat. Porcelain enamel is used as a finish for cooking utensils, sinks, ranges, refrigerators—at least on the inside—and for the inside coat of washers and dryers, wherever there may be a certain amount of rubbing against the surface.

Synthetic enamel is organic in nature, made from resins and gums, and is baked on at 300 F. It frequently is called "baked-on" enamel, under various trade names. It is used for the outside finish of washers, dryers, ironers, and often of refrigerators, freezers, and for kitchen and bathroom cabinets. This type of enamel will withstand knocks and blows without injury, but not abrasion. It is obtainable in white and a variety of colors.

Paint is an applied finish, too, but usually is somewhat limited in wear and will need to be replaced at intervals.

"Teflon." A comparatively new finish applied as a coating to the inside surfaces of housewares made of aluminum, cast iron, steel, and glass is "Teflon"[3] (Fig. 15.6a). It is a fluorocarbon resin, now obtainable in more than twenty different colors. Fused on at about 700 F., "Teflon" consequently has high heat stability and is not affected by cooking temperatures, or in fact by any food acids or alkalies, and is not harmed by the strongest detergents. The finish lasts indefinitely and pans can be washed in the dishwasher but finish will be damaged by abrasive cleaners.

Foods do not adhere to "Teflon" and no fats are usually needed for frying or baking unless desired for flavor. People who are dieting can thus eliminate unwanted fats. Before first use, however, it is a good idea to oil or grease the nonstick surface, especially in the case of frypans, griddles, and bakeware. Also cake and muffin pans used for butter cakes or those that contain fruit or

---

[3] Registered trademark for DuPont's "Teflon" TFE nonstick finishes.

a high sugar content should be greased before each use. Frypans and griddles should be preheated. Foods may burn if too high a heat is used, just as in an ordinary pan, but the food will not stick to "Teflon" and can be removed immediately without soaking. The finish is fairly soft and can be scratched, but this rarely affects the nonstick property. Scratches and cuts may be avoided by using spoons, forks, and spatulas of plastic, rubber, and wood (Fig. 15.6b). If metal tools are used, try to develop a "light touch."

Occasionally if too high heat is used, the nonstick finish will discolor. Commercial stain removers developed for use with "Teflon" are on the market, and a homemade remedy is also suggested. Mix two tablespoons of baking soda and one-half cup of liquid household bleach with one cup water. Boil this solution in the pan for five to ten minutes, then thoroughly wash, rinse, and dry the pan and wipe the surface with cooking oil.

In spite of rumors to the contrary, extensive tests performed on "Teflon"-coated pans both in Europe and the United States have proved conclusively that there is no health hazard in the use of the pans for normal cooking processes. Records indicate that more than 100 million items coated with "Teflon" are being used in 25 million different homes in America, yet no case of serious illness from their use has ever been reported. The Food and Drug Administration has stated that "Teflon"-finished utensils are safe for conventional kitchen use.

Mechanical Finishes

Metals that do not corrode may be finished mechanically; they may be polished, given a satin finish, or may be pebbled or hammered (Fig. 15.7).

FIG. 15.6b. These plastic tools are especially adapted for use with "Teflon" pans.—DuPont.

FIG. 15.7. This aluminum saucepan has been given a distinctive pebbled or hammered surface finish.—Club Aluminum.

Aluminum is frequently anodized. Anodized utensils are popular for their wide range of colors. Anodizing combines a mechanical process with electrolysis. The metal is first given the satin or polished finish, then anodized. The finished utensil will have the same shiny or dull surface given it in this first mechanical treatment.

The aluminum, is submerged in acid (sulfuric, oxalic, chromic, phosphoric, sulfonic, or boric) and subjected to electrolysis. In this process, the aluminum becomes the anode, hence the name "anodized." The oxidation that takes place in the acid bath forms reasonably durable films of aluminum oxide on the surface of the aluminum. These films vary in thickness from 0.00002 to 0.0001 inches. As oxidation continues, successive layers of film are formed, each new layer immediately on the surface of the metal, pushing previously formed layers to the outside. Thus the first layer formed stays on the outside and becomes softer and less dense as the solvent action of the acid dissolves some of the film. This condition makes it possible for the film to absorb dye, and the utensil can be finished in virtually any shade of the color spectrum, with the additional attractiveness of an underlying metallic sheen.[4]

Anodized surfaces will never wear off and are reasonably resistant to injury from stirring tools, do not stain and pit, and are not affected by alkaline dishwater, but may fade in direct sunlight.

GLASS

New uses for glass are being developed constantly. Liquid glass may be drawn into threads so fine they can be bent without splintering, and this characteristic has opened a new field of glass manufacturing.

---

[4] Adopted from Manual No. 50, *Materials and Methods*, June, 1949, pp. 79–81.

Spun Glass

The tensile strength of fibered, or "spun," glass, its light weight, and its resistance to warping make it an ideal material for articles used in the home. Being fireproof, it may be used with safety for curtains or drapes hung near open flames, and being waterproof, it withstands rugged usage in areas exposed to water splashing or inclement weather.

Fiberglas

Glass fiber is perhaps the most popular choice of insulating materials for home appliances. It is widely sold under the trade name "Fiberglas," an Owens-Corning product.

Characteristics. Fiberglas is odorless and does not absorb odors; it is moisture-resistant, does not burn, is noncorrosive in itself and will not cause corrosion on metals with which it comes in contact. It is resilient and does not settle or warp, which would allow air pockets to form. It has high tensile strength. It is light in weight, reducing the shipping costs of appliances in which it is used and making handling easier. Fiberglas has extremely low thermal conductivity and consequently makes possible exceptionally accurate temperature control in refrigerators and range ovens and, as drapery material, aids in maintaining evenness of temperature in a room. It also is widely used as insulation in portable food containers. It is a good absorber of noise when used in motor-driven appliances such as washers, dryers, and fans.

Forms. Fiberglas is manufactured in four forms suited to a variety of uses: rolls, batts, shredded, and bulk (Fig. 15.8a). It may be wrapped around the frame of an appliance (Fig. 15.8b)) or used in the form of panels. These panels are made with grooves, notches, slits, or bevels to fit the contours of any piece of equipment and may be made to order to any desired shape. Thickness varies from $\frac{1}{2}$ to 4 inches and is obtainable in almost any width and length. Rolls faced with very thin aluminum foil are sometimes used for furnace insulation. When these are coated with neoprene, a synthetic rubber, they give additional protection in areas of high humidity.

The insulation in such household appliances as ranges, roasters, refrigerators, freezers, dishwashers, and water heaters is usually Fiberglas. It keeps the heat in or out of the insulated space, as the need may be. When used in metal kitchen cabinets and air conditioners its main purpose is to reduce vibration and noise.

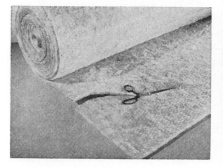

FIG. 15.8a. Three types of Fiberglas insulation to control heat, cold, or sound.—Owens-Corning Fiberglas Corporation.

FIG. 15.8b. A blanket of Fiberglas insulation is wrapped around oven and broiler compartments.—American Gas Association.

Fiberglas in the form of yarns, tapes, cords, and cloth is used to insulate electric wires, motors, etc. Added advantages of Fiberglas in these applications are the minimum thickness required and the resistance to deterioration under conditions of high temperature and high humidity.

PLASTICS

Among the materials used in the home and more particularly the kitchen, plastics may perhaps be considered in a class by themselves. Plastics are man-made substances, prepared from such every-day materials as water, air, wood, petroleum, natural gas, salt, casein, and limestone, subjected to the actions of heat, pressure, and chemicals. They have become an indispensable aid in saving the homemaker's energy and time.

Types

Plastics are divided into two main groups, according to the effect of heat upon them. The *thermosetting* plastics harden into permanent shape during the forming process because they undergo a chemical change; the *thermoplastics,* in contrast, are subjected to physical action only, and may be softened by heat any number of times and will harden again when cooled. This property makes possible the use of heat to seal together different parts of a product.

There are fourteen or fifteen basic plastics at present, but the industry has developed so rapidly since the end of World War II that other types may be expected to appear at almost any time. Four or five lead in production and their characteristics and uses will be considered briefly.

Thermosetting Products

Melamine and phenolic plastic are representatives of the thermosetting group. They usually do not scratch or break, are resistant to heat and moisture, and make good electric insulators. Melamine is used for counter tops, mixing bowls, and dinnerware and is obtainable in a wide range of opaque and translucent colors. Phenolic colors are mostly dark and opaque. This plastic is found in utensil handles, appliance handles and bases, light plugs and switches, telephones, and occasionally in wall panels.

Thermoplastic Products

Among the thermoplastics are vinyl, polystyrene, and polyethylene. All of these plastics are tasteless, odorless, and nontoxic; they do not absorb water and are not affected by the common chemicals. Vinyl and polyethylene may be used as surface coatings on fabrics and paper and are manufactured in both rigid and semirigid forms. Polyethylene is used for flexible bowls, squeeze bottles, ice cube trays, and food bags; also in sheet form for food wraps. Vinyl is sold for wall and floor tiling, shower curtains, upholstery material, and vacuum cleaner and refrigerator parts; polystyrene for tumblers, lighting fixtures, refrigerator door liners and food bins, kitchen cabinets, and air-conditioning cases.

Nylon. Nylon is usually thought of as a fabric for articles of clothing, but nylon plastic finds wide use in gears, bearings, and pulleys in household appliances, hinges, gaskets, and rollers on drawers in ranges and refrigerators, and on sliding doors.

Silicones. Then there are the silicones, a group of over a hundred different products. They are a cross between organic and inorganic substances and have some of the properties of glass. In the equipment field, silicone is used to treat the surfaces of pans, ice cube trays, and waffle grids to prevent the food product from sticking. Silicone oils maintain accuracy in range oven clocks and in the timers of toasters. Silicone rubber, a stainless and odorless product, is used in the gaskets and seals of many steam irons to prevent leakage of moisture. Other silicone products are used for the insulation of electric wires and, because of their ability to withstand high temperatures, greatly increase the life of motors and small electric appliances. As has been noted, silicone fluid is used in probe tubes for thermostatic control.

Additional Characteristics and Uses of Plastics

In addition to being used by themselves, plastics also may act as adhesives for bonding other materials together in the form of laminates for counter tops, knife handles, etc. For use in house paints, they are marketed in the form of resins because they flow on smoothly, dry rapidly, make the paint more resistant to marring, and keep white paints from turning yellow; in varnishes and oils and rubbers; in polishes that protect the surface and need no rubbing. Plastic coatings are used on bread wraps and milk cartons and on fabrics to make them water and strain repellent.

Plastics are light in weight and easily cared for; they may be wiped off with a damp cloth, occasionally with the use of warm water and a mild soap. Harsh abrasives should be avoided. Keep them from contact with a direct flame. Vinyl film, Melamine dinnerware, and polystyrene wall tile carry an identifying CS (Commercial Standard) seal of quality. An effort is being made by the plastics industry to develop standards for other products made of plastic.

EXPERIMENTS AND PROJECTS

1. To compare materials used and methods of making kitchen utensils:
   a. Assemble different types of pots and pans and accessory utensils, such as beaters, graters, cutlery, measuring cups and spoons, etc.
   b. Have the students inspect them and list for each utensil: basic metal, finish, method of forming, method of fastening on handle, shape of cover, features that contribute for or against ease of cleaning.

QUESTIONS

1. What materials are especially recommended for use in surface utensils? in oven utensils? Why?
2. How have some manufacturers improved the poor conductivity of stainless steel utensils?
3. Distinguish between stamped and drawn utensils. When is the drawing method necessary?
4. What types of finishes are porcelain and synthetic enamels? When are these finishes used?
5. Why is the cobalt coat of porcelain enamel frequently used in ovens?
6. Sometimes titanium enamel is used in the oven and also on the outside of the range. What are its advantages?
7. What three kinds of mechanical finishes are used? When are they used?
8. Are all anodized finishes alike? Explain.
9. Why are handles on range doors often attached with screws?
10. Aluminum used in cookie sheets is not a good absorber. Why? Then why is it used?
11. Two pie crusts are baked in the same oven for the same number of minutes. One pie pan is of aluminum, the other of year-old tin. Which pie crust will be darker? Why? What is the general rule to follow in such a case?
12. In purchasing any utensil, what are the important things to consider if you are to be satisfied with your choice?

Chapter Sixteen

SELECTING EQUIPMENT AS GIFTS

By Betty Jeanne Sundling*

Household appliances and kitchen utensils are popular items to give as gifts, but many times these gifts are bought without serious consideration given to their ultimate use. They may have been purchased simply because "it is the latest thing on the market" or "I saw it advertised on television."

Factors which should be considered when purchasing any gift are the occasion, the recipient, the situation, and the inherent qualities of the particular item.

THE OCCASION

The purpose for purchasing a gift will often be a guide in the selection. For a prospective bride a kitchen shower is a welcome preparation for future duties in the kitchen. Appropriate gifts for a baby shower would be blenders or food mills as they would allow the mother to prepare puréed foods much more cheaply than buying them in cans. But there are occasions other than special showers, a birthday or Christmas or wedding anniversary, or a thoughtful "thank you" after a visit with a friend. A copy of this book would also be a useful gift to assist in using appliances and utensils correctly. You should find it as valuable as your cookbooks; indeed, correct choice of a cooking utensil often determines the quality of the finished product.

THE RECIPIENT

An unused gift has little value; the gift selected will need to be adaptable to the personality, interests, age, and family cycle of the individual.

Some questions to consider before purchasing a household item for another person are:

* This chapter was written by Miss Betty Jeanne Sundling who received the B.S. degree from Washington State University and the M.S. degree from Iowa State University. Currently she is a member of the Engineering Home Economics Department of Whirlpool Corporation.

What does the individual value? One may enjoy the prestige of possessing the very latest household item while another prefers to work with a minimum of equipment. A homemaker very creative in preparing and serving foods would find use for melon ballers, skewers, or attractive serving dishes.

How flexible or receptive is the individual to the adoption of the new? A gift may be placed in storage because the homemaker does not want to change her pattern of living or does not understand the gift's potential. This kind of homemaker may be encouraged to enjoy a new-idea gift if it is accompanied by an offer to demonstrate its possibilities. The "fun" approach wins many converts to new equipment.

What are the interests of the individual? Does she enjoy making products from basic raw materials or using packaged products? The use of instant puddings, instant potatoes, presifted flour, packaged cake mixes, packaged pie crusts, prepared casseroles, or frozen meals and desserts will affect the amount and type of utensils and appliances needed by a homemaker dependent on these products. Hobbies such as gardening, sewing, woodworking, and outdoor cooking give clues to the selection of a gift. Family members interested in maintaining home grounds would appreciate receiving lawn mowers, edge trimmers, garden hoses, and garden tools. For men that enjoy woodworking, power tools would be an ideal gift. For the home decorator there are many pieces of equipment and kits to improve his or her efficiency and to transform an arduous task into a "Huckleberry Finn" project.

What are the needs of the individual? The size of the hand and the strength of the grip need consideration in selecting gifts where a firm grip is essential to efficient operation, such as electric knives, portable beaters, or any utensil with a large handle. To assure satisfaction for the recipient of an electric shaver, his type of beard, the sensitivity of his skin, and the closeness of shave desired will need to be considered. Any equipment designed to be used only in the right hand, such as certain models of electric irons, will be less efficient for a left-handed user.

The single woman might welcome household tools such as screw drivers, hammers, small repair kits, and supplies for keeping her equipment in good running order. A working wife would find much use for pressure cookers, casseroles, and easy-to-care-for bakeware and cookware. Cordless shavers, travel toothbrushes, electric shoe polishers, electric or battery-driven clothes brushes, travel alarms, travel irons, rechargeable cigarette lighters, or purse size flashlights are gifts worth considering for a traveling person.

Before buying gifts for college-bound students, it would be advisable to check the school's regulations. Gift ideas for these students are irons, hot plates, electric blankets, coffee makers, instant coffee brewers, hair dryers, electric toothbrushes, typewriters, sunlamps, bathroom scales, tape recorders, radios, alarm clocks, and good study lamps.

How much entertaining and what type of entertaining will be done in the home? A family that entertains generously at home will appreciate equipment to accommodate large quantities and a variety of accessories to match: large capacity coffee makers, heated trays, and chafing dishes, or serving carts, for indoors; and barbecue equipment, melamine dinnerware, picnic supplies, and stainless flatware would be more appropriate for outdoor entertaining.

What is the stage of the family life cycle? Is the family in the beginning, childbearing, preschool children, school children, teenagers, launching, middle years, or aging life cycles? Gifts appropriate for a beginning family may endure through a procession of children, but as the family approaches another stage—especially when the children are leaving—a new variety of needs can be filled with gifts appropriate for new interests and activities. Old equipment has been outmoded or perhaps is just shabby from use, so a new blender or rotisserie will be welcomed.

What kind of equipment does the family already have? The presence of a dishwasher will affect the selection of dishes, silverware, and utensils. Dishes designed to sheet off water easily and utensils not affected by alkaline detergents and high temperatures are compatible with a dishwasher. The presence or absence of electrical outlets will determine whether an electrical or battery-driven item will be purchased. When there is lack of electrical outlets and the individuals do not object to the high cost of battery maintenance, cordless items like shavers, vacuum cleaners, and toothbrushes would make ideal gifts.

THE SITUATION

If forethought is given to the family situation, it can serve as a guide in the selection of a gift. Factors such as design of the house, mobility of the family, location of the family, size and composition of the family, needs of the family, equipment already possessed by the family, and the occupation of the bread-winner should be considered.

Design of the house will determine the counter and storage space available for equipment. Beginning families living in apartments or trailers have little cabinet space and will welcome equipment that stacks or nests. Bulky equipment, forced into storage, may have been replaced with smaller substitutes before the homemaker has space to accommodate it in her kitchen. Versatility of a single piece of equipment (such as combination can opener-knife sharpener) is valued highly in these circumstances. If the occupation of the breadwinner requires frequent moves, equipment easily transported from one area to another should be considered — portability, compactness, and strong construction are essential.

Location of the family will influence some of its activities. Weather, degree of urbanization, and amount of privacy will determine the type and amount of entertaining, and type of activities. Where climates permit outdoor living a major portion of the year, customs tend to be more casual and gifts for informal entertaining would be cherished.

Family size will determine the capacity of the equipment and family composition will influence the selection. Mothers-to-be would enjoy bottle warmers while mothers of young children and teenagers would prefer popcorn poppers.

ULTIMATE USE OF THE ITEM
AND ITS INHERENT QUALITIES

After consideration has been given to the occasion, the individual, and the situation, then the item itself should be evaluated. Above all the gift should perform the functions for which it was designed. A frypan given as a gift should be made of a material that conducts heat evenly.

General criteria for all equipment should include sturdy construction and assembly, durability, portability, versatility, good design, good balance, performance, and ease of care. With motor-driven appliances, the size of the motor and electrical safety would be additional criteria. Heat resistant handles and legs, thermostatic controls, and electrical safety would be important points for heating appliances. An electrical appliance and its cord should always bear the UL seal of approval to insure electrical safety (Fig. 2.22).

Each appliance should be evaluated according to what it does and which features are important. In Eithel Bray Rose's study of "Factors Influencing the Selection and Satisfactions in Use of Household Appliances as Indicated by Three Selected Groups of Married Women Graduates of Ohio State University,"[1] satisfactions expressed by the majority of homemakers were: adequate performance, special features or accessories, convenience in use, and ease of care. Factors such as color, quality, finish, model, and guarantee ranked low in contributing to satisfaction. Dissatisfaction resulted from inadequate performance, inferior features or accessories, inconvenience in use, difficulty in cleaning, incorrect size, and unsatisfactory service calls.

The item should be purchased from a reliable dealer who will service it and should be made by a company that will stand behind its products. Most gifts, especially individualized ones, should be exchangeable in case of duplication.

In giving any gift be sure that all directions for operation and care are included, and suggest to the recipient that the card requesting the name of the dealer, date of purchase, and other pertinent information be filled out and returned immediately to the manufacturer so that the guarantee will be good for the time specified.

HINTS ON GIFT GIVING

According to *Merchandizing Week*,[2] the trend is to classify everything according to use. Classifications of household articles could be listed as basic kitchen equipment, home entertaining equipment, home maintenance, personal care, clothing care and construction, comfort, and leisure time equipment.

> Basic kitchen equipment: Mixers, blenders, juicers, coffee makers, clocks, can openers, knife sharpeners, cutting boards, food storage equipment, clean-up equipment, and cooking equipment.
>
> Home entertaining equipment: Television sets, radios, phonographs, door chimes, tape recorders, movie cameras, movie projectors, walkie-talkies, serving carts, and heated trays.

---

[1] Available in both microfilm and Xerox form (L.C. Card No. Mic 60–789), Ohio State University, Columbus, 1959.

[2] *Merchandizing Week,* No. 8, 1965.

Home maintenance: Lawn mowers, garden tools, sprinklers, hoses, lawn sweepers, cordless shrub and grass shears, cordless hedge trimmers, and snow removal equipment.

Personal care: Hair dryers, manicure sets, electric toothbrushes, electric hair brushes, electric comb, individual curler-dryer, hair-cutting equipment, and shavers.

Clothing care and construction: Sewing machines, electric scissors, scissors, irons, ironing boards, electric shoe polishers, cordless clothes brushes, electric washers and dryers, both available in portable models.

Comfort: Humidifiers, dehumidifiers, air conditioners, air purifiers, fans, heating pads, electric blankets, massagers, heaters, sunlamps, and cordless heated mittens and socks.

Leisure-time: Outdoor cooking equipment (barbecue equipment, melamine dinnerware, aprons, chef's hats, charcoal lighter), patio and garden lighting, summer furniture, gardening equipment, and power tools.

Many of these products are available with electric cords or are cordless. Transistorized equipment with accessories are being developed for the home, boat, or automobile. *Merchandizing Week* also lists future innovations such as an electric window washer, electric paint brush or roller, automatic rake, outdoor disposer unit, and an electric automobile washer and waxer.

As you survey the many household appliances and kitchen utensils on the market, as well as those of the future, you will find many fine gift ideas that would be appropriate for any occasion for a very special person.

REFERENCES *

GENERAL

Beveridge, Elizabeth, *Choosing and Using Home Equipment,* 4th ed., Iowa State University Press, Ames, 1963.

Changing Times. The Kiplinger Magazine, 1729 H St., N. W., Washington 6.

Ehrenkranz, Florence and Inman, Lydia, *Equipment in the Home,* 2nd ed. Harper & Row, N.Y., 1966.

Forecast for Home Economists.

Hamilton Homemakers Manual. Hamilton Manufacturing Company, Two Rivers, Wis.

Johnston, Betty Jane, *Equipment for Modern Living,* The MacMillan Co., N. Y., 1965.

Ladies' Home Journal, articles on home equipment.

McCall's magazine, articles on home equipment.

McCullough, Helen, *Housing and Household Equipment Research in Home Economics,* 1925–1950. Circ. 712, Ill. Univ. Agr. Exp. Sta., Urbana, 1953.

Money Management — Your Equipment Dollar. Household Finance Corporation.

Peet, Louise J., and Thye, Lenore S., *Household Equipment,* 5th ed., John Wiley & Sons, Inc., N. Y., 1961.

Teachers' Kit on Home Appliances. Whirlpool Corp.

VanZante, Helen J., *Household Equipment Principles,* Prentice-Hall, Inc., Englewood Cliffs, N. J., 1964.

What's New in Home Economics, articles on home equipment.

CLASSIFIED ACCORDING TO SUBJECT MATTER

Selection Factors

Money Management — Your Shopping Dollar. Household Finance Corporation, 1956.

Ranges

American Gas Association Approval Requirements. AGA (American Gas Association).

American Standards for Household Electric Ranges. NEMA (National Electric Manufacturers Association).

Choosing and Using Your Household Range, E-393, Ext. Serv., Mich. State Univ., East Lansing.

---

* Where addresses are not included, they will be found either under the list of Associations or under the list of Manufacturers, at the end of this section.

Home Economics Dept., Robertshaw-Fulton Controls Company:
  *Teaching Manual — Oven and Range Top Cooking
  Temp 'n Time Topics.*
How Your Gas Meter Works. AGA.
McCracken and Richardson, *Human Energy Expended in Using
  Built-in Oven at Different Heights,* USDA.
McCullough, Helen, and Schoeppel, Martha S., *Separate Ovens.* Small
  Homes Council.
Science Principles and Your Automatic Gas Range. ED9, Educational
  Service Bureau, Dept. PL, AGA.
*Teacher-Student Instruction Kit on Thermostatic Top Burner Cook-
  ing.* Harper-Wyman Co.
Univ. of Tenn., Div. of Ext. bulletins, Knoxville, Tenn.:
  Caring for Your Electric Range, 1954
  Selecting Your Electric Range, 1954
  Using Your Electric Range, 1955.

Refrigeration

Extension Service, Mich. State Univ., East Lansing:
  Choosing and Using Your Refrigerator, E-390
  Choosing and Using Your Freezer, E-391.
Heaton and Woodroof, *Performance of Home Freezers,* Georgia Agr.
  Exp. Sta. No. 30, Univ. of Georgia, Athens, 1962.
Home Freezers, Their Selection and Use. Home and Garden Bul. No.
  48, USDA. 10c.
Home Care of Purchased Frozen Foods. Home and Garden Bul. No.
  69, USDA. 5c.
How To Choose and Use Your Refrigerator. Bul. IS-56, USDA.
Manuals, leaflets and specification sheets from equipment manufactur-
  ers. (See list at end of this section.)
Storing Perishable Foods in the Home. Home and Garden Bul. No.
  78, Office of Information, USDA, 1961.

Electric Housewares

Forecast for Home Economists.
Ladies' Home Journal, articles on home equipment.
McCall's magazine, articles on home equipment.
Manuals, leaflets, etc. from manufacturers. (See list at end of this
  section.)

Nonelectric Housewares

*American Standard Dimensions, Tolerances and Terminology for
  Home Cooking and Baking Utensils.* Z61.1-1963, American Stand-
  ards Association.
Beveridge, Elizabeth, *Pots and Pans for Your Kitchen.* House and Gar-
  den Bul. No. 2, USDA. 10c.
————, *Tools for Food Preparation and Dishwashing.* House and Gar-
  den Bul. No. 3, USDA. 10c.
See references under Materials, Chapter 15.

Kitchen Arrangements

A Step-Saving U Kitchen. House and Garden Bul. No. 14, USDA.

Beltsville Kitchen-Workroom. Home and Garden Bul. No. 60, 1958, USDA. 10c.

Choosing and Using Your Automatic Dishwasher, E-388, Ext. Serv., Mich. State Univ., East Lansing.

Cornell Univ. bulletins, Ithaca, N.Y.:

    Guides for Arrangement of Urban Family Kitchens. Heiner, Mary K., and Steidl, Rose E., Agr. Exp. Sta. Bul. 878, 1951.

    Let Your Kitchen Arrangement Work for You. Heiner, Mary K., and Steidl, Rose E., Ext. Bul. 814, 1951.

    Kitchen Cupboards That Simplify Storage. Heiner, Mary K., and McCullough, Helen, Ext. Bul. 703, 1949. 5c.

    The Cornell Kitchen, 1952.

Heart of the Home. Picture Edition, American Heart Association. 10c.

Kitchen Sense. The Equitable Life Assurance Society of the United States, 1956.

McCullough, Helen E., *Space Design for Household Storage.* Ill. Univ. Agr. Exp. Sta. Bul. 557, 1952. $1.25.

Plan Your Kitchen To Take It Easy. Dept. Home Management and Child Development, Mich. State Univ., East Lansing.

Small Homes Council bulletins, Univ. of Ill., Urbana:

    Cabinet Space in the Kitchen. C5.31

    Handbook of Kitchen Design. Tech. Series C5.32R

    Household Storage Units. C5.1

    Kitchen Planning Standards. C5.32

    Storage Partitions. C5.11.

Standards for Household Electric Dishwashers, National Electrical Manufacturers' Association, 1961.

Youngstown Kitchen kit for setting up models of kitchens. (See illustration below.) Write for price.

Your Farmhouse—Planning the Kitchen and Workroom. House and Garden Bul. No. 12, USDA. 25c.

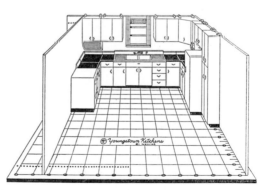

View of a model kitchen set up from kit. Walls, cabinets, and appliances are movable so that various arrangements may be tried.

Safety

Handbook for Emergencies. U. S. Government Printing Office, 1958. Washington 25.

Laundry

All About Modern Home Laundering. Ruud Manufacturing Co., 1953, Pittsburgh 1, Pa. $1.00.
Detergents for Home Laundering. Home and Garden Bul. No. 49, Office of Information, USDA, 1956. Washington 25.
Extension service, Mich. State Univ., East Lansing:
  Choosing and Using Your Automatic Washer, E-392
  Choosing and Using Your Clothes Dryer, E-389
  Problems in Textile Care, E-401
  Using Modern Laundry Aids, E-400.
How To Test Water Hardness in Your Home. Dow Chemical Company. (A 2-page leaflet containing a strip of sensitive paper for making the test.)
Hamilton *Home Laundry News.* Home Appliance Division, Hamilton Manufacturing Company.
Home Laundering Terms. American Home Laundry Manufacturers' Association. June 19, 1959.
Laundry Areas. Small Homes Council Circ. series C 5.4.
American Home Laundry Manufacturers' Association:
  National Home Laundry Conference Reports
  The 1962 Home Laundering Textbook—Teaching Guide.
Removing Stains From Fabrics. Home and Garden Bul. No. 62, 1959, USDA. 15c.
Stain Removal. Farmers' Bul. No. 1474, USDA. 5c.
Teaching Guide and All About Modern Home Laundering. Educational Service Bureau, AGA.
Washing Machines—Selection and Use. Home and Garden Bul. No. 32, USDA, 1955. 15c.

Cleaning

Choosing and Using Your Cleaning Appliances, Ext. Serv., Mich. State Univ., East Lansing.
House Cleaning Management and Methods. Farmers' Bul. No. 1834, USDA.
Hoover Home Institute, The Hoover Company:
  A Guide to Modern Cleaning Methods. 1959
  How To Take Work Out of Your Housework.
Free wall charts. Vacuum Cleaner Manufacturers' Association.
Manuals distributed by Vacuum Cleaner Manufacturers' Association.
Manuals on Household Waxes, S. C. Johnson and Son, Inc.
Vacuum Cleaner Manufacturers' Association:
  How To Take the Work Out of Your Housework. Revised 1962
  Modern Floor Care With an Electrical Polisher.

Saving Motion and Energy

Agr. Ext. Service, Purdue Univ., Lafayette, Ind.:
Fitzsimmons, Cleo, Goble, Eva, and Monhaut, Gertrude, *Easy Ways,* Bul. 391, 1953.
Barnes, Ralph M. *Motion and Time Study,* 5th ed. John Wiley & Sons, Inc., N.Y., 1963.
Coleman, Margaret, *Old Versus New Ironing Methods.* Proctor Electric Co., 1952.
Extension Service, Mich. State Univ., East Lansing:
Ironing Made Easy, 1953
Kettunen, Ruth, *Take It Easy in the Laundry,* 1954
Meyer, Olevia, *Take It Easy in the Kitchen,* 1954.
Gilbreth, Lillian M., Thomas, Orpha Mae, and Clymer, Eleanor, *Management in the Home.* Dodd, Mead & Company, N. Y., 1959.
Goodyear, Margaret, and Klohr, Mildred, *Management for Effective Living.* 2nd ed. John Wiley & Sons, Inc., N. Y., 1965.
Gross, Irma, and Crandall, Elizabeth, *Management for Modern Families.* Appleton-Century-Crofts, Inc., N. Y., 1954.
Heart of the Home, Picture Edition. American Heart Association. 10c.
Time Management for Homemakers. Household Finance Corporation.

Lighting

Better Light Better Sight News. Better Light Better Sight Bureau.
Bulletins, manuals, etc. from General Electric (Large Lamp Department):
Light. Vol. 29, No. 3, 1960
Lighting Fixture Guide, 1956. 50c.
Outdoor Lighting for Family Living, 1955
Portable Lamp Lighting Guide, 1958. 10c.
See Your Home in a New Light
Wall Lighting Guide, 1956. 50c.
Commery, E. W., and Stephenson, C. Eugene, *How To Decorate and Light Your Home.* Coward-McCann, Inc., N. Y., 1956. Paper-covered ed., 35c.
Eyes, our windows to the world. Better Light Better Sight Bureau. 10c.
Facts About Electric Wiring for the Home. National Adequate Wiring Bureau.
Film, "Bright Future," may be obtained on a loan basis through local utility company.
Handbook of Interior Wiring Design. Industry Committee on Interior Wiring Design. $1.00.
IES Lighting Handbook; the Standard Lighting Guide. 4th ed. 1966.
Light Bulbs and Fluorescent Tubes. Westinghouse Lamp Division.
Light Where You Need It. Westinghouse Lamp Division.
Lighting Keyed to Today's Homes. Committee on Residence Lighting. 1961.

Plumbing

Plumbing. Small Homes Council Bulletin, Circular Series G5.0.

Heating and Air Conditioning

Air Conditioning and Home Management. Carrier Corporation, 1960, Syracuse, N.Y.

Fuel Consumption in the Home. Superintendent of Documents, Washington 25, 1950. 15c.

Small Homes Council Bulletins, Circular Series:
  Basements. F2.0
  Chimneys and Fireplaces. F7.0
  Controls for Central Heating Systems. G3.2
  Fuels and Burners. G3.5
  Heating the Home. G3.1
  Moisture Condensation. F6.2
  Selecting Windows. F11.1
  Solar Orientation. C3.2
  Storm Sash. F11.2
  Summer Comfort. G6.0
  Window Planning Principles. F11.0.

Essential Facts About Electricity, Gas, and Thermostats

Bright Ideas for Ladies or What To Teach Husbands About Electric Wiring. Armored Cable Section, National Electrical Manufacturers' Association.

Full Housepower. National Wiring Bureau.

How To Give a Chalk Talk on Electric Wiring in the Home. National Wiring Bureau. 1961.

Manuals distributed by Robertshaw-Fulton Controls Company.

Materials available from Educational Service Bureau, Dept. PL, AGA.

Meet the New Gas Industry. American Gas Association. Natural Gas Industry. Nelson Doubleday, Inc., Garden City, N.Y.

Residential Wiring Handbook. Industry Committee on Interior Wiring Design, 1954. 25c.

Servants at the Switch. National Wiring Bureau.

Materials

Manuals distributed by Porcelain Enamel Institute, Inc.

Plastics As Building Materials. D9.0, Small Homes Council.

Steel's Competitive Challenge. American Iron and Steel Institute, Dec. 1961.

Steelways. American Iron and Steel Institute.

The ABC's of Modern Plastics. Bakelite Company.

This Formica World. Formica Corporation.

ASSOCIATIONS*

Air Conditioning and Refrigeration Institute, 1346 Connecticut Ave.
N.W., Washington D.C. 20036
American Gas Association, 605 Third Ave., New York. 10016
American Heart Association, 44 East 23rd St., New York. 10010
American Home Laundry Manufacturers' Association, 20 N. Wacker
Drive, Chicago. 60606
American Iron and Steel Institute, 150 East 42nd St., New York. 10017
American Society of Refrigerating Engineers, 234 Fifth Ave., New
York. 10001
American Standards Association, Inc., 10 East 40th St., New York.
10016
Bakelite Co., 30 East 42nd St., New York. 10017
Better Light Better Sight Bureau, 750 Third Ave., New York. 10017
Detergents Inc., 1147 Chesapeake Ave., Columbus, Ohio. 43212
Edison Electric Institute, 750 Third Ave., New York. 10017
Equitable Life Assurance Society of the U.S., 393 Seventh Ave., New
York. 10001
Gas Appliance Manufacturers Association, 60 East 42nd St., New York.
10017
Gas Vent Institute, 333 North Michigan Ave., Chicago. 60601
Household Finance Corp., Prudential Plaza, Chicago. 60601
Illuminating Engineering Society, United Engineering Center, UN
Plaza, New York. 10017
Industry Committee on Interior Wiring Design, Room 1650, 750
Third Ave., New York. 10017
National Bureau of Standards, Washington, D.C. 20234
National Electrical Manufacturers Association, 155 East 44th St., New
York. 10017
National Warm Air Heating and Air Conditioning Association, 640
Engineers Building, Cleveland. 44114
National Wiring Bureau, 155 East 44th St., New York. 10017
Plastic Houseware Manufacturers Association, 5719 W. Chicago Ave.,
Chicago. 60651
Porcelain Enamel Institute, Inc., 1145 19th St., N. W., Washington,
D.C. 20036
Society of the Plastics Industry, Inc. (The), 250 Park Ave., New York.
10017
Small Homes Council, Mumford House, Univ. of Ill., Urbana. 61803

---

* These associations publish new informational material at frequent intervals.
Teachers should request new materials at least once a year.

Superintendent of Documents, U.S. Government Printing Office,
    Washington, D.C. 20250
        (n.b. Write to this address for most of the USDA publications.
        Send cash or p.o. money order; do not send stamps.)
Underwriters' Laboratories Inc., 207 E. Ohio St., Chicago. 60611
USDA, Washington, D.C. 20250
U.S. Dept. Commerce, Washington, D.C. 20250
Vacuum Cleaner Manufacturers' Association, 1070 E. 152 St., Cleve-
    land. 44120

MANUFACTURERS*

Admiral Corporation, 3800 Cortland St., Chicago. 60647
Aluminum Goods Manufacturing Co., Manitowoc, Wis. 54220
American Radiator and Standard Sanitary Corp., 40 West 40th St.,
    New York. 10018
Blackstone Corp., 1111 Allen St., Jamestown, N.Y. 14701
Club Aluminum Products Co., 825 Twenty-Sixth St., LaGrange Park,
    Ill. 60528
Corning Glass Works, Corning, New York. 14830
Crane Co., 2474 Blake St., Denver, Colo. 80205
Dominion Electric Co., Mansfield, Ohio. 44902
Dow Chemical Co., Midland, Mich. 48640
Ecko Products, 1949 N. Cicero Ave., Chicago. 60639
E. I. Du Pont de Nemours & Co., 1007 Market St., Wilmington, Del.
    19898
Foley Manufacturing Co., 3300 N.E. Fifth, Minneapolis. 55413
Formica Corp., Subsidiary of Cyanamid, 4632 Spring Grove Ave.,
    Cincinnati. 45232
Frigidaire Division, General Motors Corp., 300 Taylor St., Dayton,
    Ohio. 45401
General Electric Co., Consumers Institute, Appliance Park, Louisville,
    Ky. 40225
General Electric Co., Portable Appliance Dept., 1285 Boston Ave.,
    Bridgeport, Conn. 06602
General Electric Co., Lamp Division, Nela Park, Cleveland. 44112
Hamilton Beach Co., Division of Scovill Mfg. Co., Racine, Wis. 53401
Hamilton Manufacturing Co., Two Rivers, Wis. 54241
Harper-Wyman Co., 8550 Vincennes Ave., Chicago. 60620
Hobart Manufacturing Co., Kitchen Aid Division, Troy, Ohio. 45373
Hoover Co., North Canton, Ohio. 44447
Hotpoint Home Economics Institute, 5600 West Taylor, Chicago.
    60644
S. C. Johnson & Son, Inc., Racine, Wis. 53401
Kelvinator, American Motors Corp., 14250 Plymouth Road, Detroit.
    48232
Lewyt Corp., 43-22 Queens, Long Island City, New York. 11101
Mirro Aluminum Co., Manitowoc, Wis. 54220
National Presto Industries, Inc., Eau Claire, Wis. 54701
Nesco, Inc., 947 W. St. Paul Ave., Milwaukee, Wis. 55116
Norge Sales Corp., Merchandise Mart Plaza, Chicago. 60654

---

* These manufacturers publish new informational material at frequent intervals. Teachers should request new materials at least once a year.

NuTone, Inc., Madison & Red Bank Rds., Cincinnati, Ohio. 45227
John Oster Manufacturing Co.,5055 Lydell Ave., Milwaukee. 53217
Owens-Corning Fiberglas Corp., Dept. 1833, 717 5th Ave., New York.
    10022
Parker Rust Proof Co., 2177 E. Milwaukee Ave., Detroit. 48211
Philco, Tioga and C Sts., Philadelphia. 19134
Preway Inc., Wisconsin Rapids, Wis. 54494
Proctor and Schwartz Corporation, 700 W. Tabor Road, Philadelphia.
    19120
Proctor-Silex Corporation, 333 West 65th St., Chicago, 60638
Robertshaw-Fulton Controls Co., P.O. Box 489, Irwin, Pa. 15642
Geo. D. Roper Corp., 1905 W. Court St., Kankakee, Ill. 60901
St. Charles Manufacturing Co., St. Charles, Ill. 60174
Speed Queen, Division of McGraw Electric Co., Ripon, Wis. 54971
Sunbeam Corp., 5600 Roosevelt Road, Chicago. 60650
Tappan Co., 250 Wayne Mansfield, Ohio. 44902
Toastmaster Division, McGraw-Edison Co., Elgin, Ill. 60120
Wear-Ever Aluminum, Inc., New Kensington, Pa. 15068
West Bend Co., West Bend, Wis. 53095
Westinghouse Electric Corp., Mansfield, Ohio. 44902
Whirlpool Corp., St. Joseph, Mich. 49023
Wiremold Co., Hartford, Conn. 06110
Youngstown Kitchens, Division of American-Standard, Warren, Ohio.
    44483

SUBJECT INDEX

Absorption system, refrigerator, 38, 46, 48
Accident prevention
  electricity, 273–75
  in kitchen, 137–39
Air conditioners
  central system, 261, 262
  operation of, 261
  room types, 262
  selection, 260
  special features, 262
Air filters, 252–53, 259
Aluminum utensils, 89, 288, 297
American Gas Assoc. Approval Seal, 33, 34
American Standards Assoc., approval, 98
Ammonia, as refrigerant, 46–47
Ampere, 267, 270, 275–76
Anodization of metals, 297
Appliance center, 130–31
Appliances
  arrangements, 110–17
  circuits, 276
  operating costs, 276–78

B

Baking sheets, 95
Bathroom appliances, 241–45
Beaters, hand, 102–04
BLBS (Better Light Better Sight) study lamps, 230–31
Bimetallic strip, 282
Bleaching, 153–54
Blenders, electric, 82–84
Bluing, 153
Broiling
  electronic, 26–27
  oven, 16–17
  portable, 76
Brushes, 184, 192–93, 194

C

Cabinets, 112–15
Cake pans, 94, 95
Can opener, 84, 101
Canister cleaners, 177–79
Carpet sweeper, 188
Central cleaning system, 180–82, 184
Chimneys, 257–58
Circuit breaker, 272–73

Circuits
  appliance, 276
  closed, 279
  general purpose, 275
  grounded, 279
  house, 275–76
  individual, 276
  open, 279
  overloaded, 279
  short, 279
Cleaning equipment
  brushes, 184, 192–94
  general, 188–91
  storage, 193
  vacuum cleaners, 174–88
Coal, as fuel, 255
Coffee makers
  care of, 67
  percolator, 65–67
  vacuum, 67
Color, in kitchen, 131
Compression system, refrigerator, 44–46
Condensers, refrigerator, 44–46
Conductors, 267
Cordless cleaner, 180
Counters, kitchen
  area, 115
  arrangement, 116, 117
  coverings, 152
Cutlery, 96–99

D

Dehumidifier, 263, 264
Detergents, 149–51
Diffusing bowls, 218
Dirt
  clothing, 153
  dry, 174–88
  effect on light, 207
  floor covering, 174
  moist, 188–93
  types, 174
Dishwasher, 122–29
Dishwashing, 202
Disinfectants, 154–55
Dryers
  construction, 162
  lint removal, 164–66
  factors affecting, 166
  use of, 162–64
Dusting, 187–88, 189
Dutch ovens, 93

ILLUSTRATION INDEX